TAKE CHINA

The Last of the
China Marines

HAROLD STEPHENS

Wolfenden

Wolfenden Publishers
P.O. Box 789
Miranda, California 95553
Voice/Fax: 707-923-2455
e-mail: wolfen@northcoast.com
http://wolfenden.com

Cover designed by Robert Stedman
Edited by Austin M. Berry

Printed in Thailand

Take China:
The Last of the China Marines
A Novel by Harold Stephens

ISBN: 0-9642521-8-X

USA $14.95
CANADA $22.95

Also by
Harold Stephens

Discover the Orient
Destination Singapore
Turn South at the Equator
Complete Guide to Singapore
Singapore by Night
Motoring Guide to Singapore/Malaysia
Malaysia
Asian Portraits
Asian Adventure
At Home in Asia
Three Decades of Asian Travel & Adventure
The Last Voyage
The Tower & The River
Return to Adventure Southeast Asia
Who Needs a Road
The Strange Disappearance of Jim Thompson

Take China
The Last of the China Marines
A Novel
is dedicated to
The men of the 29th Marines
Sixth Marine Division

In particular, I am indebted to
William (Bill) Sanner, John (Jack) Stephenson,
John (Jack) Stewart, Howard (The Terrible) Terry,
Warren (Ike) Wanamaker
and Richard (Dick) Whitaker
for providing helpful information
concerning our experiences in the Marine Corps.
All were members of
Fox Company, Second Battalion, 29th Marines.
I had the privilege of serving with them at
the Battle of Okinawa
and during our occupation in China,
as China Marines.

Copyright © 2002 by Harold Stephens
Front cover: Designed by Robert Stedman
Printed in Thailand by Allied Printers
ISBN: 0-9642521-8-X

CONTENTS

Chapter 1

THE WAR IS OVER

The date is August 15, 1945. The place, Tent City on Guam. It's late, long after midnight.

The sound, at first, was faint, far-off, like the wind that rustles the trees on the farm back home in Pennsylvania, just before a storm. It seemed I was in one of those half-awake, half-asleep dreams, thinking of home, but when I heard Cpl. Marsden moving about in his bunk, I knew the sound was not from a dream. It was real. The others heard it too, and they began to stir.

The sound grew louder.

There was a sliver of moon in the night's sky, enough to give some light to the inside of the tent. I could see Marsden sit up in his bunk. I watched him push back his mosquito net, as if that would help him to hear better. Melanowski saw him too, and spoke up. "What is it, Sarge?" he asked in a voice barely above a whisper. He had called Marsden "Sarge." Everyone called Marsden Sarge. All squad leaders were sergeants, but headquarters never got around to promoting Marsden. He became squad leader when Sgt. Hamilton was killed on Okinawa.

"Shut up, Ski," Marsden barked. Everyone in the tent was sitting up now, pushing back their mosquito nets.

"But what is it?" Melanowski asked again.

"Nothing," Marsden said. "Be quiet."

"It sounds like a fire," Stevenson said, coming into the

tent from outside. He was excited. "We had one in Camp Lejune," he continued. "It started at one end of Tent City and in minutes wiped out the whole battalion." Stevenson was the company brain. He had a year of college and answered questions no one else could answer. He used impressive sounding names, and he knew how to spell big words. He was in college and then one day out of the blue, he enlisted in the Marines. He liked to have others think it was patriotism but it wasn't. The war was winding up and he figured if he acted quickly, he'd have the GI Bill to pay for his schooling. What he never expected was that three months after he signed up, the war was anything but over, and he found himself dodging bullets and digging foxholes on Okinawa.

No sooner had Stevenson mentioned the word fire than every Marine in the 29th began yelling at the tops of their voices. "Fire, fire!" they shouted. Had someone deliberately pushed the panic button they could not have done better. It was now a scramble to see who could get out of their tents first, not only those Marines in our tent but from every tent in Tent City. The crushed coral pathways between the rows of tents suddenly filled with excited Marines, standing there in their bare feet, some completely naked, others in their skivvies. Private Terry stood naked clutching his M1 rifle.

But where was the fire? There was no blazing red sky in any direction, and no smell of smoke. The sky was clear with the moon poking over the tops of the palms that ringed the camp. The men stood baffled, confused. The sound kept growing louder, like the roar of the sea, and it crept closer and closer.

Like a roar! That's exactly what it was, a roar, a roar of voices. Men in the distance were shouting. They were shouting at the tops of their voices, and the message they had to tell came like a wave rushing to shore. "The war! The war!" they shouted. "The war, the war." Then we made out the words— "It's over!" The war was over! "The Japanese have surrendered," they shouted.

The entire regiment now picked up the chorus, shouting until they became hoarse, jumping up and down in their bare feet on the coral pathways. "The war is over," they all sang together. They became hysterical, uncontrollable. They rushed into their tents and returned toting their M1 rifles. It was against regulations to possess live ammunition but some men kept a few extra rounds tucked away for emergencies. They loaded their M1s, pointed them skyward and fired. Some Marines had tracers and they fired these too, and when they went off they left long streaks across the sky, like falling stars. Soon the sky was all streaked. No one would have been surprised had the navy gunboats offshore fired their big guns. But then, maybe they hadn't heard.

Finally, over PA speakers, the duty officer instructed everyone to keep calm, to put away their rifles and return to their tents. There would be an official announcement in the morning. We returned to our tents.

"It was that bomb that did it," Melanowski announced when we were back inside. Stevenson agreed, it was the bomb that did it. We had heard about this wonder bomb before but didn't know what to believe. We learned that on August 6th, a B-29 Super Fortress named *Enola Gay* had flown nearly 1,500 miles across the open Pacific and dropped a single bomb on a city in Japan. No one could remember the name of the city but they remembered the bomb's dimensions: ten feet long, twenty-eight inches in diameter and weighing nine-thousand pounds. Then a couple of days later, there was talk about another B-29 dropping a second bomb on a Japanese city. No one could remember the name of that city either.

After we arrived back on Guam and began training, Stevenson was made Fox Company clerk, and he came back after work with all kinds of reports. Everyone was keen to hear about the bombing on Japan. The Allies, Stevenson reported, had been bombing Japanese mainland cities since June 15, 1944. They had dropped 170,000 tons of high explosive and incendiary bombs on the enemy before the *Enola*

Gay ever appeared in Japanese skies.

"I don't care how many friggin' bombs they dropped. I told you guys to shut up," Marsden shouted for the last time. There were no more discussions about bombs, not that night. We all went to sleep.

When reveille sounded the next morning, it started all over again. Even Marsden became involved this time. From the moment we were out of our bunks, we began questioning the outcry that awoke us in the middle of the night. The war was over! What the hell was all that about? Maybe it was only scuttlebutt. "Rumors, that's all," we mumbled. They expected us to believe that crap about Japan giving up! They taught us from the very start, from the first day in boot camp, that Japan would never surrender. "They'll fight to the very last Nip, down to the last woman and kid," Col. Roston said only a few days before when we were headed in work parties down to the docks to load ships that would carry us and a million others on the invasion of Japan.

We knew the big push was coming. "Nine out of ten of you bastards will be dead in another month," the colonel's Exec officer reminded us, "so enjoy it while you can." We hated that guy; he was a rear echelon major who had just joined the 29th; nevertheless, we listened, and we reasoned, never would the Japanese give up. The 29th had witnessed this on Okinawa. How many Japanese pulled the pins on their potato mashers and fell on them rather than give themselves up? How many thousands more, soldiers and civilians alike, leaped off the cliffs at the southern end of the island rather than surrender?

Official reports were kept from the troops, but Stevenson sneaked some through. The first invading force, called *Operation Coronet* was scheduled for November 1, 1945, less than three months away. It was to be followed by *Operation Olympic.* More than two million Japanese combat troops were waiting on the main islands. In reserve were four million civilian workers. Beyond that, the Japanese cabinet had approved drafting the remaining men between 15 and 60, and women from 17 to 45, to provide 28 million people armed with grenades and sharpened bamboo spears ready to die for the Emperor. Admiral Rikihei Takuma, chief of the *Kamikaze Corps,* had stockpiled fuel and armaments for 5,368 suicide aircraft, including biplane trainers, to use against the invasion fleet. The Mitsubishi plant and the Japan Steel works were on a seven-day, around-the-clock war-production schedule. In the harbor, Japanese sailors were readying hundreds of suicide boats to repel the approaching Allied invasion; torpedoes and high-explosive charges were piled high in seaside caves.

The capture of Iwo Jima, less than eight square miles of real estate consisting of nothing more than volcanic ash, cost the Marine Corps nearly 26,000 casualties. At Okinawa, kamikaze pilots willfully crashed 7,830 fighter planes into American warships anchored off shore. They sank 34 US ships and damaged another 368. The battle of Okinawa—the largest land-sea-air engagement in history—took the lives of 23,000 Americans, 91,000 Japanese and 150,000 Okinawan civilians.

Sitting on a hill above Naha Bay, we witnessed the kamikazes in action, watching helplessly as these suicide pilots bombed our ships in the bay. We saw them come in high, the sun picking up their reflection as they dove. Puffs of black smoke from our ackack guns popped up all around them. "There, there," one of our guys would shout, and we would all look in that direction. "Here he comes!" we called, not knowing to be amused or bewildered. We were kids, all of us, and we should have been watching football games back home but instead we were watching men die.

Iwo Jima and Okinawa were over. Won at a heavy price. But what would be the cost to take more than 142,000 square miles of Japanese homeland? Planners estimated we could lose as many as one million men—more than the total of the European and Pacific theaters combined.

But we Marines holed up in Tent City on Guam were not planners. We were kids, 17 and 18 year olds. The oldest Marine was Pappy Preston, and he was 29. Terry was 15 when he joined. He had just turned 17. We figured we were winning the war but there were times when we had our doubts, when dark confusions of the mind took over. Every night on Guam when we climbed into our bunks, we listened to Tokyo Rose on the short wave. We listened to what she had to say about the war. We laughed when she spoke in her soft sexy patter about home. "Tuck in your mosquito nets, you handsome Marines," she would say softly. "Lay back your head on your pillows, and picture your 4F cousins back home, out tonight with your girls, out with your wives, driving your car that you locked away in the garage, listening to the music of Harry James, drinking bourbon and gin you should be drinking, and where are you, Marines? Where are you? I know where you are. You're not home where you should be!"

We laughed at her banter, wondered who she really was, and listened when she played "The Boogie Woogie Bugle Boy from Company B." We made remarks, and joked that we would look her up when we reached Tokyo. One by one the men grew quiet. The radio went silent and the night melted into dreamy thoughts as we drifted off in sleep wondering what our 4F cousins were doing that night.

We wondered about the war when we watched the B-29s returning from their bombing missions over Japan. They had made more than 35,000 sorties flown against targets on the enemy mainland. We watched those that survived the guns and Zero fighters, and those that didn't run out of fuel, come limping back. We heard their droning, sputtering engines before we could see them. We stopped what we were doing and looked up to watch them come into view, all shot up. What miracle was it that kept them in the sky? Some appeared like skeletons, tail sections blown away, gaping holes in their wings and fuselage, only metal rib frames showing. Still, they flew, and we watched in disbelief. But even then, some so close, lost the race. They came in low, too low, and we held our breath. Some prayed, as pilots attempted their final, desperate

approach to reach the airfield. They would disappear, and soon
we saw balls of smoke rise from over the rim of palm trees.

But the question now: was the war really over? That
morning at roll call it was confirmed. Not officially, but we
knew there was some truth to the matter when all work parties
for the day were canceled. That never happened before.

We went back to our tents and in the downpour of heat we
waited. We waited for the official word from headquarters
that seemed would never come. There was much speculation,
all conjecture, of course. From squad leader to company runner
we each had our opinions, and we were only too willing to
share them with others, wanted or unwanted. And no one
hesitated giving voice to his thoughts. Focus centered on that
thing they called the "A-bomb." The A-bomb! The US had
dropped an A-bomb on Japan. There had been talk about the
bomb days and weeks before, but no one in the 29th had the
slightest idea what this super bomb might be. With the opinions
came disagreements, but the one thing that everyone agreed
upon, unequivocally, was that whatever kind of bomb it was,
it had to be big, really big.

"It's an A-bomb," Stevenson emphasized.

"What'd hellava frigin' kind of bomb is that?" Scotty
Johnson asked.

"It's a big sonava bitch. It can lay flat a place a mile square,"
Terry chimed in. He was repeating what he had heard earlier.

"Shit, you believe that crap," announced Melanowski with
conviction. "No frigin' bomb can do that. None, I tell yeah.
We ain't gotta frigin' plane big enough that can carry a frigin'
bomb that frigin' big."

"You dumb Polack! Who said so?" snapped Terry.

"Frig you, Terry." Melanowski shouted.

"Yeah, even a dumb Polack knows it'd havda be bigger
than 500 pounds to do that much damage," added Chandler.
"And that's the biggest size our B-29s can carry."

"It's a special bomb, you dumb shit," Terry continued, his
comment aimed at Chandler this time. "This ain't no ordinary

bomb I tell you. It's an A-bomb."

"What's the A fur," asked Scotty.

"What's the A fur! A is for the first, the first of its kind, that's what," Chandler said.

"Hell, if an A-bomb can blow a hole in the ground bigger than a square mile, think what a B-bomb will do when it comes out," Cpl. Marsden said.

"Yeah, then the C-bomb's gonna come. I'd like to see that."

"You're all full of shit. I never heard of any kindah A-bomb before, and I've been reading the news all the time," Melanowski concluded.

"You stupid shit, what news you been readin'?" Terry said. "You ain't gonna find nothing about A-bombs in the stupid funny papers. That's about all the news you ever read."

"What you talking about!" Chandler said. "He can't read."

"Go stuff yourself, all of you," Melanowski said and turned away.

Marshall and Hecklinger now got into the argument. Harry Marshall was from Indiana and argued with midwest logic, the "show me" kind of attitude. He didn't like the name Harry and wanted to be called Smitty. Walter Hecklinger was from Oklahoma and what he said he considered gospel. Six foot four with the demeanor of a rodeo rider, no one argued with him. We called him Stretch.

And so the debates continued, and all we could do was wait, the curse of the Marine Corps. I felt I had to get away. I needed time to think. If the war was over, did this mean we were all going home? Already the men began talking about being home for Christmas. I should have been excited, but I wasn't. What was wrong? Like everyone else I clamored about wanting the war to end, and what I was going to do when I got home. Smitty planned to sleep for a month, getting up only to eat his mother's home cooking. Terry was going to take his discharge and blow his separation pay on the longest binge of his life. Whittington pictured himself in Saugerties in New York by Christmas. Melanowski would grab the first woman he saw and Stevenson was going back to school. Marsden didn't talk about it, but we knew he had his wife on his mind. I too had my future planned, or rather my father had it planned for me. He was awaiting the day I would return. He wanted to open a small electrical repair shop, and I would help him run it. The only problem, electricity didn't interest me. "There's a great future in electronics," he would write me but I never paid much attention.

The Marines of the 29th, for the most part, hated Guam. I guess I was one of the few exceptions. We learned we were going to Guam when we were still on Okinawa. When word came that Okinawa was secured, and we were being evacuated, three LST landing crafts immediately left for Guam with an advance work party. Rick Whittington, our company runner, was with them. Only then he wasn't company runner. He was a machine gunner like all the rest of us and had served his 87 days under fire. He and the others arrived on Guam and had the honor of erecting tents for the other eleven late-arriving LSTs that brought the rest of the men of the 29th. We could hardly call it a triumphant welcome for returning heroes. There to greet us was Whittington, with the news that he had been appointed Fox Company runner. We didn't congratulate him, but envied him, and gave him the title—Brown Noser.

No sooner were we assigned our tents than our thoughts turned to Japan, and Fox Company was soon back at the same old business, training for the coming invasion of Japan. While we went on hikes, with full gear and did close-order drill under the scorching sun, Whittington rubbed it in. Each day all he had to do was go to the Second Battalion Quonset hut and warm the bench for as long as the Battalion Exec was at his desk. When the Exec left, Whittington left. "While you guys run around in the boonies playing war, I sit on my ass and drink coffee," he boasted. Whittington was ribbed by the men, and thrived on it, but he was also our private source of information gleaned from executive orders he had to deliver. He even outshone Stevenson now as the information man. He was invaluable to us.

Tent City was far better than our accommodations on Okinawa. No one complained. It was in a way an actual city laid out in quadrants with rows of tents in neat orderly lines. Each tent quartered a squad consisting of eight men. Our machine gun platoon was assigned to one tent. Marsden was our squad leader and Johnson his assistant. Stevenson was gunner and Melanowski assistant gunner. The rest of us, Jack Chandler, Terry Howard, Harry Marshall, Walter Hecklinger and me, were ammo carriers. And there was Karl Kyley. He didn't really count. He was a nonentity. He never had anything to say about anything. He never complained, nor talked and you didn't even know he was there. He could be one of two people in the tent and you wouldn't take notice of him. Maybe that's because he was always sleeping. Even when he was awake he was sleeping. He could sleep 23 hours out of the day, using the other hour only for meals. And sometimes even the meals didn't matter.

The tents had wooden decks and the side flaps were kept rolled up during the day. At night and when it rained, they were lowered. The temperature inside during the day was unbearable, but there was no other place to go to escape the brutal tropical heat. The only shade was a tent-like structure over the Lister bags which did little to keep the drinking water cool. They joked that the cook made coffee directly from the Lister bags without needing to boil the water.

The mess hall was a huge open tent which we entered in a single long line that wrapped halfway around the tent. We had our own mess kits and canteen cups and these we had to wash ourselves in 44-gallon drums filled with boiling water. Nearby was the PX, stocked with Planter's peanuts, canned sardines and Chesterfields. The "movie theater" was an open-air semicircle with logs from coconut trees serving as seats. Navy ships supplied the movies. Lana Turner and Betty Grable were certain to bring a full house under the stars with Marines crowded around the periphery sitting on their helmet liners.

There would always be a ten- or fifteen-minute news feature by Fox Movie Tone. We cheered when we saw our ships plow through heavy seas making the landing for the invasion of Okinawa. And we always hooted, hollered and booed when we saw General MacArthur appear on the screen. If it was the Commandant of the Marine Corps or a Marine general, that was okay, but there wasn't a Marine who had a nice thing to say about a dogface army general. Some Marines went to the theater several hours early to get seats, and many even gave up evening chow not to miss out.

Until we began loading ships, we drilled in daytime and stood guard duty at night. At the docks beneath a torturing sun and under the glare of a crushed white coral roadbed, we formed long lines and passed 105-mm artillery shells from man to man, cursing the man before us to slow down. Naked to the waist, with helmet liners to ward off the sun, we made ready for the invasion of Japan. At night, as armed sentries, we walked the perimeter of Tent City. Occasionally Japanese soldiers sneaked down from the hills on raiding parties and cut through the fences. Every now and then a raider was shot, and his body had to be carted off the next day before sun up to be buried. Everyone went to look at the corpse, and praised the sentry who did him in. But even the war-hardened Marines felt pity for the badly starved dead man, mosty skin and bones. They were young, young as we were. We could have been friends had the circumstances been different. One night a newly arrived replacement went on sentry duty and thought he saw two Japanese stealing a Lister bag. He called out to give the password but there was no response. He opened fire, emptying a clip of ammo. A squad of armed Marines came running, and found a dead white water buffalo. The Officer-of-the-Day made the sentry bury it using an entrenching tool to dig the hole. He was considered lucky; he didn't have to pay a farmer for his loss.

We heard about a Japanese soldier who had stolen some Marine dungarees and had sneaked into the chow line over at the 22nd Marines. None of us could understand how a Japanese soldier masquerading as a Marine could possibly have pulled off such a stunt. But then, we always said, they weren't too bright over in the 22nd Marines anyway.

Contrary to how most others felt, I did find Guam much to my liking. While the men lay in their bunks during their time off, sweltering in the heat, beating their gums or else talking about home, I made my escape. I knew where there was a hole in the barbed wire fence along the southern perimeter, and I would go there when I could get away. I told the guys I was going to the base library, but instead I headed out into the bush. Much of Guam was out-of-bounds for GI's, and that included all the native villages, the jungles that surrounded the camps and most beaches. However, there were a few designated beach areas where we could swim. We always had to be careful. The Japanese not only sneaked down at night to steal food and supplies, their snipers took popshots at us every now and then. When this happened, our patrols went into the hills to flush them out, but with little success.

One beach that we all liked was eventually put out-of-bounds. It was a great place, very secluded. We had to lower ourselves over a cliff by ropes, and at the bottom was a small cove with white sand and a small island a dozen yards off shore. The incoming tide swept through the channel and if we caught the crest of a wave just right we could body surf right up to the beach. Then one day a Japanese sniper took popshots and the Provost Marshall closed the beach.

Stevenson and I found another beach, and while he stood guard with his M1, I dove into the surf to test the water. It was a beautiful turquoise, and refreshingly cool. I was about to motion to Stevenson to join me when I felt a sting, and then another, and another. Jelly fish, some only as big as a thumb nail. I came out of the water flying, covered with stinging welts that were so painful I could not put my clothes back on, not even my skivvy drawers. Stevenson escorted me back to camp as I walked naked through the streets to the sickbay.

That didn't stop us though. Soon after I recovered, Stevenson joined me on another excursion. We sneaked through the fence and went exploring. A couple miles from camp we were hiking along the road, ducking into ditches when Jeeps and other vehicles came by, when we noticed, high up on a ridge, a disabled Japanese two-man tank. We scrambled up the hillside to take a look. One of the tracks on the left side was blown off; other than that, the tank was functional. It was one of those so-called four-ton suicide tanks. They were quite easy to knock out; a .30 Cal. armor piercing bullet could go right through the side. Except for a .37-mm gun they had no other firepower. We opened the hatch, squeezed inside, and played like we were Japanese soldiers. It was fun. The turrets worked and by turning a hand crank I could rotate the turret, raising and lowering the gun barrel that protruded from the front. I took aim at imaginary targets and pretended to fire. I then noticed a convoy of military vehicles coming down the road below us. I made out like I was sighting in on them, and lowered the gun barrel to take aim. Suddenly all the vehicles in the convoy came to a halt. When I peered out I could see the occupants jumping out of the vehicles and diving for cover alongside the road. Holy hell! We realized what we had done! They took us for Japanese! We scrambled out of the tank and slid down the hill on the opposite side of the convoy. Fifteen minutes later, when we were on our way back to camp, we looked back and watched two P-51s dive at the hilltop and release their bombs. In two sorties the entire top of the hill, tank included, were blown away. Stevenson was more careful after that when I asked him to join me. But boredom always made him change his mind. Terry on the other hand was ready for anything, but I didn't like his tagging along. He insisted on taking his M1, threatening to shoot at anything that moved. Sometimes I thought he might have secretly wanted to get himself a Japanese sniper.

For a farm boy, Guam was my dream. Here were Kipling's

Jungle Books and Edgar Rice Burrow's *Tarzan of the Apes.*
Their characters were alive and flourishing here. I ran among
the trees, through verdant undergrowth, down sun-flecked
paths, until I became breathless and could run no more. When
I laid down with my back against the roots of a massive tree
and looked up, I wanted to swing through the trees like the
animals of the forest do, but I could hardly put my arms around
any of the trees they were so mighty. And often my expectations
were short lived. I tried to climb a coconut palm and found
that even a simple task like that was impossible for a newcomer.

I spent one afternoon in the forest; it was late when I
sneaked under the fence and returned to camp. I feared I might
be in trouble, but I wasn't even missed. The men were
preoccupied with a new subject. A new point system was
announced. Stevenson and Whittington were hot at it debating
the finer points."I tell you this," Whittington insisted, "the
CINCPAC memorandum on the Point System states if you
have 30 or more points you are eligible to go home."

"Yeah, and a Purple Heart gets you five extra points,"
Johnson interrupted.

"That doesn't mean shit," said Melanowski. "When are
we going home anyway?"

"Overseas time is double Stateside time," Marsden added.

"That's still not the frigin' answer," Melanowski said.

Gradually the conversation took another turn. The war was
over! What would we do now? We would certainly miss our
buddies. Who could understand us better than those guys with
whom we shared the same foxholes for the past year. Men
began jotting down addresses, and making promises to "keep
in touch." Harsh words were no longer uttered and enemies
became friends.

There were some who hated to see the war end. When the
news came, they may have shouted the victory call, but deep
inside there was the feeling that more than a war had ended.
Back to the farm they would go, to the steel mills, to the

coalmines, to the humdrum, the mundane. And I would go to work in an electric shop with my father. It wasn't a very happy thought. No more heroes. No more victories. No more buddies to confide in. No more war to fight. It happened so quickly, and now it was over.

News of Japan's surrender was finally confirmed. Stevenson was right. The A-bomb had ended the war. We were told that on August 28, 1945. Only a few days before, the *USS Missouri* had sailed triumphantly into Tokyo Bay and accepted the Japanese surrender. What we didn't know until later was that not far away from Tokyo Bay, last-ditch kamikaze pilots began taxiing into position on the runway, determined to sink the American battleship. There were still many Japanese in high military positions who were mindset, at all costs, to win the war. After the second bomb was dropped on Nagasaki on August 9, 1945, War Minister General Korechiki Anami told the cabinet ministers that it was far too early to say the war was lost. The general wanted one last great battle on Japanese soil. "Would it not be wondrous," he said, "for this whole nation to be destroyed like a beautiful flower?"

That chance never came, and a million American lives were saved. A last minute appeal by Prince Takamatsu, the emperor's younger brother, grounded the fanatics who could have started the whole thing all over again.

So once again we waited, and finally word arrived. We were moving out. This time no one grumbled when work parties were assigned and we headed back to the docks to load ships. "We not only brought all this crap over here," Melanowski ranted, "but now we have to take it all back."

The docks looked like a staging area that was getting ready for battle. There they were, LSTs, LSMs and PAs, all lining the water front, and farther out in the bay the 7th Fleet had moved in with its destroyers and destroyer escorts. They looked menacing, even with their guns silent. We could picture them escorting our troop ships as we steamed into San Francisco under the Golden Gate. It was a proud feeling. The victory was ours! Halleluiah!

But victory, we were about to discover, was not ours. It was only wishful thinking on our part. We would not be returning to America to a cheering, waving populace. We would be long forgotten by the time we returned. Dick Whittington, our company runner, gave us the news that was about to change everything. It wasn't what everyone wanted to hear. We knew it was going to be something drastic the way he arrived at the docks in the colonel's Jeep, skidding sideways sending coral flying everywhere. He had hardly stopped when he stood up in the Jeep. "We're not going home!" he shouted, waving his helmet liner over his head. He didn't wait for questions. Everyone stopped what they were doing and stood silent as statues. Finally, he belted it out. "The 29th is not going home," he shouted. "You know where we're going? We're going to China." He hesitated and repeated it again, as loud as he could, "We're going to China!"

We were not going home! Whittington took the full blast of everyone's fury. He stood fast. It seems, he told us, that the Commandant of the Marine Crops, the Secretary of the Navy, the Secretary of Defense, and President Harry Truman himself all had a different idea about where we were going. And, it wasn't home!

This wasn't at all what the men wanted to hear. Many of the Marines in the 29th had been with the outfit since Guadalcanal. They had been fighting for years. Now the war was over, and they were told they weren't going home. Instead, they were going to China.

It wasn't a sudden headquarters decision. All the while we were sweltering in the sun on the docks, breaking our backs, the brass knew it. They knew it and that's what was so disturbing. We had been lied to. We were heading to China to repatriate the Japanese forces. That was the reason Col. Roston gave us, but there were other factors at hand which they didn't tell us. These we would find out for ourselves later. All we knew now was that we were going to a foreign land we hardly knew existed, nor did we know exactly why we were going. We made no decisions, and controlled no destinies, not even our own. We knew of no secret orders. We were told to pack our gear, and to load the ships. We had to get ready to sail immediately. That was all we knew. We would be sailing to China in a few days.

Going to China! What was that song everyone was singing—"A Slow Boat to China, or Maybe Siam?" A slow boat to China. The words kept turning over and over in my mind—A slow boat to China. Not back to the farm, not to open an electric shop with my father, but to China. I was thrilled, Stevenson was thrilled, Chandler was thrilled, Harry "Smitty" Marshall was thrilled, Terry was thrilled, and so were many others, but we couldn't say it aloud. Marsden would have belted us. We had to grumble like everyone else. But inside we were thrilled. We were going to China!

In three days the ships were loaded and Tent City was dismantled. We were told we were going to a place called Cheefoo on the north coast of the Shantung Peninsula in northern China. None of us had ever heard of the name Cheefoo, let alone where it was. On the afternoon of the last day I broke away from my work party without anyone noticing and headed for the base library.

The place was in complete disarray. The center isles were stacked with empty wooden crates and a half dozen grumbling librarians were preparing to pack the books. "Take what the hell what you want," a sergeant growled, "and then get the hell out of here."

I went to the history section and picked up *The Dowager Empress*. There were photographs of the Empress of China taken in 1911. She looked regal, but also very mean. Would the women of China all look like her? Under one photograph it mentioned "eunuchs." What the hell were eunuchs? I tucked the book, as well as another one about the Boxer Rebellion under my arm. On the way out I passed the REFERENCE

SECTION. There they were, lined up on shelves: dictionaries, thesauruses, books on grammar, a book called *Teaching Yourself to Type* and another on *Learning Shorthand and Book Keeping the Easy Way*. I always wanted to learn to type, secretly that is, but the book was large format and too big to carry. I then noticed the language books—*How to Speak French. Spanish. Italian.* And then my eyes fell upon *Spoken Chinese*. I took it down from the shelf and didn't even bother opening the cover. I tucked it snugly with the other two books under my arm, and without asking further questions left the library and headed back to the docks. That night before lights went out and taps were sounded—Tokyo Rose had gone off the air—I began teaching myself Chinese.

We were going to China.

Chapter 2

SLOW BOAT TO CHINA

T he 29th Marines had three days to get ready to sail for China. Finally, on September 30, 1945, we made our way in a convoy of heavy trucks to the docks at Agana. Fox Company was assigned to *USS Napa*, AP 157. There were no bands playing to send us off, no one making speeches, no one waving flags. Instead we had MP's in helmet liners wearing white armbands and Sam Rayban sunglasses screaming out orders. They carried carbines slung upside down over their shoulders, directing traffic and pointing out the directions where the trucks had to line up. We disembarked and formed long lines, and with full packs and seabags to tow, we slowly filed up the gangplanks to our new quarters that would be home for the next 21 days.

We reached the quarterdeck, set down our seabags, turned aft and saluted the ship's ensign. Lt. Clark Brandmire stood at the railing with the battalion roster. "Fox Company this way, follow me," he called. He lead the way through a double set of black curtains to a narrow ladder that led down into the depths of the ship. The light was faint, a reddish glow, and almost immediately the air grew heavy. We came to one deck, and then another, and still another. We went down five decks to the very bowels of the *USS Napa*. We could not have gone deeper. "Find your own bunks," Lt. Brandmire said and left us to our own misery.

The steel-framed, canvas bunks were stacked eight high with hardly enough room to turn over once you climbed in.

Everyone struggled to find bunks near the entrance, close to the head, but I edged my way to the rear as far as I could get, and there I found a top bunk. It was a good choice. Directly overhead was a red light encased behind tiny bars, obviously to keep one from unscrewing the light bulb. The light was dim and cast an eerie glow, but with a little straining I could edge closer and then there was enough light to read.

We were allowed on deck until taps at eight, but first we had to pass through several sets of heavy black curtains to reach the open deck. There was concern that Japanese submarines hadn't got the word that the war was over. The smoking lamp was out and in the black of night there was little to see. Ships in the convoy appeared in silhouettes of black, like paper cutouts. You couldn't help wondering how the fleet managed to keep formation as it did in the darkness.

Daylight aboard brought much relief. We were required to wear our lifejackets at all times, which no one liked, but Stevenson and I found an area under a lifeboat where we could escape from the crowd and no one could see us. It took some scrambling on our bellies but the effort was worth it. Here we reclined, using our life jackets as pillows, and listened to the mesmerizing sound of the sea as the *USS Napa* rose and fell as she met each wave head on. We spent endless hours staring out at the sea with its unattainable horizon, and when we tired of dreaming we read or played cards. Sometimes we invited one or two others to our refuge. Other times we just talked, rambling on about home, wondering out loud about China. The others listened intently as I told them about the US Marines in China during the Boxer Rebellion. I told them horror stories about eunuchs from *The Dowager Empress,* stories that I read in my bunk only a couple hours before.

"You mean they cut off their balls just so they could serve the empresses?" they asked, and then they wanted to know if China still had eunuchs. I had to slow them down when they got too far ahead of me, and then that night I would read up on my history book to prepare myself.

I found the text from *Spoken Chinese* the most fun. I didn'
t tell anyone about my hidden books. At night in my bunk
under the glow of the red light I memorized a Chinese phrase
or two. Of course, I had no idea about my pronunciation but
that really didn't matter. And so I studied "Are you
Chinese"—a stupid question to ask. "Do you speak
English?"—almost as bad. "Where is a hotel? A restaurant? A
WC." I surmised WC had to be another name for "head," or
Marine talk for toilet. Then, the next day under the lifeboat, I
would spring my Chinese on my listeners. They had no idea
what I was saying, and often I didn't either, but it was fun
playing the fool. Naturally they would ask where I learned
my Chinese, and jokingly I would reply that I came from a
missionary family.

"You're full of crap," Terry said.

Stevenson always backed me up. "He's right," he answered.
"I know."

"How do you know?"

"I just know."

Our secluded area provided another service that made life
a bit easier. Washing clothes aboard a troop ship was a problem.
No washing machines. No laundry service. Marines crammed
into the heads, under the showers, and attempted to scrub away
the dirt and smell from their dungarees with salt water. Others
had found an easier way, by tying their clothes to long lines
and dragging them aft of the ship. The pounding sea usually
washed them clean, but before long everyone was crowding
the aft deck vying for space to tie their lines. Often times it
became a real mess when lines tangled and fights would ensue.
Under our lifeboat we didn't have that problem. We dangled
lines over the side, with our clothes securely fastened to one
end. At the water's edge below us, the ship cast a wake that
kept our laundry a yard or two away from the side of the ship.
It worked as long as they didn't pump the bilge.

When we weren't reclining in our hideaway, we were
waiting in the chow line. The lines were frightfully long and

incredibly slow moving. Those who were readers could get an education just while waiting. We had but two meals a day. There was no seating arrangement in the mess hall. We ate standing up with our trays resting on narrow counters that ran the length of the mess hall. There were no seconds, and with the lines as long as they were, there was no possibility of sneaking in line a second time. There just wasn't time.

The chow line formed above deck and led down the ladder to the first level. The chief cook, a fat sailor with four hitches behind him, had a pet monkey that he picked up in Madagascar. The monkey was the ship's mascot. The Marines hated him. The sailors called him Jarhead, which didn't sit well with us. He was a dreadful, vicious creature. He stood guard above the entrance to the mess hall, like King Kong, and every Marine that went through the chow line had to pass beneath this scowling, ugly beast. As we came out of the bright daylight it was hard to spot him at first, and this is when the howling, screeching animal would come swooping down from out of nowhere and snatch away a hat from the head of an unsuspecting Marine. If the Marine had on sunglasses, he would grab the glasses. Sailors roared with laughter as the monkey fled by leaping upon a boom over the sea and out of reach.

Scotty Johnson didn't think it was so funny when Jarhead snatched away his Raybans. We were surprised how calm he remained, for those glasses were his proudest possession. He wore them constantly, even when it was dark. He actually made a good show, and we all envied him wishing we had Raybans. Scotty never said anything about the incident, but we knew down inside he intended do something about it. "What you gonna do, jump through the rigging after him?" Terry asked and everyone laughed.

"You'll see," he said. "You'll see."

Scotty had mess duty the next day and that night when he returned to his quarters he carried a tiny bundle wrapped in his skivvy shirt. Still he said nothing. A few minutes after taps sounded and lights went out, Scotty climbed down from his bunk on the pretense of going to the head. He slipped up the gangway and went on deck. Less than twenty minutes later he was back in his bunk.

The next morning pandemonium broke out on deck during morning chow. The cook went into a terrible rage and every navy officer from CO to deck officer assembled at the entrance to the mess hall. The navy was stunned. Their monkey was gone. He went over the side! That morning, the story goes, he had swooped down as he always did, grabbed a Marine's hat and then leaped out on the boom, only to miss his grip and fall into the sea. At close inspection they found the boom had been greased. The CO called for an investigation. The culprit would be found, and the book would be thrown at him. But, of course, he never was. No one on deck had seen Scotty drop his skivvy shirt overboard. It was covered with lard.

On October 1st, *USS Napa* stopped at Saipan, and on October 7th we watched the southern end of Japan come into view. We lined the deck, thankful the war had ended, knowing that it wasn't this barren, inhospitable coast that would take our lives. "A hell of a place to die," Marsden said.

"The bomb saved us, didn't it, Sarg?" Chandler asked.

"Yes, maybe a million of us," Marsden replied, reflecting for a minute or two on those words, and then continued. "And maybe twenty million Japanese."

"It was worth it then, wasn't it? We'd be dead now, and all those Japs too." Chandler commented.

"Was it worth it?" Marsden repeated, hesitating over his words. We waited for we knew he would answer his own question. Finally, he replied: "Yes, it was worth it, for us, but I'll tell you, the world may not think so in years to come."

Aboard ship work parties were our daily routine. Every square inch of deck space, above and below, had to be swabbed down twice a day. Aside from the need for swab jockeys there was mess duty. Given the choice, a Marine would rather swab than stand with arms up to his elbows deep in hot soapy water.

It was a miserable assignment, but there was one even worse, and that was trashman in the furnace room. All trash aboard navy ships had to be burned. Nothing was ever to be thrown overboard. The concern wasn't the environment. The navy didn't want to leave tracks. So someone had to shovel trash into the furnaces. Each morning after chow Pappy Preston, the company gunny sergeant, appeared in each quarters, and with duty roster in hand he called out names and handed out assignments for the day. He had a tough time pronouncing names and often had to repeat himself several times to be understood. Since there were several Marines aboard with the same name as mine, or names sounding close to it, he would merely call out STEVE. I discovered, quite by accident, that by hesitating and not answering immediately, another Marine would answer up for me. Even my friend Stevenson never caught on and took work assignments that should have been mine.

This went on for about a week, until one morning instead of sneaking into my hideout I made the mistake of climbing back into my bunk and there I fell asleep. Before I knew what happened I found myself tumbling from the top bunk to the hard steel floor below. When I came to my senses I was looking up at an irate gunny sergeant straddling me with a heavy boot on each side. He was so angered that even Stevenson, who Pappy said was dumb enough to stand in for me, was assigned to the furnace room with me.

The furnace room where we burned trash was midship and the only good thing I can say about it is that it was but one floor below deck. The heat was so intense, the air so stifling, that every fifteen minutes or so, while stripped to the waist, we had to charge topside gasping to get fresh air. The door to the furnace had been removed and so vast was the opening that a boxcar could have easily fit through without touching the sides, or so it seemed. We were given wide, flat shovels to use, and we learned quickly they had a purpose other than shoveling trash. When the ship rolled sharply to starboard, we used the shovels as props to keep us from lunging into the open furnace. The fire was as vicious as the flames of Hades. It consumed piles of trash as fast as we could shovel it in. Not once did we manage to get ahead so we could rest, for as soon as we had shoveled clean the deck space in front of the furnace, another batch of trash would come tumbling down a chute completely inundating us. It never ended.

Our troubles aboard *USS Napa*, and for all ships in the China Sea, were just about to begin, however. During a break from the furnace room, I noticed the sky had turned an ominous black, and very strange was the texture of the sea. It was flat and an oily calm. Something was about to happen, and one didn't have to be an old sea dog to know that. The next morning we learned a typhoon was approaching.

The news of the coming storm didn't bother Gunny Prescott as much as did the news that Stevenson and I had been relieved from our duties as trashmen. Stevenson was summoned to company headquarters located in a tiny compartment next to the bridge. The Exec reassigned him to his old duties—Fox Company clerk. From yard bird trash burner to pencil jockey. Not bad. My calling was of a different nature. Our convoy was sailing in seas that had been heavily mined by the Japanese, and Navy gunners were put on alert and called upon to man the 20mm guns to look for floating mines. Also those Marines who had scored Expert Rifleman were called upon with their M1s to be on the lookout for mines. Having fired 307 at Parris Island, one point over the mark, my name was called. Hecklinger also got the assignment, and for an Oklahoma cowboy it was a natural, but he wasn't too pleased standing on deck with a storm coming up. "This ain't like hanging on a bronco," he said. "Why did I admit I could shoot a gun better than anyone? Hell, lettin' the cat outta the bag is a whole lot easier than puttin' it back." For me it was better than the furnace room.

During daylight hours I was assigned to stand guard duty with my M1 in a gun turret that extended far out over the superstructure to the right of the bridge. I had a clear, unobstructed view of the bridge and all the activity that was going on inside. I didn't know it but I was about to have the ride of my life.

The first words from the bridge that caught my attention were that the barometer was falling. Terrifying words to seamen. I remembered those words from reading Jack London. In one of my favorite stories of his, he wrote about the barometer falling when a hurricane was coming. Odd that I should remember this now. The average for a barometer reading was 29.90, and now the deck officer was saying the barometer was down to 29.62. The only difference between Jack London's world and ours was that we were in the China Sea, and they call the storms here typhoons. In Jack London's *Tales of the South Seas* they were hurricanes. Whatever name we gave them, there was no doubt the *USS Napa* and the ships of the convoy were directly in its path. Orders went out for Marines to remain below deck and for the crew to close hatches and secure everything on deck.

I felt ridiculous, standing in the turret, holding on to a tiny rifle, and looking out at a raging sea. This was no time to be on the lookout for mines bobbing up in a tossing sea, but I guess it was better than being cramped up below deck in our quarters, or even worse, in the furnace room.

I could not have believed it possible for the wind to blow as it did. Stevenson borrowed a foul weather jacket and came to stand with me in the turret. We were grateful we were not back in the furnace room for now the ship was pitching and listing so violently there was no mere shovel that could have kept us from falling into the open flames. On deck it was less frightening. At first, we thought it was fun. "Whoa, holy hell, look at that wave, over there," we'd cry and found it all amusing. But when the wind increased, and tore at our bodies, we now looked at each other in dismay. Was this really happening? Soon we stopped laughing. "I had better get back inside," Stevenson said and I was alone. I was going to call him chicken but I knew in my heart I wanted to be with him.

The wind grew even more frightening. There's no describing it. How can one describe a nightmare? It tore at my clothes, threatening to rip the buttons from my jacket. I felt the flesh on my face distort with each blast of wind and I had to turn away to breathe. It was a monstrous thing, and the most monstrous thing about it was that it increased and continued to increase.

It was incredible! The sea, which had risen at first, was beaten down by that wind. It seemed as if the whole ocean might be sucked up into another sphere, another world. There could be no force now that could control this hellish thing we call a typhoon other than, perhaps, the very sea itself. The storm reached a point where the driving wind actually flattened the sea, but it did not reduce the swell. Often when I tried to find the LST to our starboard it had completely vanished from view, lost in the trough between two mighty waves, and then it would reappear, shedding water on every quarter as is it rose. How high were the waves? The masts on the LST were at least 40 feet above water. God forbid, when I looked again I remembered that LST. It was carrying 3rd Phib Corps Motor Pool, and Sammy was aboard. Poor Sammy. I knew him from Okinawa. Samuel Carver Washington. He was a driver and a mechanic with Motor Pool, a black man from Alabama. Blacks were not part of the fighting corps, but they did serve as drivers in motor pools. I saw Sammy at the docks when we were shipping out, and he said he was going to sleep on his 4X4 on deck. No way was he going below deck. The very thought of the ocean made him seasick. I wondered where he was now. I wondered if maybe even his 4X4 had washed overboard.

As time passed, it became so dark it could have been another day and I wouldn't have known the difference. I had to get away for a spell and see what was happening below deck. I really wanted to be with my buddies. I told the deck officer I had to make a head call.

I descended the five sets of ladders and worked my way to

the bow where my bunk was located. Here the ship tossed and heaved at its worst. The bow dropped so violently, it momentarily took one's breath away. There was vomit everywhere, down the sides of the bunks, on the bulkheads, over the floors. It was dreadful! It made walking slippery, almost impossible. Men lost their balance as they dashed for the head, and they came down the isle head first, feet first, sidewise, rolling over and over, twisting and squirming. Now and again a man caught a grip on a bunk; but the weight of the bodies behind tore his grip loose. It was a melee, a curse, but as terrible as it was, there was still bantering and joking among the downtrodden men, even some laughter when someone went tumbling by.

I hadn't been to the galley but we heard that it suffered the worst damage of all. A heavy cooking range broke away from its fastening and crashed from one side of the galley to the other taking out all the tables. It had to be lassoed like a wild steer before it could be stopped. They said Stretch should have been the one to do it, but at the time he couldn't get out of his bunk.

I knew at once, no matter how terrifying the sea might be, I would be much better off topside. I went back to my turret. What happened next I shall never forget. The turret where I stood was a good 50 feet above water, but when the first sea— there were three that I recall—broke over the entire deck, in one mighty flush it flooded the turret. I was swept from my feet but managed to grab on to the railing. The second sea sent the LST to our port—Sammy's LST was to our starboard—so far over in a roll that her whole underside became exposed. I was certain she would continue to roll and not right herself but she miraculously rose again. The third and worst sea was yet to come.

The situation continued to worsen. Had we not been in the path of the storm, conditions may have been better. "Who makes the decision for the Navy?" Stevenson asked when he came back on deck between lulls. He answered the question himself: "Someone back in the Pentagon says 'steam ahead at all costs,' and that's what they do, at all costs. Would a day or two or three make any difference? Would those guys called communists do any more than they have done already?" He continued to rant about miscalculations and military ineptness, about the thousands of Marines who lost their lives at Iwo because no one took time to consider the tides. He ranted but I lost his words in the roar of the sea, or maybe I just stopped listening. I was shaking from something more than the cold.

Stevenson had joined me during a lull, but in the absence of the wind and pressure, the sea rose. It jumped! It leaped! It soared straight up! It sprang up from every point of the compass. We had passed through the eye—when the wind temporarily stops—but leaving the eye of a storm is far worse than entering. We were about to meet the full onslaught of wind and wave.

Just at that moment the *USS Napa* flung down to starboard. The third sea hit us. It didn't merely hit us, it struck, it slammed, and it bombarded, all at once, in one powerful, mighty blow. It came so violently, so shocking, that it felt like the earth might have fallen from its axis. There was no system to the waves now, no stability. They were hollow, maniacal seas. They were higher than forty feet now, or fifty, or a hundred. What did it matter? They were not seas at all but mountains of tumbling water.

The tragedy was there was no avoiding it. The helmsman could only steam ahead no matter what. There were splashes, monstrous splashes which you could only hear and not see. We were flooded, the entire APA, with a mighty sea that rose up from nowhere. No one saw it. It just came. It came and fell everywhere. Perhaps it was more than one wave; maybe two or three waves that had collided, rushed together and collapsed upon one another. It was the sea gone mad!

For sixteen endless hours the storm continued, and when we were about ready to give up, no longer caring, it ended. It ended as abruptly as it began. They say the China Sea is shallow, and it doesn't take well to typhoons. But when the winds stopped, the seas stopped with it. I went back to my bunk and fell into a death sleep, despite the filth and stench.

I was in bunk the next morning when I became aware that the ship had slowed down. Suddenly the thought came that we were in a minefield. I was needed on deck. I grabbed my M1 and rushed topside as rapidly as I could, knocking everyone off the ladder who had already started to form the chow line.

I reached the turret and looked out at sea. It was a shocking, abominable sight. The sea as far as the eye could behold was littered with smashed, wrecked junks. These poor junks, they were literally torn apart by the typhoon, ripped wide open, beaten into a pulp, smashed into kindling wood, annihilated. The typhoon had dissipated but it had left a ravenous swath of destruction and death. The convoy had slowed down to half speed, and as we slowly churned forward we glided through a sea of death. On every quarter was wreckage, not one or two, not even a dozen, but a fleet of demolished junks, all devoid of life. There were the bodies, yes, lifeless bodies tied to the masts and rigging, floating corpses. There was not one single sign of life among the sea of wreckage. All morning we continued, but by afternoon our convoy could no longer linger, searching for life, and with a rendezvous to keep, it resumed speed. Night came and we could only imagine ploughing through such human carnage in the darkness.

Our destination was Cheefoo, a seaport on the north shore of the Shantung Peninsula. On the morning of October 9th, we caught our first view of the Chinese mainland. It appeared in a darkened silhouette off our port bow, and as the day grew brighter—there was no sun—the land began to take form. The sea turned from yellow to the color of mud and we knew we were near. A voice came over the PA system announcing it was the coast of the Shantung Peninsula.

China came as a shock, not at all what we had anticipated. It was dismal, mountainous and barren. There was no sign of life, not a tree, not even a shrub. There was no color. It was gray and hard. Even when dawn turned into day it was bleak. That first view was disappointing, but what came next was far worse. It was the smell. Far out at sea we could smell China. It was like no other smell we had known before. It was a musty, unforgiving smell, nauseating to the senses.

As we sailed along the coast, Marines stood at the railing studying the shoreline: a sheltered cove with junks at anchor. Some at least had survived the typhoon. Farther on a fishing village nestled in a valley came into view.

There was something else. It looked so odd at first. Near the fishing village was a long and narrow line, as if someone had taken draftsmen's dividers and had drawn a pencil mark from the edge of the sea to a diminishing point in the far mountains. As we sailed closer, we saw it was nothing more than a wall, a wall without apparent purpose. But still it was there, a Chinese wall, our first wall, but not our last.

Later that morning I was at my post in the turret, drinking a cup of coffee a sailor on duty had given me, when Stevenson appeared. By the look on his face I knew he had something urgent to tell me. "We are not going to Cheefoo," he blurted out. "No Cheefoo landing."

The words hit me like a weight, like one of those barbells you try lifting but it's too heavy and you have to drop it. The barbell hit me right in the chest. After all this, we were not going to China. I was going to the electric shop, to work for my old man, to sell radio vacuum tubes. I hated vacuum tubes at that instant more than I ever hated vacuum tubes before. "What in the hell are you talking about?" I shouted back.

"Take it easy," Stevenson said, looking around. "We're not going to Cheefoo. We're going to Tsingtao."

That was better but I didn't say so. I didn't know where Tsingtao was but nevertheless it was still China. "Why's that?" I asked, calmer now.

"The communists," he said. There was that word again. Over the last couple of weeks that same word was tossed around but none of the Marines would admit they had no idea what a communist was, except that it had a bad connotation. Stevenson continued and I listened, as though I understood.

Major General Keller E. Rockey, the Commanding General, IIIAC, had arrived in Cheefoo shortly before to discover communist troops had already seized the city from the Japanese. They installed a party official as mayor, and were not sympathetic to the request from Admiral Thomas C. Kinkaid, Commander of the Seventh Fleet, that they withdraw before the Marines arrived.

Vice Admiral Daniel E. Barbey, Commander, VII Amphibious Force, recommended that the landing be temporarily postponed. Gen. Rockey concurred, that the Cheefoo landing be delayed, and that the 29th Marines would land instead at Tsingtao with the rest of the 6th Division.

Tsingtao, Cheefoo, what did it matter? China was China and no one in the 29th cared much where we landed, just so we would get off the tub we were on as soon as possible. Our division commander, Major General Lemuel C. Shepherd, Jr. and a small staff had transferred to the Destroyer Escort *Newman* and were en route to Tsingtao. The rest of the convoy followed in close pursuit. *USS Napa* arrived at dusk on October 10th and stood off shore for the night. The following day the rest of the convoy arrived, minus half a dozen LSTs that had lost their rudders. They were in tow.

Together we steamed into Tsingtao Harbor and dropped anchor. The rattling of chains in their hawseholes could be heard clear across the city. What a splendid show we made. From all the riggings, from the bridges to the tallest masts, signal flags, colors and ship's ensigns flew aboard every US vessel in the harbor.

Never did the port of Tsingtao see such a massive flotilla enter its harbor as it did on October 11, 1945—APAs and AKAs, LSMs and LSTs, and other various landing craft, all escorted by the 7th Fleet with her destroyers and destroyer escorts. Ships stretched as far as the eye could see.

Against the splendid backdrop of American ships was the flotilla of Chinese junks. The contrast of ships was never so keen. By the hundreds junks were rafted together, their masts appearing like a forest of trees in a New England winter scene. One could easily have leaped from one vessel to the other and crossed a mile or two of harbor without touching water. They were ancient wooden craft, sea-worn vessels, never having known a coat of paint, only the eyes at their bows were done up in bright colors. Their rigging was hemp, thick as a man's wrist, and their stays were cables blackened with tar. They had rudders that stuck high out of the water, and aside their gunwales running fore and aft were massive leeboards that could be raised and lowered. Their sails, of course, were lateen, and badly sagging. The junks were right out of *Terry and the Pirates*. They had probably been there when Genghis Khan and Marco Polo sailed past.

From aboard ship we could look over the harbor towards the docks where masses of humanity began gathering. Some sat along the docks, their feet dangling over the sides, while others squatted atop buildings, and still others scampered up telephone poles and any higher places they could find. The din of those voices seeped out across the water like the humming of a swarm of a billion bees.

Before our anchors settled on the bottom, hundreds upon hundreds of bumboats, or sampans besieged us. Single oarsmen who stood at the stern sculled each boat. They came waving small American flags, shouting joyously, and quickly displayed their wares: silk robes, embroidered drapery, jackets embossed with golden dragons, ladies garments of mostly dresses slit up the sides, paper lanterns, scrolls with fancy designs, and whiskey, bottles of whiskey—White Horse scotch and Hubba Hubba vodka. Soon more boats arrived, these with young maidens half hidden under tarpaulins. With braided pigtails, bangs, powdered white faces and lips painted bright red, they smiled revealing gold-filled teeth. They definitely weren't Vargas girls. Their presence brought howls and screams from the Marines who crowded the railings.

With a shipload of Marines threatening to jump overboard and Chinese hawkers ready to climb aboard with their wares, orders were given to the deck watch to keep the boats at bay. It was not a task easy to fulfill. Whether or not any women got aboard that first night is questionable, but whiskey did, in bottles with neatly printed labels, certified to be genuine and safe by one Dr. Wong, MD. By morning a couple of Marines from Charley Company were in the sick bay with hoses stuck up their noses, and several others had reportedly gone blind.

At dawn another wave of bumboats began to arrive; MPs with carbines were mustered on deck. When threatening warnings to the gathering bumboats had little effect, the deck officer gave the order to bring out the fire hoses. These high-powered hoses could tear the bumboats apart, sending them to the bottom in an instant. I don't think the Chinese boatmen were aware what was about to happen. I moved over to the railing and looked over the side. Chinese hawkers, many dressed in rags, stood in their boats with their arms lifted up to the Marines along the railing, beckoning us to buy their wares. They looked so pathetic, pleading with us, and I felt sorrow for them. A dozen sailors pulled the limp hoses up to the railings. Two men at each hose grabbed the muzzles and waited for the final order.

It was worth a try. In Mandarin Chinese, a language I had never spoken aloud before, I shouted out—"*Ni zou, ni zou bah.*" Go, go! Go home.

I was more shocked than anyone else standing there. It worked. The bumboats withdrew. The deck officer gave me a startled look. "Where did you learn Chinese?" he snapped.

"I just learned it," I said.

Terry had joined us and stood at my side. "His family were missionaries," he said.

"Shut up, Terry," I said and tried to push him aside. He wouldn't leave.

"What's your name, Marine?" the officer asked.

I told him, and when he asked what outfit, I had to tell him that too—Fox company, 29th Marines.

That afternoon before chow I was summoned to the bridge. What had I done now? I held my hat in my hand and stepped onto the bridge. A dozen Marine officers, with Col. Roston, our battalion commander lording over them, were gathered around a chart table with a map spread out before them. I breathed easier when I saw Whittington standing to one side. He was on duty. He wore his white duty belt with a canteen on the left side and an empty .45 holster on the right. A slight smirk came to his face when he saw me. He then stepped up to Col. Roston. "Sir, here's Private Stephens," he said and stepped back. I was even more dumbfounded than before. Were they going to court-martial me right here and now? Or was this all some kind of a mistake?

Col. Roston gave me the once over. I wondered if he might be expecting someone else the way he looked at me. "I hear you speak Chinese," he said. As I stumbled for words, he continued: "The 6th Reconnaissance Company is going ashore in the morning to secure Tsangkou airfield." Why was he telling me this? "Another landing party is going ashore with them, to negotiate for quarters for the regiment. Unfortunately no officer aboard speaks Chinese. You will go as their interpreter."

I felt the blood drain from my upper body; my knees were about to give way on me. The feeling was far worse than looking up from my foxhole and seeing a banzai charge coming my way as it did at the southern end on Okinawa. "Sir," I said, my voice breaking, "my Chinese is not good."

"Nonsense. It will come back. A little practice. Report on deck in shore uniform at 0800," he said and turned to other matters at hand. I was horrified. What was I to do now?

"That's hot shit," Melanowski said gleefully as he dug into the bottom of my seabag looking for my greens. There was no need. Cpl. Marsden stepped forth and offered me his uniform, all neatly pressed. Stevenson volunteered to let me wear his barracks hat. It was the only barracks hat aboard the *US Napa,* maybe in the whole fleet. I missed chow that evening. I had to study my Chinese handbook. I climbed into my top bunk but to my horror the light had gone out. The storm must have had something to do with it. I went into the head and sat on a toilet and studied, until I was run out. "You som' kinda nut or sumptun," the MP said. "Get the hell out of here!" I went back to my bunk, laid my head down on my life jacket and went over the phrases in my mind. I was progressing. "Are you married?" "Do you have your own rice bowl?"

Chapter 3

CHINA IS A WALL

During the early morning of October 11, while the 7th Fleet stood offshore, the first of the division's transports docked at Tsingtao's wharves. The 6th Reconnaissance Company disembarked and was soon on its way to secure Tsangkou airfield, about ten miles from the city. Two VMO-6 observation planes launched from the escort carrier *USS Bouganville* flew low overhead above the docks and headed toward the airfield.

At 0750 I reported to the bridge on the *USS Napa*, and along with two Marine officers transferred by motor launch to the *USS Bouganville*. Once aboard we were escorted to a stateroom next to the bridge. Gathered around a conference table were a dozen officers and ranking enlisted men. Both officers and men were dressed in their green uniforms. I had never before seen so many campaign ribbons and decorations as I did that morning. Maj. Glen Wallis from the Adjutant General's office stood with his back turned talking to his aide in a tone that was hardly audible. In one hand he carried a black-leather brief case; in the other a swagger stick. At his side was Capt. John Johnson, also from the Adjutant General's office. With the exception of a young pimpled-face lieutenant I had seen all the officers at one time or another. Everyone in the room carried side arms. Staff NCOs stood in the background. Lt. Brandmire was off to one side. He gave a scowl when he saw me and motioned that I stand in the rear behind the NCOs. I do believe that he expected me to salute him, but since I wasn't armed or wearing a duty belt, I wasn't required to salute. I moved to the back as he instructed. I shoved Stevenson's barracks hat farther back under my arm and hated myself for bringing it. Not a single officer or enlisted man in the room had a barracks hat.

Maj. Wallis withdrew some documents from his carrying case, unfolded one, scanned it quickly and then looked up. "Lt. Austin is from G2," he said, glancing over at the lieutenant with the pimple face. "Some of you gentleman may already know him." Lt. Austin smiled. Maj. Wallis continued. "We are not going ashore to engage in combat," he began. "That's not our mission. We are on friendly soil. Tsingtao is under General Chiang K'ai-shek's control." General Chiang K'ai-shek—a name we all knew, one of the good guys. "Lt. Austin will explain in more detail the situation in Tsingtao."

Lt. Austin from the G2 Section stepped forward. "I am pleased to announce that Tsingtao is backed up by armed irregulars recognized by the Central Government, the Kuomintang," he began slowly. What he lacked in appearance, his voice carried in authority. "The Nationalists are running Tsingtao. The communists, however, hold most of Shantung Province, right up to the countryside at the outskirts of Tsangkou airfield. Japanese troops are holding the rail route leading into the interior." I glanced around at the others and wondered if they had the same thoughts as I did. What were the Japanese doing holding rail lines? Weren't we supposed to repatriate them? "Until Nationalist troop units arrive at Tsingtao in sufficient strength to replace the Japanese, there is little hope of rapid fulfillment of repatriation plans. The IIIAC has the enormous task of processing over 630,000 Japanese military and civilian repatriates in North China. We expect to proceed smoothly so long as the Japanese can reach American-controlled areas."

"But we don't expect any armed conflict," Maj. Wallis spoke up. Lt. Austin didn't like being interrupted.

"The colonel is right," he said. "However, the disciplined

strength and tactical and technical know-how of the Japanese will keep both the Nationalists and the Eighth Route Army under control." The Eighth Route Army I learned was another name for communist forces.

"What happens when the Japanese leave China?" a warrant officer asked.

"Only time will tell. We can't speculate," Lt. Austin replied. "In the meantime, the Nationalists are on their way as I speak. The US 14th Air Force is airlifting 50,000 men comprising the 92nd and 94th CNA, the Chinese Nationalist Armies, to Peking from central and South China. The Nationalist are also known as the Kuomintang. The important thing to remember is that we must be careful. We don't want to let our men agitate the situation. We are here to liberate not to conquer."

Maj. Wallis thanked the lieutenant and reminded him that his staff officers are well aware of what is important and what isn't. He then pointed to a map on the table. "Gentlemen, this is a map of Tsingtao," he said. "You will each get a copy. You know our mission now. An advance party under Col. Best, from Division Quarter Masters, will make arrangements for billeting our troops and will obtain information regarding the local civil, military, and political situation. Lt. Brandmire will accompany him." Lt. Brandmire snapped to attention and saluted. He attempted to snap his heels but his bootstraps got in the way.

The 6th Reconnaissance Company had left the docks by the time we disembarked. Our small motor convoy consisted of five 4x4 weapons carriers and three Jeeps with the tops of all the vehicles removed. Lt. Brandmire motioned for the two Marine guards and me to be seated in the last Jeep.

"You swinging with the brass," the driver said as I began to climb into the Jeep. I couldn't believe my eyes. It was Sammy from Motor Pool, from the "Night Fighters Squadron" we called them. "I always knewed you were sumptun."

"Hey, Sammy, I'm not one of these guys," I said. "I'm only a private."

"Yea, boss," he said and saluted from behind the driver's wheel. I was about to push his hat down over his eyes but I noticed Lt. Brandmire watching us.

The lead Jeep, with Maj. Wallis and Capt. Johnson sitting upright in the rear of the vehicle, moved slowly through the arched gate and entered the street. They met with sudden loud cheering and a tumultuous welcome of enthusiastic applause. We were stunned, completely overwhelmed at the reception that awaited us.

First impressions they say are lasting. If this be the case, those who were there that day in Tsingtao on October 15, 1945, will forever remember the landing and the reception we received. No ticker tape parade in New York City for a returning victorious army could have been more grand. The streets were one continuous mass of humanity, a carpet of happy, smiling, waving people. In every direction I looked there were people. They jammed the streets. They crowded the alleys and doorways; they hung out the windows and looked down from rooftops. There wasn't a telephone pole, a signpost or a tree that didn't have people clinging to it. They waved and they cheered. Each and everyone there that day, without exception, babies included, held small American flags which they waved frantically.

An armored Chinese military vehicle was waiting outside the gate and turned into the stream of people when they saw us coming. They led the way as the masses parted to let us past. But barely. Chinese officers in dark brown uniforms and Sam Brown belts sat riding in the lead vehicle, but unlike the rest of us, they remained somber and unsmiling.

We drove through the city, passed a twin towered church and up a long hill to a cluster of stone buildings surrounded by a high wall. The sign at the entrance had Chinese characters with the name "Shantung University" underneath. Our entire route, from dock to university, had been lined with people. There wasn't an inch of standing room to spare. Inside the gate were more people, but now they formed two lines. We passed through the lines to another reception party standing at the doorway to the main building.

The officers and senior enlisted men in our convoy stepped out of their vehicles. Chinese officials in long ankle-length robes bowed slightly from the waist and then extended their hands. Soon everyone was shaking one another's hands. One Chinese official, upon seeing the two guards and me sitting in the Jeep, motioned for us to join the others. It was an awkward situation. We made overtures thanking him and remained seated. The Chinese official ran up to Maj. Wallis and pointed back towards us. I couldn't hear what he was saying but he was speaking in English. What a relief. I suddenly relaxed. They wouldn't need to count on me for Chinese. Seeing our predicament, Maj. Wallis signaled for us to join the party. The Chinese delegation now shook hands with the two guards and me, and pushed us ahead to join the others. Lt. Brandmire was not too pleased.

The main building had been turned into a banquet hall, and we were the guests. It was a banquet deluxe, course after course, lasting two hours.

The meal finally ended and the staff officers were ushered into another room. Col. Best from Division Quarter Masters gave Lt. Brandmire his orders and rushed off to join the staff officers. Before any of the Chinese delegation could lead me away, as I was hoping they would, Lt. Brandmire summoned me to follow him. "We have our orders," he snapped and led the way to an outer courtyard.

The university had been turned over to the division for our billets. Lt. Brandmire's task was to see that classrooms were emptied out and made habitable. Since none of the Chinese in the work party spoke English, I was assigned to assist him. The thought was frightening. I didn't know that much Chinese, but there was no use trying to explain to Lt. Brandmire.

I was at Lt. Brandmire's mercy. He now had me where he wanted me. I had to stand at attention while he gave me instructions. He was a most irritable guy who suffered from some kind of disillusionment. He was downright nasty, and it didn't take a head shrink to reason it was his diminutive size that made him that way. His first name was Clark, named after Clark Gable they say, but he was no Clark Gable. The men in our company could see through him, and I think he was aware of this. He was a non-combatant dealing with combat Marines. His was defensive, which made him a bit cocky. When he walked, he strutted. He wore non-regulation boots with straps and tucked his trousers into the boot tops. This alone would have been enough to make the troops dislike him. Marines like their officers to be regulation. Lt. Brandmire was not.

The Chinese foreman came rushing up to us when he saw us coming. He was a shadow of a man, dressed in a long black robe slit up the sides. He wore a felt hat, had a row of gold teeth and carried a slate for jotting down notes. "Ask him if the buildings are empty, and make sure no one is living in them," Lt. Brandmire said.

"You want to know if the buildings are empty?" I asked.

"Yes, I want to know if the buildings are empty," he said and then abruptly stopped. It seems he suddenly remembered the briefing where Maj. Wallis said it was his duty to gather information about the local military situation. "Find out about security," he added. "How many National Army troops are guarding the city." He looked at me with cutting eyes and then at the foreman.

I searched my mind for words. Troops. Soldiers. Guards. I didn't remember seeing them or any words like them in my *Spoken Chinese* book. Not one. "Go ahead, ask him, private," the lieutenant barked.

In my best Mandarin Chinese I addressed the foreman. "Sir, what is your honorable name?" I said. I remembered clearly, when addressing anyone older than me, I had to call him "honorable." When referring to my name, I had to say that my "humble" name was so and so.

The foreman smiled and bowed from the waist. He repeated

his name in Chinese, which I immediately forgot as soon as he had said it. Chinese names are hard to remember, especially when their last names are really their first names in line.

"What did he say?" Lt. Brandmire asked impatiently.

"He said there are many."

"How many, damn it! Ask him how many!"

"Sir, are you married?" I asked. The foreman looked at me as if I were asking, 'are there green elephants in Tibet?' He didn't reply, only nodded. This wasn't going to do. I had to get an answer from him. "How many children do you have?"

He fired back his answer, so rapidly I couldn't catch one single word. "What did he say? What did he say?" Lt. Brandmire questioned.

"Sir, ah, he's not quite sure," I answered. "Ah, he will get a full report for you later."

"Very good, very good. How long will it take his men to clean up this place?"

"Honorable, Sir," I began. "What is the color of your rice bowl?" And to Lt. Brandmire I replied, "They can do it in a couple hours."

Other questions followed and I was able to learn where the WC was located, and what time the restaurant opened. I even think the old Chinese foreman liked me, although he must of thought I was a bit whacko.

The Seabees and Engineers came to our aid. There was no time to dally around with our quarters. The Chinese coolies were too slow for them. They stormed into the building with sledge hammers, axes and shovels. Opening the double windows wide, they began tossing everything in the class rooms out the windows—glassed-in display cabinets with jars containing strange specimens, weights and scales, vials, glass bottles, books and files with papers, charts and graphs, and anything that moved. Even things that didn't move and were bolted to the floor, they smashed apart and threw those out the windows too. They then built wooden bunks, two high, and for each room brought in an oval kerosene heater.

A high brick wall surrounded the compound; pieces of glass were embedded into the concrete capping that topped the wall. Over this engineers strung rolls of barbed wire and immediately guards were assigned to patrol the inside of the wall.

We had to pitch our eight-man tents again, but not for long. In a few short days we of the 29th Marines moved into our new quarters. That first night, when we were still in our tents, chow went early, and as we sat around in front of our tents wondering when we would get our first liberty, Melanowski came running towards us. "You can get laid," he shouted. "You can get laid right here on base." He grabbed his wallet from his seabag and ran off with everyone in our squad in close pursuit. I had a hard time keeping up with Stevenson.

At the far end of the compound was a cluster of pine trees matted with thick bushes. It was dark now but there was enough light to see a gang of Marines in a long line. "Get in line," they shouted as Stevenson and I approached to see what was going on. "A buck, that's all it costs," one man said. I recognized the voice, Cpl. Wilson from the Hoopa Indian tribe in northern California.

"Who's the woman?" Stevenson asked.

"What the hell does that matter," Cpl. Wilson replied.

"Yeah," said Pfc. Robinson who was near the end of the line, and his second time in line, "what's the difference. Stand them all upside down and they all look alike."

"Right," agreed Hecklinger. "How's a man gonna find out. Good judgment comes from experience, and a lotta that comes from bad judgment."

And so a couple dozen Marines from the 29th became indoctrinated. It wasn't actually a Pearl Buck romance, not what Stevenson and I had in mind when we talked about China aboard the *USS Napa*. But our time was to come.

Chapter 4

FIRST LIBERTY

Everybody on their feet!" Cpl. Marsden sounded out. "Fall out in five minutes," he continued, "helmet liners and rifles."

Marsden had a harsh Oklahoma cowboy voice that commanded respect, and we all hated him for it. When our officers couldn't find anything else for us to do, we had short order drill, and Marsden had to rally us into action. I think he hated it as much as we did but he kept it to himself. It wasn't that we were lying around all day doing nothing; it was just that somebody up above wanted us to be miserable. Of course, the basic reason for Marines to be in China was guard duty, no matter what anybody said. We were told we were going to China to repatriate the Japanese forces, to send them packing back to Japan where they belonged, but after only a short while we began to wonder about this. Instead of sending the Japanese home, we began using them as guards. The Japanese and their puppet troops continued to hold the rail route from coastal towns to Peking. "Until the 4th Marines in the north can take over," Whittington had said a minute or two before Marsden poked his head in the door. Whittington had heard the staff talking about it that morning at HQ.

"Isn't the Nationalist Army supposed to be doing that?" Chandler asked.

"They can't even take care of the communists," Whittington replied. "There's talk about a civil war but Col. Roston said no one is allowed to call it a civil war."

"What do we call it then?" Hecklinger asked in his Oklahoma accent. "If you find yourself in a hole, the first thing to do is stop diggin'."

"Skirmishes," Whittington answered.

"What's the difference? We can get killed in one as easy as the other," Melanowski answered. "What are we guarding anyway?"

Just then Cpl. Marsden opened the door and shouted instructions, and Whittington was out of there faster than a banzai charge, back to his bench in front of Col. Roston's office. While we gathered our helmet liners and rifles, the grumbling began. We had been in Tsingtao two days and we had already stood guard duty, had field training and now we were having short order drill, and there was no mention of liberty.

Our guard duty began even before we had settled in our new quarters. We guarded our headquarters, supply buildings, coal dumps, ammunition dumps, airfields and dock areas. We even had guards to guard the guardhouses. Everything in China needed guarding at all times.

The prize guard duty was the main gate. Sentries here were corporals with sergeants in charge, all picked for their neatness. They manned the gate twenty-four hours a day, and checked every person and vehicle passing in or out for a proper pass. Compound guards were privates and PFCs. They patrolled the entire university, which was surrounded by a stone wall. The wall rose to a height of eight or ten feet, more in some places. The top of the wall had jagged shards of glass embedded in the concrete, like many buildings we saw in Tsingtao when we arrived. Where the wall was not so high, rolls of concertina barbed wire were strung. The most miserable guard duty was the docks. It was as bad as guard duty could get.

The dock area was gloomy and depressing, not a place you'd call cozy. The warehouses, row after row of them, were unpainted with roofs of broken tiles and tiny barred windows high up out of reach. A high wall surrounded the entire area.

The warehouses all looked alike and the only way to distinguish one from the others was by the numbers painted on the corners. Rats were so numerous in the area that even in broad daylight they didn't bother taking cover. Doors on the buildings were huge, crossed with iron straps and studded with bolts. During the day there was all sorts of activity in the area. Military trucks loaded with cargo from the docks arrived one after the other, and gangs of Chinese coolies set to work unloading crates of stores and stacking them in the warehouses. The crates included everything from Bourbon whiskey for the officers' mess to winter underwear for the troops. There was canned tuna and gallon-size tins of fruit cocktail. It seemed half the space in warehouses was taken up by cartons of fruit cocktail. Someone in America was making a killing on fruit cocktail. Never did an occupation army anywhere in the world have more fruit cocktail than the China Marines.

At night the picture changed. Guards had prescribed areas to patrol, and with their loaded M1s slung over their shoulders, they walked their posts. It was lonely and wearisome. Officers-of-the-guard made periodic inspections by Jeep, and sentries called out, "Halt, who goes there!" as if they didn't know. Sentries reported their posts were secured at which the officers and their drivers drove off into the night. Young lieutenants liked to sneak over the wall but that stopped when Terry unloaded a clip of ammo over one's head one night. They were more careful after that. Sentries counted the minutes of their watches, even the seconds, until they were relieved.

When not on guard duty, we had field training. We stripped down and cleaned our M1s, our carbines, our .45 pistols and our .30 Cal. machine guns, blindfolded. No sooner had we put them together than we had to take them apart again. Smitty could field strip his carbine behind his back faster than anyone else could. We had map reading, first aid drill, compass orientation and on Saturday morning we were scheduled to go on a conditioning hike. All this duty and no liberty yet. And now they called us out for short order drill. Who wouldn't beat their gums?

The morning sun came out warm, and for two hours we drilled—"One, hup yah left, one hup yah left." Everyone would be in step, heading straight into a wall. Then, at the last minute, "Left flank hooh, right flank hooh, to the rear hooh." Sometimes there were so many "to the rear hoohs" in session we got dizzy, to the delight of the drill sergeant.

At noon, just before chow call, Cpl. Marsden appeared with a grin on his face. "Okay you leatherheads, liberty call at 1600," he said and cheers went up from every man on the drill field. He continued: "Take the afternoon off and let's see some shined shoes." We didn't walk; we ran back to our quarters.

The only man who wasn't pleased was Stevenson. He didn't get off duty until 1700. He carried his boondockers back to his desk after chow, grumbling, and began the slow process of spit-polishing them. He took his barracks cap with him. Not all of us had dress shoes in the early days, only GI issue ankle-high field boots we called boondockers. We wore them in combat and later for dress as well. They were made of rough brown leather but if you polished them hard and long enough you could get a shine on them. It wasn't mandatory that we shined them but nevertheless Marines prided themselves in the fine gloss they could get on their boots. If you could see your reflection, you had reached perfection. We didn't have dress-green jackets, only field jackets, the ones with four pockets on the outside. A couple guys had Eisenhower jackets. These were cut short and came down to the belt with a slanted pocket on each side. They were smart looking and the envy of everyone.

We spent the afternoon spit-shining and pressing our trousers and telling one another what we intended to do on our first liberty.

For the two days we had been in Tsingtao we had listened to talk about the best liberty spots in town. There was all kind of scuttlebutt, good and bad. We heard one didn't have to venture too far. Right outside the main gate was Sophie & Marie's, a neat little bar that served great steak sandwiches. They said it was run by an old White Russian woman named Sophie and her daughter Marie. That was as far as some of the Marines said they would go, until they heard the damn steak was really dog meat.

Even before we went ashore we knew the names of all the bars and taxi dance halls in town. We had our own intelligence source—the grapevine. Some guys said they were headed for the ABC Bar. "That's for American, British and Chinese," Terry said with certainty.

"No, the Tivoli," insisted Smitty, "that's the place to go. It's first class. They have table cloths, and it's located in the center of Tsingtao, in the tallest building in the city." Other names were tossed out—Prime Club, New York Bar, and Cherry Club. The New York Bar, someone remarked, had White Russian hostesses. But the word was that the best place in town was the EM Club—the Enlisted Man's Club.

"A good meal of steak, eggs and potatoes cost less than a buck at the EM Club," Hecklinger announced. "Drinks, ten cents for any kind of beer and five cents for any kind of liquor or mixed drink. I reckon that's fur me. It don't take a genius to spot a goat in a flock of sheep."

We didn't talk about museums and art galleries; we talked about bars, eating and women, and not necessarily in that order. A heated subject was the bordellos; one, we heard, had a thousand women under one roof. We all agreed we had to go see what they had to offer and look over the merchandise, but the big question was, where would we go first? Some opted to check out the whorehouses first, while others couldn't make up their minds whether to get drunk or to eat first. Our machine gun squad elected to start at the EM Club first. It was settled, unanimously, the EM Club, and we would stick together. Buddies watched over buddies.

Clean-shaven, trousers with creases that could cut fingers,

and faces that shined as bright as our shoes, we headed to the Fox Company office to pick up our liberty passes. We beamed with joy as we bounded into the office, but sadly Stevenson became crestfallen when he saw us. "You aren't gonna wait for me," he whimpered, threatening to tear up our passes. He had another hour before he got off duty.

"And waste an hour," we all growled. We finally convinced him we'd meet him at the EM Club in town.

As Stevenson handed me my pass, he said he had a message for me. "Col. Roston wants to see you at 0800 Monday morning," he said.

"What about?" I asked. Any time a Marine had to see the Old Man it had to be for Office Hours, for some offense or infraction of the rules, but I hadn't done anything wrong, not anything that I knew about.

"He didn't say, but it must be something important. He had discussed it with the Exec."

"Why Monday? Why not now, or tomorrow morning?" I asked. "You kidding. We go on a hike at 0600 tomorrow," Stevenson snapped. "You forget!" He then changed his tone. "But hey, buddy, we get liberty tomorrow when we get back from the hike, and all day Sunday too." I immediately forgot about Col. Roston and Office Hours.

The moment we stepped out the gate half a hundred rickshaw drivers, two lines of them that extended far down the hill besieged us. "Hey, Joe, hey Joe, rickshaw," they called out, holding on to their rickshaws with one hand and extending the other in pleading gestures. At the slightest signal from a Marine, they dashed forward. We made our selections, agreed to ten cents a ride, and in a phalanx like charging chariots shot down the hill to the EM Club.

We learned instantly that rickshaws are delicately balanced machines. A heavy-set Marine could lean back in his seat and lift the driver right off his feet. A couple of Marines tried to put drivers into the seats and take over but it didn't work. It took skill, balance and practice to pull a rickshaw. We saw scores of other rickshaws farther down the road parked by the wayside. They were serving as shelters, even homes, for their owners. The drivers had covers over the tops, and many were stretched out fast asleep.

We were about to have our first real look at a Chinese city. There were no waving, cheering people now. What did greet us was reality. It was like looking through a kaleidoscope and not seeing colors but instead a scene of gloom and despair. To farm boys like most of us were, who had only seen Charleston, South Carolina, when we got out of Parris Island boot camp, this was shocking. We were too bewildered to make comments. No one cracked jokes or made wisecracks. We couldn't comment, only stare in disbelief. Every direction we turned there was something startling to see. We were awed by the Chinese, the confusion of traffic, the vehicles, the noise, the filth, the dilapidation, the smell. Charcoal burning trucks bounced over torn pavements, some so heavily loaded we thought their axles might bust. Some did, and traffic had a devil of a time getting around them. Battered buses with people hanging on the outside like flies on flypaper rolled past, their exhausts kicking out evil black smoke. On some, passengers sat on top. Nationalist troops in columns of two marched through the streets. Policemen in black uniforms and Sam Brown belts across their chests stood on concrete posts at busy cross sections, blowing whistles and waving their arms frantically. No one seemed to pay attention to them. Stalls with dirty sagging canvas awnings overhead lined the sidewalks, and here merchants sold their wares and customers argued with them about prices. Motorcars with doors falling off, and some tied with twine to keep the doors on, rumbled past. None of the signs, not a single one, could we read. They were all in unintelligible Chinese characters. We could only imagine what was behind the signs and closed doors.

The saddest thing we witnessed were the heavy, overloaded carts, pulled not by animals but by men, human beings. It was inhumane to watch. These carts were the backbone of the transportation system. They were on all the streets, clumsy carts, with two huge wooden wheels with spokes and steel rims. The coolies that worked them did so with backbreaking effort. Two, sometimes three men labored in unison at each cart to keep it in motion. Over their shoulders they slung ropes, and upon these they bent their weight as they pushed, and at the same time they pulled on the two handlebars sticking out from the front. They slid and often fell to the pavement, bloodying their knees and elbows, but not giving up. When their carts became rutted and stuck, they twisted and turned them sideways and pushed and pulled again until they had them free. Such a curse against humanity that man should labor so hard.

And among all this traffic, rickshaws shot in and out, darting away from oncoming trucks and avoiding crashing into other rickshaws. Rickshaw boys called out warnings and threats that no one seemed to heed. Now and then an immaculately kept rickshaw, shiny black and polished, with neatly crafted gold trim, ambled past. They were the envy of everyone. Their drivers were smart; they wore new canvas shoes; their clothing was uniform and clean. They pulled well-dressed Chinese men and women, and some school children. Whether man, woman or child, these passengers sat back smug and arrogant and looked upon the world around them condescendingly. Some of the rickshaws, not the wealthy ones, had young boys running along side, and when they came to an incline the boys helped push. Some boys couldn't have been more than seven or eight years old. These drivers and boys wore castoff clothing. No two pieces were the same.

The masses, the throngs of people, moved along the sidewalks and out into the streets as recklessly as the traffic. Many, mostly school children, had their faces covered with white surgical masks. Men wore long robes, slit up the sides. Women wore simple dresses that reached below the knees, also slit up the sides. Every fifth person had a pockmarked face. Smallpox had disfigured them permanently. All the women had bangs, and when they smiled, which wasn't often, they revealed gold teeth. As we looked over the scene, there was lack of color, no pastels or light colors among the whole lot. Things were either black or brown. The Chinese, the shoppers, the merchants, the pedestrians, they all appeared oblivious to the beggars, and beggars were as numerous as the shoppers. There was no escaping them—lepers, the blind holding on to sticks following young children, men with missing limbs, young girls hardly old enough to be mothers yet still cradling infants, and child beggars who came in hordes running after our rickshaws. "No mama, no papa," they called. "Kumshaw, kumshaw!"

Mingled with all this chaos and confusion was the smell of China. The smell wasn't anything in particular but everything in general. It was a blend of the whole of China. It was a smell we first detected far out at sea, and it was the same smell that followed us ashore. It was the unwashed bodies, the human waste gathered to fertilize their crops, the garlic they ate to sustain their lives. It was a smell that would never escape us.

There were some souls we saw—we couldn't call them beggars for they didn't beg—who appeared to have never washed in their lives. Their skin was black, black as coal miners coming from the pits, their hair uncut, matted and tangled, and their clothing tattered rags as filthy as their bodies. They had to have demented, sick minds, for there could be no other excuse for their existence, and yet, we wondered, wasn't there a place for them to go other than the streets of Tsingtao.

The fleet of rickshaws carried us to the EM Club without mishap. Upon seeing the three-story redbrick building with a sign WELCOME SAILORS AND MARINES, our mood quickly changed. We each gave our rickshaw boys the money due them, but they demanded more and ran after us. We charged into the club leaving them on the steps below. Laughing and hollering, happy that we were still in one piece, we burst through the doors like conquering heroes.

The EM Club was, indeed, an escape from a nightmare world outside into a haven of retreat, a house of fun, but to all who entered, it was also an entrance to a volatile world. Anything could happen, and did happen at the EM Club. There were no women, only service men in uniform. The noise was deafening. The floor vibrated, the walls shook, the ceiling threatened to collapse, and with jabbering, shouting, hard-drinking Marines from the 6th Division and sailors from the 7th Fleet, the place was unhinged. There must have been a hundred tables or more, and clustered around them were groups of Marines and sailors, not together but separately. They mocked and sneered at one another, sailors vs. Marines, and any minute threatened to pounce upon the other. The more beer they consumed, the more tense grew the situation. Among this entire melee, waiters carrying trays laden with cans of beer and glasses with harder stuff scurried dutifully among the tables. The waiters accepted willingly, although not gleefully, the jibes and jeers from the carousing band of brothers. At some tables empty beer cans were stacked as high as a Marine or sailor could reach, that is, while standing on a chair attempting to place another can on top. When a mountain of cans toppled over it was mayhem. Dare the man who might deliberately have knocked over a pile of cans. He was sure as hell dead meat.

Behind the bar was a large mural painted across the entire wall. The mural was a masterpiece, the EM Club's *piece de resistance*. It depicted various scenes common to China and to seafaring men. One scene showed King Neptune in pursuit of a beautifully endowed mermaid. He chased her at high speed, leaving a large foaming wake behind him, his long white beard streaming in the wind. He had a wild lustful gleam in his eye and there was no doubt what his intent was if he caught her. Behind him came Queen Neptune. She was in full pursuit of the King, leaving a large wake behind her too. She was terribly ugly, having a long nose with a large wart on the end of it. Her bare breasts were long and stringy like an old woman's. One long tit was thrown back over the top of one shoulder. The other tit trailed in the breeze under her other arm. Her eyes were shooting sparks and fire. It was quite apparent she was mad as hell. The mural had a drunken mouse on it and the custom was for new guys to find the mouse. If they couldn't find it, they had to buy a round. The more drinks they consumed, the harder it was to find the mouse for he was hidden behind a table leg lapping up spilt liquor. It was apparent the mouse was very drunk. It was really quite a work of art and very funny.

We found a table, marked out our territory and began swilling down cans of beer at ten cents a can. Hecklinger bought a box of Havanas, and soon we puffed on cigars, leaned back and boasted about what a great life we had. Stevenson arrived an hour later, all smiles, wearing his barracks hat, and immediately challenged everyone at the table to see who could chug-alug a beer faster than he could. He easily won the first round since most of us had our fill and were drunk by then. A swabbie at the next table made a remark about Stevenson's hat, a most sensitive thing to do. Chandler defended his buddy, fists began flying and the machine gun squad of 2nd Platoon, Fox Company, 2nd Battalion, 29th Marines, was kicked out and banned from the EM Club on their first liberty ashore in Tsingtao.

"Never mind," shouted Smitty out in the street. He had his sleeves rolled up, and the Hawaiian girl tattooed on his left forearm seemed to dance in agreement. "Hey, boys," he stammered, gyrating from side to side, "we go dancing, you know, dance." He held his arms stretched out, like he was holding his dance partner. "Go dance, drink, you know, whiskey." He puffed his chest, tilted his head back and smacked his lips, pretending he was kissing a woman. Terry turned his back and would have pulled down his trousers and drawers to expose his butt if we hadn't pushed him away, with Smitty attempting to plant a foot in his rear. It was all worth a laugh.

Agreed, we'd go to the Prime Club, all except Hecklinger.

He wanted to strike out on his own. "If you're ridin' ahead of the herd," he said, staggering from one side to the next, "take a look back every now and then to make sure it's still there with ya. I'll find ya'all when I look fur ya'all."

We called rickshaws and instructed the drivers in our newly acquired pidgin English—"You takee us chop chop Prime Club lookie see." The lead rickshaw boy said he knew the place, but we had doubts as our convoy shot through crowded streets and into back alleys, avoiding the main traffic route. The driver knew his business. A block before we reached the club we could hear the noise, a boisterous mixture of shouting, merry making and music. Feeling our liquor and in a jubilant mood, we gave the rickshaw boys more than they agreed to; they still complained and ran after us as we charged up the stone steps to the Prime Club.

The club was jam-packed and about ready to burst at the seams. It was marvelous. Dance music came from a four-piece band assembled upon a raised platform at the far end of the room. Behind them hung the sign THE TSINGTAO CHARIOTS. They were a comical lot, more like characters in a comic strip than a real live band. They wore Western suit coats and long trousers. The coats were ill fitting and the trousers hardly reached down to their shoes. One man was perched on a three-legged stool in front of an upright piano, and another sat half-hidden behind a set of battered drums. A saxophonist and an accordionist stood in front of a microphone. They were playing "Golden Earring" when we entered, not like Benny Goodman on sax and Gene Krupa on drums but their music was good enough to fill the dance floor with GIs swooning over their taxi-dancer partners. The music ended, Marines and sailors returned to their tables and the girls went back either to the tables where they had been sitting or else to their chairs along the wall. With only a brief delay, the band took up the beat and began playing "Give Me Five Minutes More," or what sounded like "Give Me Five Minutes More."

The Prime Club was a rectangular room about the size of a

basketball court. The dance floor was in the very center of the room. Tables three deep flanked the dance floor on three sides. The remaining side was lined with straight-back chairs. Here the taxi dancers sat. They were a pathetic-looking bunch of women and one felt pity for them. They tried to look their best, but sadly they had little to work with. Their dresses were motley, some Chinese, some Western. They were certainly more attractive in their Chinese clothes than they were when they wore Western costumes. Somehow they didn't look right in silk dresses with ribbons and bows their tailors made for them from pictures in the Sears & Roebuck catalogs dating back to the 1920's. When it came to their attempting to wear high-heel shoes, which very few women had, they were a catastrophe. Surprisingly, no one laughed at them; GIs treated them as ladies, and in most cases the guys were proud, and protective, of their women.

However, these women were very clever. They didn't miss a clue. They saw us coming, and smiled beguilingly and ogled any of us who happened to look in their direction. We had to grab Smitty by the shirt to hold him back when he saw the line up. Scotty and Chandler weren't much better.

We looked for a table but all were taken. The room was heavy with smoke and the air charged with high-powered excitement. Through the smoke we had a difficult time telling if a dancer across the way was pretty or if she was pockmarked. Things were in a blur, like photographs out of focus. I attributed the blur to the smoke but most likely it was due to our consumption of booze. We did a lot of stumbling, and we felt we could lick any swabbie in the joint.

We stood at the bar, waiting, and when a table was free we rushed in to grab it, outmaneuvering a couple of sailors who thought twice about arguing. A bow-tied waiter in a white apron brought us two extra chairs and took our order. We had several choices of whiskey, all certified to be tested as safe to drink, but we settled on local Tsingtao beer, which the waiter called *pijiu*, and Hubba-Hubba vodka, which we had heard was the safest booze to drink. We ordered *pijiu* for everyone and two bottles of Hubba-Hubba. When the order came we poured out a peg of Hubba-Hubba for each of us and attempted to down them straight. We couldn't stop the embarrassing tears that came to our eyes. The rotgut vodka numbed our tongues and burnt all the way to the bottom. We agreed it was fine stuff and ordered lime soda mix for the next round, with ice, but the waiter said they didn't have ice. The band now began playing its rendition of "Zip-a-Dee-Doo-Dah" and made it sound like a polka. Smitty found a girl he fancied and asked her to dance but discovered he first needed a ticket to dance. The dancer led him to a booth near the entrance. Ten-cents a ticket to dance, or 50 cents per hour for a lady to sit at a table. If you paid for a girl for an hour, you could dance as much as you liked, or you could spend the time talking. The girls also ordered their own drinks. We paid for the price of whiskey but figured it was only tea, but we weren't allowed to taste.

The crowd became unruly, the music louder and the women more aggressive. They no longer sat at their chairs but now wandered among the tables, running their fingers through a man's hair. They asked to sit at tables, and if rejected, they stormed off mumbling "Cheap Charley." Disagreements over the women began to break out. Men sized up one another. Tensions were building.

Scotty brought a girl to the table. She was part Korean and spoke barroom English. She was quick to reprimand him when he admired a girl at another table.

"What's with you?" Scotty asked. "You can look around and I can't."

"Me no likee man him butterfly," she admonished him. "When girl sit your table, and you pay money, no one can come talk her. No dance with her. You furstay?

"I furstay," he said, "but me no likee. Me have one girl friend, okay. You have many boy friend, that okay."

"Now you furstay. You only one girl flend. Me. You smart man," she said and they got up to dance.

At a few tables away there was a ruckus between two Marines from Baker Company. The shorter of the two men grabbed an empty Hubba-Hubba, knocking over the drinks on the table as he stood up, and was about to swing it at the other Marine. The Marine squared off with both fists. All hell was about to erupt. The band took the cue and began playing "The Girl that I Marry" as loud as they could. At that moment the girl sitting with them rose to her feet and stood between them. We couldn't quite make out what she was saying but it was obvious the Marine with the bottle had paid time for her and the other one butted in. I couldn't take my eyes from the woman. She was lovely, not beautiful, but striking.

I thought for sure she was going to get slugged, and having just enough vodka in me, I rushed over to their table. I was unaware that all my buddies from the machinegun squad, five of them, had followed behind me.

"We're okay, okay," the woman said. She spoke with a slight English accent, not fractured English like most of the bargirls there spoke. As rapidly as the argument began, it ended. The woman had everything under her control.

"A real pro," Terry muttered when we sat down. We ordered more vodka and bought tickets to dance. There was more to pick from when you weren't saddled with a girl at your table. I danced with a few girls but I couldn't take my eyes from the one at the next table, the girl who prevented the fight. She was tall for Chinese, and slight of figure. It was her smile that was so beguiling. She had two dimples. I was tempted to ask her to dance but it was obvious she had been bought for the night. She was aware that I was watching her.

Two more fights broke out that night; each time, the band played louder. The last fight became a free-for-all and the Shore Patrol was called. Word got around the paddy wagon was coming. Everyone rushed back to their tables, straightened their chairs and tried to cover up their torn shirts, black eyes and broken teeth. We appeared to all outsiders like a loving bunch of babes in arms when the SP's arrived. Nevertheless they stood around, and a half-hour before curfew they ushered us out to our waiting rickshaws.

The girls waved us good-bye and asked that we come again, which each of us promised we would do. But love stopped at the door. Taxi dancers in the clubs were not permitted to leave the premises. There was no need to explain to the rickshaw boys where to take us. They knew exactly. They dropped us at the main gate, but shortly before we arrived there, we all became disturbed by something we saw. A young Chinese boy, perhaps seven or eight, was asleep in a sewer pipe. When he heard our singing, he stuck his little head out from the sewer and with sad eyes watched us go by. The sight of him stopped us all from singing. We went through the gate in silence. Our defense was not to make comments. We pretended we didn't see him.

For those who had gone ashore the night before, the conditioning hike into the hills was sheer agony. Hecklinger suffered the most, and he wouldn't tell us where he had been. "Always drink upstream from the herd," he said.

No mercy was shown us that morning. Those who didn't go on liberty took advantage of the situation. They talked about having greasy porkchops for noon chow when we got back. Marsden, who hadn't gone on liberty, spoke about a dog he saw that got smashed on the road the day before. "His guts was all over the road," he emphasized.

"Yeah, and the flies and stink," Kyle chimed in.

"How in the hell would you know," Stevenson barked at Kyle. "You've never been out of the sack long enough to know what the road outside looks like."

"You're right," Kyle said. "The only time I want to go out that front gate is when I leave China and go home."

We all felt sorry for Kyle, and at the same time we hated him. There he was, marching right along with us. Poor Kyle, he had never exercised a day in his life; his arms were skinny as tooth picks and his skin was pasty white. But what was so annoying about him was that the conditioning hike didn't bother him, not at all. He not only kept up, he was in better shape than most of us.

Our hike took us past the racetrack, beyond the city limits into the hills to a Shinto shrine. The shrine was a tower about 60 feet tall with windows looking out on each floor and had a four-cornered roof with eaves that curled up at the edges. We were too beat to climb the tower and instead sat around in front and rehashed the events that took place the night before. We all agreed we'd go back to the Prime Club again that night.

Stevenson and I went on liberty after lunch. The others slept and we couldn't get them up. We had no idea where we were going. Rather than take rickshaws into town we decided to walk. It didn't matter. Two rickshaws followed close at our heels, and in the end I paid them off anyway.

Along the road to the university the bars and restaurants were open and their owners stood out front and called us to enter. The specialty in all the restaurants was the same—steak and eggs. We continued on towards town, trying to understand our new world.

Tsingtao was a hilly town that sloped toward a wide bay. Looking down we could see ships and many hundreds of junks at anchor. We came to a square and at one end stood a big Lutheran Church with twin steeples. Across the square from the church was a row of buildings, and one of them had a hand-drawn picture of a bathtub and shower. Beneath the picture in small letters was the word BATHHOUSE in English. We entered to investigate. We were surprised to find a gigantic pool with warm water that filled the room with steam. We wanted to swim, but first, we learned, we would have to go through a cleansing process. We were each ushered into a little cubicle, whereupon my attendant gave me a towel and hung a wooden tab with Chinese characters on a peg near the door. He bid me to take off my clothes. Reluctantly I stripped down to my skivvy drawers, and he demanded those too. I took the three dollars I had, crumpled them up in my hand and held them tightly. The attendant then took my clothes from the room and pointed to a tub steaming with hot water. The water was so hot I could hardly put in my big toe, but the attendant insisted and pushed me in. He hung another tab on the peg. I could hear the same thing happening to Stevenson on the other side of the wall. He was squealing about the water being too hot.

My attendant washed me down, one arm and one leg at a time, while I held my cupped hand with money over my private parts. Two more attendants appeared, one with a straight razor and soap, the other with a pair of scissors and a nail file. One attendant pushed my head back and began shaving me while I still sat in the tub. He shaved not only my face but my ears as well, even my eyelids and forehead. The other man busied himself cutting my toenails. More tabs went up on the peg. Next came a rubdown like I never had before. Actually, to be honest, it was the first one I ever had. I heard Stevenson moaning, "Oooh, ouch, ahhh." A boy brought hot tea. More tabs. I was given another towel, with another tab added to the peg. They then led me out to the swimming pool. Stevenson was already in the pool with only his head and toes sticking up above the water. For what seemed like an eternity we basked in the pool, until our flesh crumbled and our faces lost all color. Finally, they asked that we get out of the pool. Back in our cubicles our clothes were hanging, washed and neatly pressed. More tabs had been hung on the peg.

"How much money do you have?" I asked Stevenson. He only had a dollar, and I cringed as we approached the cashier. He got out his abacus and began adding up the bill. It came to $1.27 each. We had enough money left for a bottle of Hubba-Hubba at the Prime Club, and a little for our rickshaws, but not enough for dance tickets. But first, feeling on top of the world, we had to check out Ping-Pong Wooley's, the whore-house some called the Thousand Assholes.

The rickshaw boys were still waiting. They beamed when we told them where we wanted to go. I doubt we could ever have found the place on our own. It had a number of entrances but finding them was the secret. The House of Pleasure could also be reached from a number of small bars through hidden tunnels and passageways, but you had to know them. The rickshaw drivers deposited us in front of an arched doorway and said they would wait for us here. We looked at each other, Stevenson and me, took a deep breath and entered, like gladiators entering the ring.

We found ourselves in a large courtyard, expecting lions to charge, or at least something to happen. It was quiet for a moment, until a resonant gong sounded, and then like a movie screen bursting into life, a thousand women appeared. The court yard was flanked on all sides by a building four-stories high, and on each level facing the courtyard were long open corridors, and here the women stood, waving and shouting to us. They stood there, every age, in every stage of dress. Moments later sailors and Marines appeared, their women at their sides, only to disappear when they saw it was only two more customers who had arrived.

What do we do now?

The answer came soon enough. A half dozen mamasans appeared, little old shriveled up women, some with bound feet, each grabbing for our arms, beckoning us to follow them. One, more persistent than the others, spoke in broken English. "Come, you lookie see," she said. "No likie, no money."

"Right, no money," Stevenson said and pulled out his empty pockets. He wasn't lying. He didn't have any money. I had the money, but the mamasan didn't know that, and no amount of pleading would convince her otherwise.

"Melican plenty money," she said and pulled us with her up a pair of steps to the level above. Suddenly a bevy of girls surrounded us. They tugged at our sleeves; they pulled at our coats. We learned quickly not to admire any one girl for then it was much more difficult to refuse them. Eventually the mamasan realized we weren't serious and demanded that we get out. We left, and said we'd be back.

Our rickshaw drivers were waiting, but when we tried to tell them we would walk, as we had little money, they explained in gestures and arm movements it did not matter. We could pay them later. Okay, okay. They took us to the Prime Club.

Being Saturday night, the Prime Club was even more explosive than before. We found a table, ordered a bottle of Hubba-Hubba and bought a handful of dance tickets. Stevenson used the tickets doing the tango with Judy, a part Japanese girl he met the other night. And the girl that I so admired came to the table while her date went to talk to Marines at another table. "I'm Ming-Lee" she said. I was delighted she remembered me. She suggested I come back during the week, when the club wasn't so busy. I said I would, but I wasn't about to get on the Ferris wheel. She was attractive, and had a nice charm, but on a Ferris wheel one can't always get off.

There was no money for more vodka or dance tickets; reluctantly we had to go back to the base. In the rickshaw I was proud of myself. No way was Ming-Lee going to catch me in a trap. "But then," I said to myself, "she is lovely." I soon forgot her when I saw the little boy in the sewer. I wondered what he ate, if he did. Where were his parents?

Sunday was a lazy day. Those who were not on guard could sleep in if they wished. Kyle missed both morning and noon chow. Sammy checked out a Jeep and took eight of us all squeezed together for a ride to the beach area north of town. We passed some beautiful beaches with homes nestled in the hillsides where affluent Chinese lived. In the summer months rich Chinese and many foreigners came by train from as far away as Peking, and from Shanghai by coastal boat. But it was winter now and the hotels and inns were closed, except for a hotel high on a rocky edge of a jutting peninsula. It was an officers' quarters now, and, of course, out of bounds for enlisted men.

Before turning in that night, Stevenson reminded me Col. Roston wanted to see me at 0800 the following morning. "You have a way of messing up a guy's perfect day," I said to him.

"Think of Ming-Lee instead," he said. I thought about Ming-Lee, and about the kid sleeping in the sewer.

Chapter 5

THE COLOR OF YOUR RICE BOWL

A few minutes before 0800, my hat in my hand, I was standing in front of Stevenson's desk at Fox Company Headquarters. He was waiting for me. Whittington was sprawled out on a bench at one side, reading a much-worn copy of *Esquire*. He always had some smart remark to make but this morning he was quiet. I wondered if he knew something that I didn't. "You had better go right in," Stevenson said. "The Old Man is waiting for you." He knocked lightly on the door, opened it and announced to Col. Roston that I was there. He then stepped aside to let me pass. Once inside the office, I stood at attention, prepared for the worst but it didn't make it any easier. I felt like I had a .45 cocked and pointed at my chest.

All kinds of thoughts danced through my head, but none were even close to what Col. Roston had to say. "At ease, Stephens," he said, looking up from his desk. The .45 misfired. This was a good sign. He always had the troops stand at attention when he saw them in his office. But then, I thought, it could be bad news and he was being easy on me. If that were the case, something drastic must have happened back home. He would be sending me back Stateside. I didn't want that. I wanted to stay in China. Some one cocked the .45 again.

"There's a missionary lady here," he began, choosing his words carefully. "She's British, and I feel, rather we feel, kind of sorry for them. For seven years, Mrs. Murray, her husband and their kids were in a Jap concentration camp. The youngest was born in camp." He leaned back in his swivel chair, almost tipping over backwards. What did this have to do with me? Then the thought came to me. That was it, certainly! I had joked with the guys that I came from a missionary family. There had to be a connection. Col. Roston had it all wrong. I didn't know any missionaries. I had never even met a missionary. I had no idea what a missionary even looked like. How was I going to explain this now? "Mrs. Murray, that's her name," he continued, "she contacted Fleet Headquarters. She wants to offer her services as a teacher, to teach Chinese." I wasn't aware of it, but I might have even smiled. I wasn't going Stateside. The .45 was uncocked and was put back in its holster. Col. Roston had something else in mind.

"She teaches Chinese," I said, not quite knowing where this was going to lead, but I felt I had to say something.

"Yes, teaches Chinese," he replied. "I'm relieving you of all your duties. You will continue with your study of Chinese, starting this afternoon. You will study at the Murray home, at their request, and Motor Pool will provide transportation. Your expenses will be paid out of Company funds. Mrs. Murray will report to us your progress. Any questions?"

"No, Sir," I replied. I wanted to thank him but I thought it best not to, mostly because I didn't know how to thank him.

"You lucky bastard," Stevenson said when I came out of the office. The door to the colonel's office had been ajar and he and Whittington eavesdropped on our whole conversation. "Now you can really find out what those girls down at the Prime Club are saying."

"Who's the brown-noser now?" Whittington asked.

The Murrays lived in a residential area out near the racetrack. It was wooded with tall pines that hummed in the wind as we drove by in the Jeep. Sammy knew the area, as one of the staff officers moved into a house there, and he had no difficulty locating the Murray place. He offered to pick me up in a couple of hours but I said I'd find my way back. With an open-gate pass I wasn't worried about being picked up by the MPs during non-liberty hours. Earlier that morning I thought I was going to be court-martialed and now I was as free as the wind in the trees above. I was floating. I thanked Sammy, walked up the steps to the house and was about to knock on the door, and stopped short. How our moods can change. I suddenly felt uneasy. Uncertain. When the door opened, what would I discover on the other side? I was soon to find out. A young girl of about six or seven opened the door. She stood there, looking at me, saying nothing.

"Who is it, dear," a voice from far inside said and presently an elderly lady appeared. She hastily introduced the young girl, Sally, her daughter and promptly sent her way.

"I'm Mrs. Murray," she said and bid me to come in. Some quick calculations and I placed her to be about 50 years old. It was very hard to tell though. She could have been much younger. She was dressed all in black—the shawl around her shoulders, her dress, her stockings, her shoes. She was very skinny. Her eyes were deep and hollow, with dark shadows beneath. The most prominent feature about her was her lower jaw. It jutted far out. When she spoke, I could see her teeth were very bad.

"Come into the drawing room," she said. "You must be my new student." I acknowledged that I was and followed her into a study with books on one wall and large bay windows facing the ocean on the other side. A table with a lace tablecloth was set in front of the windows, and upon it were books, writing tablets and pencils. Mrs. Murray was ready for business. I realized at that moment I hadn't brought any study material with me, not even a pencil. "Do sit down," she said and pointed to a chair at the table. Her accent was very proper English. She spoke like one of those British actors you see in the movies. I was fascinated by the way she talked.

Awkwardly I took a seat. "You are American," she said. "We had a few Americans in camp." She hesitated as though she had said something wrong. "Your colonel must have told you, we were prisoners under the Japanese." I nodded. "Your colonel is such a delightful man." She waited for me to say something, and then continued. "How long have you been in the army?"

"Ma'am, I'm not in the army."

"But you are a soldier."

"No, ma'am, I am a Marine, United States Marines, ma'am. I am in the Marine Corps."

"My, my, my," she said. "I thought all boys in uniform were the same." I was aware someone entered the room from behind. Mrs. Murray glanced in that direction. "Oh, my, you must meet Mr. Murray," she said. I turned to see an elderly gentleman standing there. He was stooped and quite frail. He needed the use of a cane to support himself. He advanced slowly, reached out and we shook hands. I was used to firm handshakes, not one like this. I thought his hand might break. I quickly withdrew my hand. He sat down in a high-back chair with the utmost discomfort. Then he gave a deep sigh, and with his cane between his knees, he rested his two trembling hands on the curved handle.

"I hope I didn't interrupt anything," he said. He spoke softly and it took an effort to understand him.

"Not at all, dear," Mrs. Murray said. "We are just getting acquainted. "Mr. Stephens tells me he's a Marine and not a soldier."

She called me mister. No one had ever called me mister before.

"Of course, of course," he said. "They were American Marines who rescued us from camp. We were very lucky. You fellows arrived before the Russians. Had the Russians been first, or Mao's forces, we would not be sitting here now."

I asked what outfit had rescued them. Mr. Murray didn't know names of outfits but he did go into great detail about what had happened. He repeated several times that he was grateful to the Marines. "Eight years is a long time." He interrupted our conversation for a moment and asked a servant to bring us tea. "The world has completely changed," he continued. "China is not the same, and never will be." He spoke almost in a whisper and had to stop often to catch his breath. The anguish of those long years in prison showed on his face.

"Now, now, Henry," Mrs. Murray interrupted, "you mustn't upset yourself." Turning to me, she said, "Mr. Murray is under doctor's care. He must take it easy." With that Mrs. Murray helped her husband to his feet and led him to a more comfortable seat on the sofa. Tea was served on the coffee table in front of the sofa.

"You do drink tea?" Mrs. Murray said. "I know Americans drink coffee but we English must have our afternoon tea."

We spent the next hour at small talk. The Murrays wanted to know were I was born and about my home. We discussed briefly my studies, and Mrs. Murray reminded me we would begin lessons the next day at 1400. I would be the only student but there may be others later. She had a Chinese-English dictionary but she suggested that I get one of my own. If the PX, which she called the army store, didn't have one for sale there would probably be a shop or two in town that did. Our meeting over, we said our good-byes and I left the Murrays sitting in the front room. I was happy to walk through the woods and listen to the wind in the pines again.

By the end of the week, my studies with Mrs. Murray became a matter of routine. I would arrive every afternoon at 1400 and study until 1600. It wasn't all studies, however. We took the time to talk about many things and I came to know much more about the Murrays. She had fascinating tales of old China to tell. She was a marvelous storyteller. "There was so much to do here in China," she said. "And we were needed." They settled in Cheefoo and traveled throughout north China before the war. The Japanese invaded in 1938 and their world was turned topsy-turvy. Their first daughter Clara had been born in 1927.

Although she lived with them now in their big house, she stayed pretty much on her own and remained out of sight. Once I got a fleeting glimpse of her when the Murrays invited me to dinner one evening. It was only a glance for she darted back into her room, thinking I had gone. I could sense that something was wrong but I could not quite put my finger on it. I was sure in time I would find out. I didn't want to ask.

My classes in the beginning were most difficult and I didn't think I would ever learn Chinese. Mrs. Murray admitted she had used the wrong approach with me. "We will study vocabulary every day followed by basic grammar," she said at our first class. "You will learn to conjugate verbs."

"Conjugate verbs," I said.

"Yes, conjugate verbs," she said. "Certainly you conjugated verbs in school, didn't you?" I didn't want to tell her that I dropped out of school in the 9th grade to join the war effort and began working in the steel mills, and on my seventeenth birthday I joined the Marines. My mother and father had to sign my papers and agreed to let me join since the war was winding down, and I pleaded with them that if I enlisted, before it was too late, I would be entitled to all kinds of benefits. I could study electrical engineering under the GI Bill. No one had even the slightest notion that the war was a long way from over. Nor did anyone know that I really didn't want to study electrical engineering. My parents signed my enlistment papers and I left for Parris Island.

That first night when I returned from the Murrays to the barracks, I studied verb conjugations. It wasn't that difficult and I figured I could easily bluff my way through now. A couple of hours and I knew all the answers.

"Today we will study verb tenses," Mrs. Murray began the next day. I knew them: past, present, future. "In Chinese we do not have the pluperfect and conditional tenses that you have."

Pluperfect, conditional tenses, I had no idea what she was talking about. It was obvious I had to learn English grammar before I could learn Chinese grammar.

Except for the little money the Murrays made from tutoring, they had no other income. Whenever possible I brought them gifts from the PX that I smuggled out the gate— shampoo, Lux soap, toothbrushes and toothpaste, a Gillette safety razor and blades. Mr. Murray had never seen a safety razor before. "What they don't have these days," he said. They were pleased with anything that I brought. In spite of their ill health, and problems with their daughter, they looked to the future with hope. They planned to establish themselves in another mission, perhaps in Cheefoo in the north.

Once I got beyond the stumbling block of grammar, my Chinese studies went a lot easier. The second week I could put simple sentences together. Before long I was beyond "What is the color of your rice bowl?" I memorized phrases and kept repeating them over and over in my mind, and sometimes aloud, to the annoyance of others. I learned children's poems.

Mrs. Murray was a good teacher. "Chinese is a very simple language," she explained. "It's a language of poets, but not scientists. In the next million years, the Chinese could not develop a bomb like you Americans did. It's not within their language to do so."

"But you said they were the first to invent gunpowder, and the compass."

"Yes, they did many great things, but China also closed its doors for many hundreds of years. They lost trust in the West."

The Marines were harsh skeptics when I came back to the barracks and told them that the Chinese invented gunpowder long before it was ever known in the west, and that the Chinese were the first to use a compass to navigate. "That's bull shit," Terry said when I mentioned it. "Look at their bloody trucks. They burn charcoal to run."

"They don't have gasoline, that's why," Chandler butted in. "They don't have money."

"They're backward sons of bitches, that's why. If they

weren't they'd make money and buy all the gasoline they wanted. They never invented nothing."

The guys didn't always like to hear what I had to tell them about the Chinese, and they really became annoyed when I went around spurting out Chinese. "Shut up you friggin' gook lover," they said when I overdid it. Nor did they like it when I came back smelling of garlic. The Chinese couldn't cook without garlic. The second time I came back from dinner at the Murrays they ganged up on me and put my bunk out in the hall for the night.

The guys mocked me for my Chinese, but they also picked up their own street vocabulary, which one could hardly use in polite company. They learned curse words and went around the barracks cursing one another in Chinese. Before long they were using the words freely in town. It amused them to learn that to offend someone in Chinese, you called them a turtle.

My education with Mrs. Murray was more than learning Chinese. She started me thinking on serious matters that never entered my mind before. She found books for me to read on their bookshelves. A whole new strange and often mystifying world began to open up. But when she began talking religion, I became uncomfortable. I was not pleased by the way she forgave the Japanese for their atrocities and the pain they caused her and her family. No Marine could.

"How can you forgive them?" I asked in anger after she had just told me about public executions when the Japanese beheaded their victims, and prisoners were forced to watch, even her young daughters.

"They are God's children. We are all God's children," she replied.

"Maybe, but you don't let your kids do what they want to do," I said.

"It's in the Bible," she said. "If you want to believe the Bible, the Japanese were under the influence of the devil disguised as the Emperor. To the Japanese, the Emperor was the light of the world; the devil, the Bible says, transforms himself into the light of the world. It says so in 2nd Corinthians, Chapter 4, and in Revelations 12. It states how Satan blinds the minds of the people and misleads them. To answer your question, unless you believe that the Emperor was God, it is obvious by the Bible that the Japanese were possessed by the devil. Now, you don't believe the Emperor was god, do you?"

I listened but these things I dared not repeat back at the barracks. I couldn't go around saying the Japanese were not at fault for what they did, that it was really the fault of the devil. But I could discuss such things with the Murrays.

Mrs. Murray was sympathetic, and yet on the other hand she appeared to be calloused. In her 30 years in China, she formed a view of the world that was perceived quite differently than most others viewed it. When I mentioned about the kid I saw sleeping in the sewer every night, she didn't feel the compassion for him that I did. Then I found myself in complete disagreement with her about another incident that took place a few weeks after I began my studies with her. It involved a beggar boy.

At the front gate of the university, a boy, about fourteen or fifteen, came often to beg. He made quite a pathetic sight. He couldn't stand upright and to get around he had to crawl on all fours like an animal. He had pads on his knees but still the skin was as hard as shoe leather. His legs were sticks, almost withered away from disuse. A navy surgeon saw the boy on several occasions when he passed through the gate on his way to the navy hospital. The surgeon was deeply moved by the boy's agony. One day he had his Chinese assistants bring the boy into the examining room. After x-rays and consultation with other doctors, the surgeon concluded that the boy could walk again. It would take several operations perhaps lasting many months. After reams of paperwork with navy headquarters, he got permission to operate, but not at navy expense. The surgeon put out an appeal to raise money, and within a couple days the whole regiment was prepared to pitch in. The kid became a *cause celebre*. The surgeon located the boy's parents and gave them the good news. Their son could be made whole again. The parents refused. The surgeon was astounded. He argued that we were living in a modern, scientific world, and there was no room for pagan superstition and false religious beliefs.

The thought came to him that perhaps Mrs. Murray, being a missionary and understanding these strange religious matters, might be able to intervene and convince the boy's mother to change her mind.

"The boy's mother would never change her mind," Mrs. Murray said emphatically.

"But there's a good possibility that the boy could walk again," the doctor insisted.

"And what would the family do?" she replied, not wanting an answer. "The boy is their sole income. If he could walk, he could not beg. It's as simple as that."

The boy never did have the operation.

We were warned that winters in North China were extremely cold and often vicious. But during the month of October 1945, the weather in Tsingtao was delightful. We had changed from summer khaki to winter greens, and we all wished we hadn't. Often after my Chinese classes—with my field jacket over my shoulder and my schoolbooks under my arm—I walked into town along the terraced walkways that followed the ocean. It was a long walk, several miles, but I enjoyed it. The pathway followed the curvature of the sweeping bay and passed small hillside shrines and pagodas that stood on rocky precipices. I would miss evening chow at the barracks and have dinner at a Chinese restaurant in town. The guys often joined me. We had special restaurants that we favored. These were real Chinese where only the Chinese ate. You didn't find them at street level, like the restaurants that catered to foreigners. These were usually on floors above, and to find them you had to know where you were going. Signs were in Chinese and unless you knew where they were, you missed out. They were noisy places, all very much alike—divided into cubicles, with green walls.

I liked to meet the guys at a Chinese eatery near the dock area. Not everyone would have agreed with our choice. But the food was extraordinary. We had to climb a narrow staircase, with broken steps that creaked with each step, and with walls that were dirty and black with age. At the top of the stairs was a counter with two scrolls of Chinese characters, one hanging at each side. Paper lanterns suspended from the ceiling cast a reddish glow upon the scene. Behind the counter sat a Chinese gentleman in a high-neck robe. He looked more like a scholar than a cashier, but the way he handled money, we assumed he was the owner. We had gone to the restaurant a dozen times, and not once did he even smile at us. But then, he never smiled at anyone. On the wall behind the counter was a board with pegs, like the one in the bathhouses, and here waiters on their way from the kitchen to the dining rooms would hang tabs with numbers on them. The old man gathered the tabs when customers were leaving and with an abacus added up the bills. The sound of the clicking abacus beads echoed through the restaurant. Whenever the man saw us coming, he would hit a bell on the counter and instantly a waiter appeared, a Chinese version of a French *maitre d'*. He carried menus and a towel over one arm. He would lead us to our dining area, always the same one.

The restaurant was a labyrinth of cubicles, some only large enough to seat two people, while others could host a banquet. The entrances to the individual dining rooms all had curtains but rarely were they drawn closed. As we walked to our dining area, it was amusing to watch the Chinese engaged in dining. They ate course after course, which you could tell by the dishes stacked up outside the entrances. Entire family clans— grandmothers and grandfathers, uncles and aunts, husbands and wives, brothers and sisters, and all the clan kids from tottlers to teenagers—sat around circular tables with center pieces that rotated with the swish of a hand. These were family affairs. Those rooms where there were men only—business men most likely feasting their clients and associates—had hostesses in silk dresses who sat with the men, making sure their wine glasses were filled, feeding them with chopsticks— a morsel of this, a morsel of that. Their drinking games were loud and boisterous. One game they all played—scissors, paper, and stone. Two men played at a time. Each would throw out his right hand, with either his fist closed, or flat open, or else shaped like a pair of scissors. Scissors could cut paper; paper could cover stone; stone could break scissors. With each thrust of the hand they simultaneously called out as loud as they could in Chinese. Those who won roared with laughter while the loser had to down a small cup of local wine. The wine, which came in colorfully painted bottles of every size and design, was actually distilled rice whiskey, and very strong.

In time we could name all the dishes. *Shui djouses* and *youmen sun, muxu rou* and so many more. We learned the names of their whiskies, but regardless of the name, they all were nasty tasting. With the Chinese, the saying goes, the worse it tastes, the better it is for you. We discovered the Chinese drink not because they like the taste, but they drink to get the other person drunk.

The mechanics of eating with chopsticks didn't come easy. They played havoc in the beginning, but there was no other choice. It bothered us to see little kids eat noodles and rice with chopsticks, and not drop a noodle or grain of rice. In time we became proficient and boasted among one another who was the best.

When we took any new guys to our hangouts, we made sure we ordered *Wuja Pee*. It was the worst tasting of all the local whiskies, and the most powerful. We learned to play the games, and in time we were louder than the Chinese. Often as they passed by, they poked their heads into our cubical and gave us thumbs up.

I loved those hidden restaurants, but I always suffered from guilt when I came out of a restaurant, picking my teeth with a toothpick, feeling contented and over stuffed, and then entered the real world of Tsingtao. I felt guilty that I could eat so well while people were literally starving to death on the streets. I felt this way, but it didn't seem to have any affect on all those Chinese who had dined so well in restaurants.

I always wished I could bring Ming-Lee to dine with me, but that would be impossible. I could go to the Prime Club and sit with her, that was fine, but we could not be seen together in public. It was frustrating. We wondered what would happen if we did take a girl out on the town, to a nice restaurant. What would they do? We found out when we heard about a Marine from Easy Company who talked a taxi dancer at the ABC Club to step out with him. The girl should have known the consequences, but obviously the guy was pretty convincing. It was dark when they entered the street in front of the club. The girl had pulled her coat high up around her face to help disguise herself. But the coolies in the street recognized that she was Chinese, very *bu hao*, a Chinese girl going out in public with a white man. The coolies began hurling stones at her. Several stones hit the Marine. The two tried to get a rickshaw to take them away but none of the rickshaw boys would come to their aid. Fortunately for the Marine, an MP Jeep patrol was passing and managed to get the injured Marine into the Jeep just in time. No one knew what happened to the girl. When the Marine recovered he went back to the ABC Club but the girl was not there. He never saw her again, nor did he ever find out what happened to her.

Ming-Lee lived with the other girls above the Prime Club. I was waiting for her to come down one evening when I noticed, standing at the bar, a Chinese man in western dress. He stood out from the other Chinese men in the club. His coat was a tweed sports coat, heavy wool, and his slacks were dark gray. He wore brown loafers. His hair was long for a Chinese, but neatly trimmed. He had a smile that never left his face. His teeth were white and even. He saw me sitting alone at my table and came over. "My name is Roger," he said and offered me his hand. His grip was firm. His accent was strange. It was Chinese, but different. I noticed in the leather trim on his shoes, in the small openings, he had U.S. .25 cent pieces lodged.

"I'm waiting for my girl," I said.

"You from 29, maybe I think. I like 29 malines. Vely good. Good malines on Okinawa. You BAR man?

It was hard not to like someone who liked the 29th Marines. How did he know all about the 29th? "I'm a machine gunner," I said.

"Ah, mashin gunner. You Sugar Loaf Hill. Many good maline, 3,000, maybe die Sugar Loaf. You on Sugar Loaf?

"No, I came right after."

"You come repacemen draft. What number? I forget," he said and pulled up a chair. It was still early and the place was near empty.

"You know a lot about Marines," I said. "What do you do, sell Tsingtao beer to the PX?" I didn't like him moving in the way he did. I was anxious to be alone with Ming-Lee and he was getting in the way. Still, I was curious about him. He didn't quite understand what I had said.

"You no like Tsingtao *pijiu*?"

"No, I asked if you sell beer. You know, to the PX."

"No, me no sell. Me newspaper man. Chinese newspaper."

"You a reporter?"

"No, no reporter. Work office."

"You mean you are an editor?"

"Maybe what you say."

Ming-Lee appeared at our table, all smiles and jolly. Roger and I stood up. She knew Roger and greeted him. They had a few words but my Chinese wasn't good enough to gather what they had said.

Ming-Lee looked very pretty standing there. Her hair was brushed back and she wore a Mexican blouse and skirt. I was blunt with Roger. "You must excuse us," I said. "I want to talk to Ming-Lee. I have something I want to tell her."

"Vely good," Roger said. "Maybe you wanna be no one

else. Okay." He bowed. We shook hands and he left.

"You want to tell me something," Ming-Lee said when we were seated.

"Yes, I do," I said. "I missed you."

The formal surrender of the 10,000-man Japanese garrison in Tsingtao took place at the racecourse on October 25th 1945. We had roll call at 0500 that morning. With rifles, helmets and full field packs we marched in force to the racecourse.

We made a splendid show that morning. The entire 6th Division, from company runner to mess hall cook, lined up on the green, with armored vehicles flanking both sides of the troops. Somewhere ahead of us the generals from the United States, Nationalist China and Imperial Japan were gathered for the surrender ceremony. General Lemuel Shepherd and Lieutenant General Chen Pao-tsang, Chiang's representative, took the surrender in the name of the Chinese Central Government. Gun salutes were fired, planes flew overhead and speeches where made.

It was an impressive ceremony that made newsprint around the world. That's what we heard anyway. The only thing we knew was what we could see, and that was the top of the helmet of the Marine who stood in front of us. For an October day in north China it was not cold like the books said it should be. It was hot, almost as hot as Guam. Marines standing in ranks began to pass out and dropped like lead soldiers. Trucks with red crosses painted on the sides were there to pick them up.

The town of Tsingtao celebrated. Throughout the city banners went on display. Chinese and American flags appeared everywhere, and the Nationalist Army paraded through the streets. In the hills the Eighth Road Army looked down at us.

The CO gave each of us a certificate. It had the flags of the United States and the Chinese National Government printed across the top, with our names below, our proof we had taken part in the surrender. We passed the certificates around and had one another sign their name with their address. We vowed we'd all keep in touch and never forget that day.

The day we received our certificates, we also got word that we were shifting quarters. Fox Company was moving into the Strand Hotel near the racecourse. We were thrilled at the news; we were moving into a hotel. To celebrate, we went to the Prime Club. Ming-Lee came to sit at our table. Roger came to the table too. He said he had something to tell me and called me aside. "You want see Ming-Lee Sunday. Good. I take her to beach. Meet you there."

I didn't care what the others thought about Roger. He had his merits, and I was going to make the most of them. Roger kept his word. I spent that Sunday with Ming-Lee at the beach. What a marvelous time. China duty was the best!

Roger took Ming-Lee back to the Prime Club at the day's end. The rest of us, filled with good cheer, returned to the university by rickshaw, singing and laughing all the way, urging our drivers to beat the other drivers in a race, but as we neared the gate we drew solemn. We knew what to expect— the kid living in the sewer. And there he was. His tear-stained face, smudgy and forlorn in the cold, shamed us coming back filled with booze and so joyful.

He brought back the image we had of all the street kids that roamed the back alleys of Tsingtao. Chinese children are beautiful and lovable when they are in health; their almond eyes sparkle; their cheeks flush. But what we saw were shrunken scarecrows with shallow eyes; hunger had bloated their bellies; weather had chapped their skins. Their voices had withered into a thin whine that called only for food. We had to be callused to survive. Outwardly we displayed our indifference, but I don't think there was a Marine who didn't suffer inwardly, even the most stoic and toughest of us.

Chapter 6

RESCUE IN THE NORTH

The Strand Hotel in Tsingtao became the pride of Fox Company, 29th Marines. I don't think there was a Marine who moved into the hotel that didn't write home and talk about it. It was a three-story colonial-style building located at the outskirts north of town facing an open beach. The Strand was built by the Germans who occupied Tsingtao before World War I, but who had to give up their claims in China at the end of the war. The legacy they left was more than a grand hotel, however. It was a brewery from which Tsingtao beer came. We were grateful to the Germans for both, the hotel and Tsingtao beer.

Trucks transported Fox Company with all of our gear from Shantung University where we had been billeted to the Strand. Here they deposited us, with our weapons, packs and seabags, on the street in front of the hotel. There we waited, sitting on our helmets, while the Chinese gathered to take a look at the new tenants. Seeing the crowd gathering in front of the hotel, more Chinese stopped to investigate. They in turn brought even more people to come for a look. Soon we had a wall of inquisitive bystanders surrounding us, all pushing and shoving to get better views. There was no holding them back, until Terry took out his K-bar, flipped it over and grabbed the blade end of the knife in a very dramatic maneuver. The mob backed up slightly not knowing what to expect. We knew instantly what Terry had in mind. About a dozen yards away stood a tree bare of leaves with the trunk exposed. A few Marines sat smoking around the base of the tree. Had they been aware of Terry's intent, he may not have pulled it off. Nevertheless, he took aim—we held our breaths—and he let fly the K-bar. It zipped through the air with a swish and stuck point first with a thud into the tree. The mob let out a sigh and moved farther back, leaving us breathing room. Terry calmly withdrew his K-bar, wiped the blade on his sleeve, put the knife back into its sheath and again sat down on his helmet.

Finally Lt. Brandmire appeared with Gunny Sergeant Pappy Preston at his side. Pappy Preston made the announcement. Rifle and machine gun platoons were assigned to the bottom two decks. The top deck was for storage, with a small area set aside for quarters for Chinese houseboys. The houseboys were there for the officers and staff non-commissioned officers only. The rest of us would have to clean our own rooms and shine our own shoes. He instructed us to take our gear and follow Cpl. Marsden to our new quarters on the second floor.

Never did we expect such luxury as when we stepped into the room, or squad bay as Pappy Preston called the rooms. It was spacious, with double bunks, consisting of one single metal bunk bolted to the top of another single bunk. Marsden had us hang our gear in one corner of the squad bay. We placed our skivvies, socks, utilities and personal items in our seabags, which we secured by padlock to the head of each bunk. Under our bunk we slung our rifles on two blanket roll straps. Each Marine strapped his pack, or 782 gear, along with bayonet, cartridge belt and canteen to the foot of his bunk. We draped our laundry bags over the head of each bunk.

There was no central heating and we could already feel the cold for winter was beginning to set in. We had one tent stove, which Melanowski lit, and immediately smelly diesel fumes filled the room. "Quit bitching," he snapped. "Be happy you're not sleeping in a tent." He changed his tune later in the day when the stove blew up and sent soot all over the room. We didn't stop grumbling; then we had the first of many field days.

Toilet facilities at the Strand Hotel weren't so grand. We were fortunate enough to have fresh water, but it was ice cold. We discovered this the next morning when we had to wash and shave. That evening, and every evening that followed, we had water for thirty minutes, for those who could stand a frigid shower. This occurred only if the water pipes had not frozen during the night. There was no heat in the heads. Shaving in ice water while shivering from below zero temperatures became a daily ordeal. Yet, we dared not to fall out for rifle and personnel inspection without a shave.

Due to uncertain water hours, we were all issued two canteens and every man made sure he kept his canteens full at all times. You never knew when the pipes would freeze, or if for some reason the water would not come on at the designated times.

Heads had no flush toilets because of freezing temperatures and water shortage. The frigid temperature made calls of nature something to complete as quickly as possible. Human waste was scraped out from beneatn the round holes where we sat, collected in buckets and kept in a pit outside the barracks. Coolies bailed the pit out frequently, hauling the waste into the countryside to dump on the fields for fertilizer. We called these coolies "honey dippers." Often times they scraped beneath the holes while we were still sitting there. It required some getting used to.

Eventualy we did have hot showers, but it took effort to get one. The Engineers Unit, located three hundred yards down the hill, constructed a large shower room with hot water showers. They allowed infantry companies to use the showers for an hour each evening. This required careful planning on our part, for it was very cold and dark on the path to the shower. Chandler came back cursing the first night; he had been late getting there. He had soaped up his body when the hot water went off. He had to finish with an ice cold shower. We quickly learned not to forget our soap or towel, nor be late.

We had a neat laundry room on the bottom floor. Jerry Ruker ran the operation. If we didn't want to do our laundry ourselves, which none of us did, we deposited it with him and he sent it out to a Chinese laundry. It came back the next day washed and pressed; even our skivvies got pressed. Sgt. Herman Willis was in charge of the Chinese cleanup force. We called him "Pops." He was older than any of us, having reached his 29th birthday. Even the officers, many who were much older than he was, called him Pops too.

The mess hall was heated but we had to wait in long lines in the cold to get into the hall, and then we had to wait in line again to wash our mess gear after we ate. Three 50-gallon steel drums with the tops cut off were placed outside the exit door of the mess hall. The first drum in line had a screen on top and here Marines dumped the leftovers and refuge from their mess gear. The liquids filtered to the bottom leaving only solids. The next drum was filled with hot soapy water, and the last drum contained fresh water. When we came out of the mess hall we dumped our leftovers into the first drum, washed our mess gear in the second and dunked away the soap in the third drum.

The mess sergeant issued passes to coolies who attended the clean up detail. They stood diligently over the first drum and when the garbage piled up they poured the contents into wooden buckets. At first we thought they were collecting the garbage to feed their pigs or other farm animals, but we later learned they were collecting the garbage to eat. No matter how rotten or old the discarded food was, the poor Chinese coolies collected it for food.

Some Marines found the matter disgusting and scoffed at the coolies. "You're worse than pigs," they shouted and took their cigarettes and butted them in the garbage. Later the coolies took the butts and stuffed them into their pockets.

We still used the university. There was a 4x4 weapons carrier that served as a bus and ran scheduled runs. The base movie hall was there, and they had a first class gym with a basketball court and weightlifting room. The library had a new shipment of books from America. I had finished reading *The Dowager Empress*, and found other books on Chinese history I checked out. One book I found most interesting was titled *Chinese Warlords*. I began reading about Feng Yu-hsiang, the Christian Warlord who baptized his troops with a garden hose. I missed chow that night reading it. The author of the book talked about another warlord, Chiang Hsueh-liang, who had captured Chiang K'ai-shek. I couldn't wait to read that chapter.

The Strand Hotel suited me fine for more than one reason. It was closer to the Murrays, and I could walk to my Chinese classes without Sammy having to drive me.

I came to enjoy my afternoons at the Murrays. Sally was becoming friendlier, especially when I brought her little gifts from the PX. I also helped out the family with sweet smelling bars of soap and tubes of toothpaste. They were truly luxuries for them. Clara continued to keep her distance but she no longer fled as she once did. The real shock came when Mrs. Murray told me Clara had met a Marine sergeant and had been seeing him. I was puzzled how she got to know him, shy as she was.

"She was walking home one afternoon and he picked her up in his Jeep," she explained after I asked her. "He seems like such a nice fellow."

Mrs. Murray talked freely about the mission and how happy they had been. "Mr. Murray came to China before the Great War, when Tsingtao was still under the Germans," she said one afternoon when we were having tea after my studies. "He spent the war in China, and came back to England on leave at the end of the war. He was so handsome, and had so many exciting stories to tell. China then was at the end of the world, and to even get here one had to be an adventurer. I was only eighteen when I met him. He was much older, almost twice my age, and I fell in love with him. I was the one who proposed. Can you imagine that? We married and spent our honeymoon on a steamer to Shanghai. From Shanghai we took a coastal boat to Cheefoo. Clara was born in Cheefoo."

Another advantage of living in the Strand Hotel was that it was closer to the beach. There were three beaches, and all were secured areas set aside for recreation for the troops. Although it was too cold to swim in October, it was still a fine place for weekend beer parties and barbecues. Marines could meet their Chinese dates here and not fear reprisals. It was here on Sunday that Roger brought Ming-Lee. I was as happy as the day I got out of bootcamp.

We didn't do much, only held hands and walked up the beach and talked about things most Marines talked about. We couldn't talk about the same things kids back home talked about. Ours wasn't football games and proms and Saturday night parties. The war deprived us of these things and we only knew about them from what we read in *LIFE* and *Esquire* or from letters from back home. We could only talk about killing Japs and what great buddies we had and the fun we had at the Prime Club a couple nights before. The bargirls in China listened to their men, and this is what made them so special. Marines could unburden their souls to women who hardly knew what they were talking about and it made these GIs happy. Each guy, however, thought his girl was different. I thought Ming-Lee was different, and of course, she was. She not only listened to me, she asked me questions. She was special, I guess, because she thought that I was different. I was becoming very fond of her. She was becoming my escape. I didn't realize it but I had gotten on the Ferris wheel.

We walked up the beach to where the officers' hotel stood on a rocky precipice. "It's the Dung Hi Fandian in Chinese," Ming-Lee explained. "Before the Americans came, rich Chinese from Shanghai stayed there during summer months."

One of the things we talked about was my concern for the boy who lived in the sewer pipe at the main gate near the university. "It's getting cold now, and there must be some place that will take him, like an orphanage," I said. Ming-Lee offered to check around and see what she could find. When I went to see her at the Prime Club the next night she said it was impossible to find a home for him. The orphanages in Tsingtao, she said, were already over crowded.

Back at the squad bay the next morning before roll call we discussed the boy. We knew the kid was certain to die unless we did something about it. "We can bring him here, can't we?" Melanowski suggested.

"You're out of your friggin' mind," Terry admonished him.

"Why, what the hell can they do to us? Throw us in the brig for saving a kid's life!" Melanowski replied. They got into a heated argument. Hot-headed Melanowski didn't like to be told he couldn't do something.

We thought the subject would end here, but it was only the beginning. Instead, the two toughest, meanest guys in the Marine Corps, Terry and Melanowski, turned out to be the most soft-hearted of any of us. That night, without us being aware of what was taking place, the two men had Sammy drive them in a Jeep to the sewer outside the main gate, found the kid and wrapped him in blankets and brought him back to the Strand. They scrubbed him up, dressed him out in some old uniforms, rolled up the trouser legs and shirt sleeves, and hid him out in a supply room on the third floor. They fed him that day with food they sneaked from the mess hall. The next night when Cpl. Marsden was playing poker with the staff NCOs in their quarters, they brought the kid to our squad bay. Their plan was all very cleverly orchestrated, but not everyone in the squad was in agreement, until they saw the boy. The very sight of him was enough to soften the heart of the most hard-hearted Marine. There the kid stood, frightened to death, in a uniform with the legs and sleeves rolled up, but with a face full of smiles. We all agreed the boy should spend his nights with us in our squad bay where it was reasonably warm, and in the day he could hide out in the supply room.

We called him Little Lew, for lack of a better name. He was about the size of a peanut and frightfully skinny. He quickly gained our trust and soon began picking up English words. We hadn't the faintest notion how long we could keep up our deception, but we were determined to see our plan through. We felt the gamble was worth it, considering what might have happened to Little Lew hadn't we acted. Still, we reasoned, it was not fair to Cpl. Marsden. This wasn't his doing but he was the one who would get into trouble when the boy was discovered living in the barracks. And sooner or later he would be discovered. That we knew. What we had counted on was that we could trust the houseboys on the third floor. We felt they too would feel compassion for Little Lew. We were wrong. They went running to Col. Roston.

Pappy Preston came to our defense. Who would ever have imagined that an old geezer like him would have feelings for a little kid he didn't know? Stevenson was on duty in the office when Pappy, with Little Lew in hand, went to see Col. Roston. We were torn apart inside when Pappy left the squad bay holding Little Lew's hand and walked down the corridor. The kid, not as high as Pappy's waist, looked so pathetic in his oversized uniform, walking with the gunny sergeant who was so fat his uniform bulged at the seams. At the last moment, before they were out of sight, Scotty ran down the hall with Stevenson's barracks hat and plopped it down on Little Lew's head. Little Lew turned and smiled, and with his little hand sticking out his sleeve, he waved.

Stevenson reported later what had transpired in Col. Roston's office. "There's Pappy with the kid standing in front of the Old Man," he began. "And what does he do? He says to the colonel, 'What can we do with him?' Before the colonel could say anything, he continues. 'What's been done has been done, Colonel. We can't throw him out. He has no mother, no papa, no one, and no home will take him. It isn't the question of money; all the boys will kick in for him.' Then the Old Man asks him, 'Whose idea was this?'"

We all held our breaths. Stevenson lit a Chesterfield and continued. "'Sir,' he says to the colonel, 'the idea came from the 22nd Marines.' I gotta hand it to Pappy. He was using strategy. He says to the colonel, 'You know, their CO let them adopt a Chinese orphan too. They call him Charley Two Shoes. And Motor Pool has a kid too, Bulldog Drummond.'"

Stevenson knocked the ashes on his cigarette into the cuff of his trousers, took a deep drag and continued. "Pappy knew at that minute he had the colonel whipped."

"What happened, what happened then?" we all asked.

"Col. Roston softened," Stevenson said. "There was Little Lew, standing there with big eyes wide open."

"Okay, okay, what happened," we demanded to know.

"What happened," Stevenson said. "What could happen? The Old Man agreed that Little Lew can stay."

They probably heard us in the headquarters office on the ground floor when we sounded off with one big loud cheer. We congratulated Pappy Preston when he returned with Little Lew. Both of them were beaming.

"There's more to it than that," Pappy Preston said when things settled down and he made certain Little Lew was comfortable in his new home. He then explained the conditions under which we could keep Little Lew. We had to arrange a fund that would finance his keep. He had to go to school every day, and have a doctor and dentist look him over. We had to pay for a tailor and have uniforms made. Most important, he had to follow rules as we did. He would be issued a chow pass and gate pass but he could not abuse his privileges. In short, Little Lew was the official mascot for Fox Company, 29th Marines. We set up a bunk for him in the corner of the bay. He was the happiest kid in Tsingtao. We began planning immediately for the coming Christmas a few weeks away. This was going to be a very special Christmas, but fate had its hand to play.

Mrs. Murray didn't agree with Little Lew moving in with us. "Children are not mascots," she said. "Furthermore what will happen to him when you Marines leave China?"

"We don't intend to leave," I said. "We'll always be here."

I believed it, wholeheartedly. In the meantime, Little Lew fared well. He attended the school for dependents children, and he learned English rapidly. He was well liked and was loved by everyone. We no longer used foul language in his presence, and even Melanowski stopped cursing. We fitted him with a uniform and Pfc.'s stripes. When we took him into town, he would sit huddled up beside us in a rickshaw. He became the envy of every kid in Tsingtao. It was true, he was only a kid, but then most of us, when it came down to the question of age, weren't much more than kids ourselves.

Winter came to North China in a fury. One day it was warm; the next it was freezing cold. For the Chinese who had little left after years under the Japanese, it was a matter of survival. For many, as more and more refugees pushed into the city, starvation was inevitable. The sick, the lame, the lepers, they walked the streets in rags, the lepers with flesh eaten away to the bone. Most pathetic were the child beggars, the true victims of war. There were hordes of them in shreds of rags. They had never seen a wash or a full meal in their entire short lives. When winter finally set in, they, along with the lepers, were found frozen in doorways. Trucks drove through the streets of Tsingtao each morning picking up frozen corpses in alleys and doorways. In our hikes in the countryside we watched wild dogs gnawing on the bones of the non-survivors half buried in the snow. These poor unfortunate souls didn't even make it to the city to die.

China for the Marines was a far cry from the steaming jungles of the South Pacific. We had to adapt and we had to do it quickly. No more sweltering heat and torturous sun. The cold was penetrating; even our new issue of cold-weather clothing was inadequate. It consisted of parkas, tank pants, mittens, long underwear, shoepacks and what we called Mongolian piss cutters, fur-lined hats with earflaps.

The business-minded Chinese of Tsingtao began preparing for the coming holidays. Strings of bright lights began to appear all over town, trees were decorated, and welcoming banners were strung across store fronts, restaurants and cabarets. At

Fox Company we began making arrangements for Christmas parties and the chaplain organized a Santa Claus party for orphans to be held at the mess hall. Marines began decorating the gym at the university for the Christmas and New Year's Eve dances. We began making plans. Roger let it be known he would escort the ladies from the Prime Club. Ming-Lee and Judy looked forward to the occasion and began planning what they would wear. Marines sent home special orders, and packages began to arrive from Sears & Roebuck with the latest women's wear. It was indeed going to be a happy holiday season for all.

But fun and games weren't in the cards for Fox Company, not this Christmas. The cold winds were bringing trouble.

When the Sixth Marine Division landed in Tsingtao rather than in Cheefoo, the first order of command was to establish aerial reconnaissance missions in an effort to accomplish two things. First was to monitor all Japanese movements; the second was to keep Marine Headquarters informed of communist activity on the Shantung Peninsula. In layman's language, we were there to spy for Chiang.

While we were planning Christmas parties and dances, two F7F Tigercats and an SB2C Helldiver were flying reconnaissance north of Tsingtao and became disorientated in bad weather. All three aircraft were forced to land along the northern coast of the peninsula. The Helldiver aircrew survived and made their way back to Tsingtao overland. One F7F crash-landed in the sea near Wei Hai Wei. The Chinese recovered the body of one of the crewmen, but they were unable to locate the second.

The Tigercat that crash-landed had been recording the movement of Chinese troops and was carrying valuable photo surveillance equipment. It made an emergency landing on the beach at the end of the peninsula. Before he was rescued by the Chinese, the pilot, Lt. Bland, radioed Division Headquarters in Tsingtao that the plane was still intact and should be flyable.

Division Headquarters, independent of Washington, made the decision to dispatch as quickly as possible Fox Company, 29th Marines, from Tsingtao to retrieve the aircraft and make an attempt to fly it back to Tsingtao. The site where it crashed was 500 meters inland from the beach. The terrain was flat with very little rise in the ground, and if it remained frozen, the plane should be able to take off.

We got our orders. Fox Company was about to take on the whole Chinese communist army. Col. Roston briefed us. We were to board an LST and travel to the north coast of the Shantung Peninsula and go ashore where the Tigercat crash landed.

To carry us ashore, we would have three amphibious Ducks aboard the LST, all with 30 cal. machineguns mounted on the bows. The ducks would off-load while we were at anchor. Radio contact would be maintained between the LST and Division Headquarters in Tsingtao while constant ship-to-shore communications would be kept by radio. Rick Whittington was assigned as radio operator. If it was not possible to fly the plane off, we were instructed to salvage the instruments and photo equipment, destroy the plane, and then get out as fast as we could.

We were issued rations and ammunition. Uniforms were utility with cold-weather parkas, leggings, steel helmets and field marching packs. I contacted Roger and asked him to pass the word on to Ming-Lee and Judy that Stevenson and I would not be around for Christmas. I wanted to see her and tell her myself but all liberty was canceled.

It was a nasty cold morning on December 17, 1945, when we boarded LST 755 in Tsingtao harbor. The rope flag halyard at the bow had to be thawed out before we could raise colors. There appeared to be even more junks in the harbor than when we first arrived three months before. We felt sorry for the Chinese sailors who stood on their decks, tending lines with trembling fingers. They shivered in the cold and we could just imagine them at sea in their leaky ships with waves of icy seawater breaking over their decks. It didn't seem much better for the sailors aboard a rusted freighter who lined the deck and watched us depart.

A sharp, biting wind blew in from the sea, and regardless of us not being accustomed to the cold winters of north China, we braved the weather, lined the railing and watched the shoreline disappear into the distance. I had my Brownie box camera with me but my fingers were so numb I couldn't click the shutter.

We arrived at Peng Lai the following morning. Col. Roston and a small landing party were the first to go ashore. Whittington with a radio strapped on his back went with him, along with a *LIFE* photographer, an interpreter, two enlisted men and the Duck crew. I was pleased that we had an official interpreter, especially when I learned, even though I was beyond "what is the color of your rice bowl," that he was to contact the communists and offer them reward money for caring for the pilot and crew member. He would also ask the communists for a "guarantee of safety" while our landing parties went to the downed aircraft to see what could be done.

Col. Roston and his men carried a briefcase packed with Chinese money. We watched them as they pulled along side the LST before going ashore. "Hey, Whittington, you know how to use that thing," Terry called out and Whittington gave him the finger. The second rifle squad and our machine gun squad were ordered to stand by. We would be boarding the second Duck to escort aviation personnel to the aircraft.

From the deck of the LST we watched Col. Roston and his party draw near to the shore. About 500 yards before they reached their destination, a rowboat manned by four armed soldiers approached. From the LST, with rifles ready, we watched the soldiers board the Duck and place the rowboat in tow. Whittington reported over the radio that all was well, and that the soldiers were guiding them to an unmined stretch of beach. The Duck reached the beach, and as Whittington later reported, they caused concern when they left the water and drove up the embankment. Suddenly about a hundred Chinese troops appeared from nowhere and came running to assume positions along the parapeted top of a 50-foot wall fronting the sea. We lost no time boarding the remaining two Ducks and headed toward shore as fast as we could.

As we were rapidly closing the distance to the shore, we noticed the Chinese troops had disappeared; then but minutes later they had reappeared, this time wearing Japanese steel helmets. Whittington who was on the beach guided our two Ducks through the mines whereupon we entered a massive seagate. The Duck with our aviation personnel aboard headed directly for the downed aircraft. The others headed off in the opposite direction toward the town, with the briefcase filled with money. We were fearful for their safety.

The Tigercat was undamaged, but the hardened ground began to thaw, making take-off impossible. We attempted to pull the plane to higher ground with the Ducks by attaching cables to each landing gear but that too failed. I was trying to get photographs with my Brownie when Stevenson came running. "I can't believe it," he said, out of breath. "Those commie bastards brought a carpet bag filled with American money and wanted to buy the plane." There was no sale.

The lieutenant from G-2 took charge of operations. He lost little time climbing aboard the plane followed by the aviation mechanics and a demolition man from headquarters. We took position around the plane. Several dozen Chinese troops arrived and were helpful when they formed a cordon around the plane and kept the local Chinese from approaching closer than 500 meters. The men with the money bag left.

We had to complete our mission before nightfall and get back to the LST. The men worked quickly. They removed heavy cameras from the nose of the aircraft, and stripped the navigation equipment. They carried two 5-gallon Jerry cans of fuel aboard and returned with empty cans. The last Marine to leave the aircraft was the demolition man. He set a charge, timing it to go off in an hour, enough time for us to get back to the beach. We returned to the seagate as quickly as we could. The third Duck with Col. Roston and his party had not returned. We waited for them as long as we could. Night was falling.

We still were standing on the beach, preparing to board the Ducks, when there came a terrific explosion. We turned to see the plane on fire. Darkness was almost upon us and still the other Duck was not in sight. We had no alternative but to follow orders and return to the LST. We could only make wild guesses what had happened to Col. Roston and his men. As we returned to the LST, we could see the silhouette of the burning plane against the night sky.

Back aboard the LST we stood at the railing searching the darkness, looking for some sign of the others. We were thinking the worst when we heard shouts coming through the darkness. The Duck was returning. We gave a shout of victory. They had made it! They had out-smarted the communists. A few minutes later and we could hear their voices, more clearly now, and then their laughter. We knew that sound. Oh, how we knew it—drunken Marines. The LST opened the gate, lowered the ramp and the Duck drove aboard.

Whittington gave the account of what had happened. The town of Peng Lai had anticipated the arrival of the Marines and was waiting with full honors. The streets through which they were escorted were emblazoned with freshly painted posters in English, decrying US interference in Chinese internal political problems, and at the same time fervently wishing long life for Presidents Harry Truman and Mao Tse Tung.

They were taken to the office of the Mayor, Mr. Ba Nan Kong, and introduced to Brigadier General, Sun Rai Fu, Commander of the Tung Pei Hai Military area, and Mr. Chang Hsao, editor of the local newspaper. A banquet hall where they dined was also plastered with banners, together with pictures of Mao, and a flaming red map of China. "According to the map," Whittington said, "practically all of China was in communist hands." Gen. Sun Rai Fu refused to accept the money offered by Col. Roston for safeguarding the aircraft.

The dinner party at the Mayor's house was a full-blown ten-course affair with various wines, brandies and palate cleansers, served by a battalion of waiters. After almost a week onboard the LST, the banquet meal was an unexpected treat. The Marines were completely baffled by the feast, and after months in the field, they were certainly not the most refined dinner guests ever to share the Mayor's table. The drinks were generous. One Chinese host became a bit loud and offered continuous toasts which only served to increase the guests' alcohol intake. Whittington admitted he tried to follow the Colonel's lead, as far as table manners went, and thought he did fairly well for a slightly tipsy 19-year old kid from Saugerties, N.Y. However, the Marine next to him, to everyone's dismay, drank the contents of his finger bowl, which he thought was just another exotic course. "It was like something from out of *Terry and the Pirates*," Whittington said, "although no 'Dragon Lady' ever appeared."

With the sky over Peng Lai ablaze in a red glow from the burning aircraft, LST 755 departed that same evening for Tsingtao. It was a two-day voyage at best. We spent Christmas Day at sea. To brighten up morale, several men put on a skit, which ended abruptly. Terry went drag with a mop for wig and a padding under his shirt for breasts. A sailor made a witty remark, Terry punched him out, and the fun ended in a brawl. No sooner was calm restored than an oil line broke and sprayed oil over all our bedding. We spent the night cleaning up the mess. But Fox Company, 29th Marines, did have a Christmas feast, a day later on December 27th back at the Strand Hotel.

On December 31st I took Ming-Lee to a dance at the Shantung University Gym, and Stevenson took Judy. Ming-Lee looked very lovely in a western dress and high heels. I was experiencing a feeling I never had before. Could it be that I was falling in love? But Marines don't fall in love.

Chapter 7

MRS. DJUNG AND HER DAUGHTERS

One terribly cold afternoon in March as I walked through the pines on my way to the Murrays for my Chinese lesson, I seriously thought I might freeze in my tracks before I ever got there. Even with my parka pulled over my head, with only my eyes exposed, I could not keep out the cold. It was so bad Sammy and the other maintenance men couldn't get the Jeeps nor any of the vehicles in Motor Pool started. To add to my misery, a biting wind blew in from the sea causing the tops of the pines trees above to quiver and moan mournfully. The wind, the cold, the stark bleakness, it all seemed to be a kind of premonition that something terrible was going to happen. When I reached the Murray's house I knew my instincts were right. Something was wrong. Little Sally wasn't at the window. She had gotten into the habit of waiting for my arrival each afternoon, and I could count on seeing the curtains move as she peeked out a window. And when I knocked on the door, she'd open it slightly, quickly dash away, and I'd shout out, "Whoop, who was that?" I would look around and mutter aloud that it must be a ghost. I could then hear her giggling in another room. No curtains moved now; I had to wait several minutes before someone came to open the door. This time it wasn't Sally. It was the amah. She said nothing and led me to the study and asked that I wait. I sat there for the longest time, wondering what could have gone wrong. It seemed an eternity, like on

Okinawa when we heard a "screaming memie" overhead and braced for an explosion. More often than not they were duds. Those were the worst kind, when nothing happened and you still waited. This was the same. The shell was overhead but when was it going to land?

Finally Mrs. Murray appeared. I could immediately see that she was distraught. She had been crying. "Clara is in the hospital," she said sadly. She was searching hard to find the right words. "She attempted to take her life last night," she said in a voice hardly audible.

I didn't know what to say. Her words came like a powerful poison dropped into a crucible. Clara attempted suicide! I knew that she had been acting strangely and I suspected something was wrong, but I wasn't sure what it was. But I did reason that it had something to do with the war and the Japanese. Mrs. Murray turned away while she wiped her eyes with a handkerchief. Turning to face me again, she spoke of her husband. "Mr. Murray is taking it very badly," she said and asked to be excused. I mumbled a few twisted words and quietly left. I didn't feel the cold this time as I hurried through the pines and went straight to Fox Company headquarters.

"I'm glad you came straight here," Whittington said with some urgency in his voice when I entered the office. "Lt. Harper, the new exec officer, said he wants to see you. The guy from G2 is with him now." Before I went into his office, as I stood over the kerosene stove warming myself, Whittington and Stevenson briefed me on Lt. Harper, USMCR. He had just arrived a few days before by ship from Stateside, Officers' Candidate School in Quantico. "He's a 2nd lieutenant wonder boy still wet behind the ears," Stevenson said. Whittington agreed. The regiment had been getting a fresh lot of officers and green troops for replacements, and the old battle-hardened Marines had a difficult time accepting orders from noncombatants wet behind the ears. I gathered after talking to Whittington and Stevenson that this new man, Lt. Thomas P. Harper, was one of them.

I knocked and entered his office. I really didn't expect to find Falstaff sitting behind the desk but I did. There he was, a fat, flushed-face Marine officer in full green uniform with an expert rifleman's badge on his chest above the left pocket. He was smoking a cigar, more for effect than for pleasure. I'm sure he wasn't enjoying it, not like Col. Roston enjoyed his cigars. For a moment I thought he might get sick as he took a puff. He was fat but I can't say he was jolly. In fact, he was rather grim and to the point. I wouldn't have taken him seriously except for the question he fired at me.

"What do you know about Clara Murray?" he barked. I noticed at a glance that he had my record folder on his desk. His question threw me completely off guard. Why did he want to know about Mrs. Murray's daughter? He didn't tell me to "rest at ease" but I did anyway. I told him all that I knew, that Clara kept pretty much to herself, and not once had I talked to her directly, and that the Murrays had private matters they kept secret. It was true. I often wondered about the two girls, how they faired in a Japanese prison, but it was never mentioned, and I didn't ask. "That's about all I know about her," I said.

I had forgotten all about the G2 officer that Whittington mentioned until I saw Lt. Harper glance in his direction. He was sitting in a chair to one side. Lt. Harper motioned to him and he stepped up to the deck. I recognized him, Lt. Austin, the baby-face officer from G2 who held the briefing before we first came ashore in Tsingtao.

"Did you know she was dating a Marine from Baker Company?" Lt. Austin asked.

"I knew she was seeing someone from the base here. Mrs. Murray told me, and she was concerned who he was. But I didn't know him."

"You say you didn't know him. You never saw him around?"

The lieutenant was trying to trick me into a trap, like a teacher does in school when she doesn't believe a student.

"Sir, I didn't say that. I said I didn't know him but I saw him once when he came to pick up Mrs. Murray's daughter in a Jeep."

"But you do know that the girl is under age," the lieutenant from G2 spoke up, "and that the sergeant could be charged with rape if the Murrays wanted to press charges."

Good lord! My heart began to quiver, like the quivering of those trees in the pine forest that I had just walked through. The poor Murrays, all that they had suffered, and now this. My face must have registered my disbelief, and there was still more to come. Lt. Austin continued: "Then you didn't know she was under age?"

"I never thought about it at all," I said. The trees stopped quivering. I was being accused of something and wouldn't let it happen.

I must have been convincing. Lt. Harper got up from his chair, walked around to the front of the desk where I stood and laid a folder down before me on the desk. He opened it and pointed to the heading. It was a dossier on the Murrays.

"Sir, you asked about the sergeant and Mrs. Murray's daughter. What is it you want me to tell you?"

Lt. Austin came to my defense. He asked Lt. Harper that we all sit at the conference table in the adjoining room. He called for Whittington to join us. When Whittington came in and was seated, he began.

"The sergeant that's involved with Clara Murray, we are transferring him immediately back to the States. The Murrays can still press charges—the girl is barely eighteen—but that's not why we are here."

That's the way to go, I thought. Transfer the guy and forget about the girl. What agony had she suffered? Obviously she loved the guy, enough to attempt suicide, but that didn't matter, not with the Marine Corps reputation at stake. The two officers waited for my response. "You're packing him off. Why are we here then?" I finally asked, bluntly.

"We are trying to gather evidence against Japanese, for

their war crimes, and we want the Murrays to testify."

I was more confused now than ever. Why did the Murrays have to testify? About what? Lt. Austin could see the puzzled looks on the faces of both Whittington and me. He spread open the Murray file on the table and once again began talking like a college professor.

"In 1937, Japan launched a full scale invasion of China," he began. "That same year the Nanking Massacre took place, better known as the Rape of Nanking. The American gunboat *USS Panay* was bombed and sunk near Nanking. Japanese troops soon occupied all of North China. All foreigners, non-Chinese that is, were herded into concentration camps. The Murrays were among them. "

The three of us, Lt. Harper, Whittington and me, became mesmerized by the tone in his voice. He spoke with conviction. To win a point, like the Sophists, he asked questions that we couldn't answer. "Do you know where I am leading? No. Well, let me tell you, the Japanese didn't travel alone. They brought their women with them. Their women! Only they were special women. They were sex slaves. This is what Clara Murray became, a Japanese sex slave."

The words came as a chill wind but without the cold. Lt. Austin hesitated, as though waiting for a question he knew we wouldn't ask. Letting his words sink in, he continued: "Instead of sex slaves, the Japanese called them *jugun ianfu*, meaning military comfort women. It's a euphemism for enforced military sex labor for the Japanese Imperial Army in the name of Emperor Hirohito. It's the Japanese way of hoping to obscure the dreadful reality behind the term. The number of victims involved is estimated at nearly 200,000, though it is possible that the figures are even higher. Who were they? Chinese, Taiwanese, Filipina, Indonesian, as well as Dutch women taken prisoner in the Dutch East Indies."

Suddenly the world before me lit up, as if one of those Nip memie bombs had exploded right before my very eyes. This was no dud. Lt. Austin's words were a sledgehammer blow right in the midsection. As a movie opens up on the silver sceen, suddenly it was all there. Ever since Okinawa, something had been deeply puzzling me. I had found it too horrible to talk about, even with my Marine buddies. There are some things we bury deep inside ourselves and this was one of them. When we were mopping up in the south, we entered the caves where the Japanese had been holding out. Only after intense shelling and with Napalm poured into the air vents were we able to flush them out. Not many surrendered, and those who did came out with their hands up, heads shaven, wearing only strips of loincloths for covering. Their Emperor wouldn't be happy with them now, surrendering as they did, but still, we felt pity for them, until we entered the caves. Those who didn't die from our shells and Napalm lay dead from their own hands. They had committed *harikari*. But there was a sight even more dreadful than dead Japanese soldiers who split their guts open with sabers or ended their miserable lives with bullets in their heads. Almost without exception, in nearly every cave, we found women who had been massacred, and all were completely naked. They had not a stitch of clothing on their bodies. Many had their hands bound behind their backs with cord or wire, wire that had cut so deeply into the flesh their hands were nearly severed. They had struggled. Sometimes it was less than an hour after a shelling when we stormed the caves, and already by then maggots began their work. It was a horrid sight that was to haunt us long after, one that had no explanation, until now.

The G2 officer must have been able to read my mind. "You saw it on Okinawa," he said. Turning to Whittington, he asked, "And you too. What did you see?"

"I especially remember one clear, warm day," Whittington began. "It was sunny, about our 79th or 80th day of fighting, and we were on the southern tip of the island. We were on a high cave-infested bluff overlooking the South China Sea. Navy ships were cruising just off shore blaring surrender messages through their PA systems. Navy sailors with rifles were exchanging fire with Japs we could not see. I was in a group of ten or fifteen Marines wrestling with 55-gallon barrels of napalm. We were pouring the stuff down the cave air vents. Gunfire and grenade noises were everywhere. Every once in a while a Jap soldier or an Okinawan woman would appear out of nowhere and jump off the cliff. I remember it as one of the most surreal moments of my life."

"Did you go into the caves?" Lt. Austin asked.

"Yes, and there were the women who didn't jump. They were dead."

Lt. Austin began again. "Toward the end of the war, the supply of women was dwindling, and there was more indiscriminate kidnapping of women by the Japanese Imperial Army under the enforcement of the Military Compulsory Draft Act in 1943. This is what you saw on Okinawa. At the end of the war, survivors of military sexual slavery were not informed of Japan's defeat. During Japan's retreat, to keep the facts from becoming known, they massacred these helpless women, by driving them into trenches or caves and either bombing or gunning them down."

Lt. Austin went on to explain how each woman was made to serve an average of thirty to forty soldiers per day, with more soldiers waiting in line. Women who were not submissive were brutally beaten and tortured. Escape was impossible due to strict surveillance. Japanese soldiers were reminded that women were their common property.

"Women from the working class and farmer families were assigned to lower-ranking soldiers, while Japanese and European women were for higher-ranking officers. Clara Murray became officers' property."

Lt. Austin read from the dossier, a horror story from real life. It was part medical report, and mentioned things like antisocial personality disorders, shared psychotic disorder and psychotherapy. The report listed eyewitness confessions by prisoners who stated that every woman caught by the Japanese had been raped, without exception. When Japanese soldiers couldn't find women to rape, they had been seen copulating with sows in some districts. In places where the villagers had not had time to hide themselves effectively, the women were captured, herded together, stripped naked, and driven forward by the imperial army as beasts of burden until they reached their destinations.

"Witnesses reported that Mrs. Murray was raped when she was eight months pregnant," Lt. Austin continued. "On resisting, she was beaten and her lower jaw was broken. Her daughter was born a month later. Clara Murray was twelve when they were captured. Age meant nothing to the Japanese. She spent six years handed from one officer to another, until she no longer had her senses. We want to treat this as war crimes, but our difficulty is that no one wants to come forth with their own testimony. Every witness points a finger at someone else. We had hoped Mrs. Murray and her daughter might help, until this last incident with the sergeant."

"And you want me to see what I can do?" I said.

It was an ugly affair and I didn't think I could confront Mrs. Murray by asking such horrid questions, but I had to agree that I would at least try. But there was no need. When I arrived at the Murrays the following Monday afternoon, Mrs. Murray announced Clara was out of the hospital and that they were returning to England. She used the pretext that they thought it was best for Mr. Murray who could recuperate back home and regain his health so that they could return to China.

"We have a teacher for you," Mrs. Murray said. "She is Chinese, and from a very prominent family here in Tsingtao. Her name is Mrs. Djung. I have told her all about you, and she is looking forward to meeting you. She has two very lovely daughters."

It was several weeks before the Murrays left and I spent as much time with them as I could. Col. Roston agreed to my continuing with my studies and had Stevenson extend my gate pass. With Mrs. Djung's address written in both English and Chinese characters I set out one day soon after the Murrays left to meet my new teacher. I wanted to take a rickshaw but none of the rickshaw boys could read so I walked. I knew the general location of the address, along the seawall that I had often walked after my Chinese classes.

Often on my long walks from the Murrays into town I wondered who lived in these grand stone houses that faced the sea. They had to be rich. Some of the houses had shiny black rickshaws parked in front. I soon found the house I was looking for, set back from the road behind a high stone wall. Like on most walls in Tsingtao, along the top, pieces of glass were embedded in the concrete. Stone steps led up to the doorway. I rang a bell and listened. I could hear it ring inside the house.

An amah in black-and-white dress opened the door. I said in my best Chinese that I would like to see the lady of the house. She put her hands to her mouth and chuckled. I was used to this by now. Chinese didn't expect white men to speak their language, and if they did, they laughed. It was annoying. I was about to admonish her when Mrs. Djung appeared. She wasn't anything like I expected. She was quite stunning, a very proper Mandarin Chinese lady.

She was, indeed, handsome, and very dignified. She was unusually tall, for a Chinese, standing about five-eight or nine. Her hair had strands of gray and was drawn back into a bun. She wore octagonal glasses, without rims. She reached out her hand and smiled. It was a frozen smile, like on a porcelain figurine.

"Mrs. Murray has had nothing but nice things to say about you," she said. Her accent was very British. Her coldness vanished, and I found I was beginning to like her. As she led me into the house, still holding my hand, two young women appeared from another room. "These are my daughters, Mae and Rose," Mrs. Djung said.

"Mother is very pleased that a foreign student is coming to spend time with us," the girl named Mae said.

She was dressed in western clothes, a woolen plaid skirt

and a heavy knit sweater. Like her sister Rose, who was dressed much the same, she was very pretty. I stumbled for words and didn't quite know what to say. I could feel the palms of my hands grow wet, and I wished to drop Mrs. Djung's hand.

"Mae is right," Mrs. Djung said. "We are looking forward to having you with us. So come in and sit down and tell us about yourself." I explained briefly about my studies with Mrs. Murray, and we conversed for a bit in Chinese. At first I was embarrassed, speaking Chinese, but that soon passed when neither she nor her daughters laughed. The conversation returned to English, and it was obvious they wanted to practice their English.

"We are having an early dinner," Mrs. Djung said, "and we hope that you can stay. We can get better acquainted, and tomorrow we can begin our lessons." I said I could stay. "Dr. Fenn will be here. He's a professor at the University of Shanghai, visiting Tsingtao for a few days. You will like him."

"Maybe you will be more comfortable in the study," Rose said. "We have to leave you alone while we get ready for dinner. Mother supervises the kitchen. We are having northern Chinese food. I hope you like Chinese food, do you?"

The study was paneled in dark mahogany with fine oriental rugs on the floor. Behind a glassed-in bookcase were rows of books. I glanced at the titles, some Chinese, a few French but mostly they were English. Several photograph albums sat on an oval table near the windows. "You can look at the albums if you wish," Rose said and left. I was alone. I felt like I was in a museum.

I was curious about the albums. There were three, and I began looking at them starting with the largest one first. Captions under the photographs were in English. The shots were unlike any I had seen before. There was a beach scene, two people walking up a sandy beach, but you could not see their faces. The photograph was taken from the back and showed their footprints in the sand. Another was a silhouette of two people sitting on a wall, facing one another, but they were totally in the dark, and again you could not see their faces. The background revealed an open sea with a setting sun reflecting upon the water. Junks in the far distance left their wakes upon the still water. These were not like the photographs we Marines took—photographs of us standing posed in front of temples, sitting in rickshaws, clowning around at the beach, and with us always facing the camera. These were so different. Whoever it was, they took photographs of details rather than whole subjects. There was a close-up of the peeling bark on a tree. Another one was the crevasse between two rocks, with a blade of grass growing in the opening. They reminded me of pictures you see sometimes in *LIFE* magazine, when the photographer tries to be creative.

Dinner was a formal setting: napkins in silver holders, cutlery laid out in proper order next to the plates, two types of drinking glasses, both cut crystal. There was no revolving centerpiece like I had seen in most restaurants. When we were seated, with Mrs. Djung at one end of the table and Dr. Fenn at the other, the servants began to arrive with platters of food. Mrs. Djung explained each dish. They were delicious. I favored most, a dumpling called *djow-dze*. Mrs. Djung was very pleased when I had several servings.

Dr. Fenn was very polite. He spoke slowly, choosing each word carefully. He was a frail man. He was dressed in a long robe, like the Chinese gentlemen I had seen in cabarets, with wide sleeves in which he often slipped his hands when he wasn't using them. His fingers were long and delicate, and his wrists so slender they appeared they might break if he picked up a weight. He didn't talk directly to me but through someone else. "How does Mr. Stephens like Tsingtao?" he would ask Mrs. Djung, and the others at the table would all turn to me for my answer. I didn't mind. Maybe it was the custom, I being the youngest one there. I found it rather amusing.

"Does Dr. Fenn live in Shanghai?" I asked Mrs. Djung, and everyone turned to Dr. Fenn. I could play the game too.

The conversation drifted from one thing to another, with occasional questions as to what my thoughts were about the matters they were discussing, and then it turned to literature. "Dr. Fenn and I were discussing an issue the other day," Mrs. Djung said, "and maybe you can help. We have read so much about Western culture, and now we have a foreign student among us to explain it." I smiled, and said I would be pleased to help in any way I could. I liked Mrs. Djung.

She continued. "Tell me," she said. "Do you think the philosophy of Kierkegaard had much influence on Christianity or led to the philosophical existentialism movement?"

"Huh?"

"Kierkegaard," she repeated. "You know, Jean-Paul Sartre."

"Huh?"

Our conversation after that changed to other more mundane topics, like how much effort it takes to make a good *djow dze*. "You know, no two cooks make them the same way." I said that was nice to know, and no one bothered to ask me any more questions.

Existentialism, Kierkegaard, Jean-Paul Sartre. The names were swimming in my head when I got back to the Strand and I couldn't wait until I could tell the others about my night at the Djungs. Marsden, Pappy Preston, Melanowski, and Chandler were all huddled around the kerosene stove, warming their hands. Pappy Preston had the floor. "When I get back to the States," he was telling the others, "I'm going to make it up to my wife; I'm going to make it up for all the time we lost not being in the sack together."

"You can never make it up," Marsden said. "A piece of ass lost is a piece of ass gone forever."

"Why can't you make up for it?" Melanowski asked.

"Because you should be getting it anyway, as much as you can, without thinking of making it up," replied Marsden. Seeing me there, he said, "Come on, Stephens, sit down. What do you think?"

There was no use telling him about Kierkegaard, whomever the guy was. Nor would I even dare mention him. "I think you're all full of crap," I said and felt better.

Marsden slapped me on the back. "You're okay, kid," he said, trying to be nice. We had a run in that morning and he knew I was still holding a grudge. I didn't feel like shaving and thought I could get away with it. None of us had much of a beard. The oldest Marine in our bay was nineteen. Pappy was 29, an old man by Marine standards, but he was only visiting our bay so he didn't count. I thought I could get away with it, and I felt good about it for Lt. Brandmire didn't notice during morning inspection. But Marsden did. He tore into me when we got back to the squad bay.

"You'll shave now," Marsden demanded.

"Okay," I retorted, somewhat of a smart aleck. "I'll shave."

"Dry shave," Marsden said.

"Okay, dry shave," I replied, still with a smirk on my face. What was the diffence? I remembered my first home leave after boot camp, and the pride I had that I shaved now. My father looked at me. "Put some milk on your chin and let the cat lick it off. That's all the shave you need."

Marsden detected the smile on my face. "You'll shave laying under your bunk, and don't come out until you look like a proper Marine." The others stopped stowing their gear and looked toward me for my response. "You have your choice. Shave or no liberty for a week."

Marsden didn't need to make threats. He had his own way of settling accounts. I did as he said. I shaved, without soap or water, lying tightly squeezed under my bunk. I knew I would never appear again at roll call unshaven. It wasn't the agony of dry shaving that bothered me; it was the feeling of losing favor with Marsden. We all respected that guy. It goes back to Okinawa, and even before that.

Marsden went though some heavy battles in the Pacific; he had enough points to go home but he was needed to help get the troops into China and settled. He volunteered to extend for a few months. We knew he wanted to get back to his wife. He carried her photograph around with him in his wallet. She was a big woman, dark, Italian looking. She had plain features with her hair combed straight back. Marsden was proud of her, and to him she was beautiful. He had another photograph of her with their two sons. He showed the photograph whenever he could.

He wasn't a braggart. He was what you call "calm and collected." We were on the southern tip of Okinawa, bedded down in foxholes preparing for the final mopping up operations. Japanese soldiers and civilians escaping from caves attempted to filter through our lines. No one knew for sure if they were attempting to surrender or were coming to locate and report our positions. It was night and Chandler was on watch. We heard him slide back the bolt on his M1 and slip a cartridge into the chamber. Then he called out, "Halt, who goes there!" A moment of silence and Chandler called again, "Give the password!"

We were all awake now, waiting. Marsden leaned far out over his foxhole, and in the soft light of night we saw him take careful aim. He squeezed off one round, took aim again, and fired a second round. Then came silence. Not a sound was heard. The next morning, not more than fifty yards away, only a few feet from foxholes where the Second Rifle Squad was dug in, two Japanese soldiers lay dead, both shot through the head. They had died instantly, before they could lob their potato mashers into the foxholes. Marsden made no comment, except to call out to the squad leader to throw some dirt over the bodies to keep the flies from carrying them off. Heavy fire kept Fox Company from advancing that day, and by the next morning the dirt over one body was piled a couple of feet high, to keep the flies away and the smell down.

No, Marsden was not a braggart, but he did demand respect from his men. He got what he demanded.

Mail call that same morning put us all into a happy mood. Melanowski produced a newspaper clipping stating that Ben

Hogan continued to dominate the world of professional golf. "Now hear this," he said, waving the clipping above his head, and began reading it aloud again. "As the year's top money winner, he takes home $42,556.36." There followed sighs and whoops from everyone.

Other information followed. A horse named Assault, with a clubfoot, finished first in the Belmont Stakes in June, becoming only the seventh horse in history to win the Triple Crown. There were hoots and boos, and money to be bet, when Smitty announced the St. Louis Cardinals and the Brooklyn Dodgers were deadlocked with identical records.

"The Cardinals won two straight games in the National League playoff," he shouted. "And they went on to defeat the Boston Red Sox, four games to three, in the World Series."

Everyone listened when Hecklinger read aloud about a star movie performance by Harold Russell, a veteran who actually lost his hands in the war, that eventually won him a special Oscar. He then read about another movie that got everyone thinking, a drama about three veterans home from the war trying to adjust to civilian life. "It's called, 'The Best Years of Our Lives,'" he said.

"What best years," Melanowski said. "Not here in China."

"When you get back home, stupid," Terry sounded off and an argument started.

It was April and spring was beginning to show its face. Conditions in Tsingtao were improving and life for the Chinese was getting better. All the privates in Fox Company made Private First Class, or PFC. Some PFCs were promoted to corporal. The guys gave me a surprise when they sewed my Pfc. chevrons on my green skivvy shirt. With good weather we no longer minded our conditioning hikes into the hills north of the city, and on Sundays when we were not on guard duty we took long walks, some into the countryside. When the 7th Fleet came to Tsingtao, that was something else. The town became undone at the seams. We were advised to stay in our quarters but we didn't want to miss the fun. Merchants pulled down WELCOME MARINES signs and put up WELCOME US NAVY signs. You could be certain prices would go up. We had two currencies, FRB, the provincial currency, and CNC, the Chinese National Currency. FRB was around 900 to one dollar. That was on the weekends. It was less during the week. It climbed to 2900 when the fleet was in. American dollars could always be used.

Roger continued to be a good friend and he was helpful when I wanted to get Ming-Lee out of the Prime Club. He brought Ming-Lee and Judy to the New Year's dance at the university for Stevenson and me, or we would never have been able to get them out. When the weather was good and Sammy was free, we'd make long drives into the countryside. The guys didn't like Roger hanging around so I had to make excuses to him and then meet him somewhere in town. They called him a freeloader, which in part was true. He drank with us and he ate with us, and he would grab a dance ticket from the table any time he wanted one, but he never offered to pay. I didn't mind. Roger was good company. Through him I was beginning to learn something about China. Like most of the guys, I knew nothing about the country before we came, neither its history nor its politics. We had no idea about the forces at play. All we knew was that we had to stand guard duty. What was happening behind the scenes was far beyond our comprehension. Even the very name communist—we had no idea what it stood for, except, they said, it was something bad, some kind of evil force. We may not have known what was going on, but we couldn't stop feeling that something was wrong. There were times when we drove through the countryside, and after meeting and talking to the people, we could feel a gloom that was unexplainable.

Chapter 8

ROGER, ROGER

As we remember things in life, our minds also tend to forget them. This has to be an inborn mechanism that keeps us from going insane. Cpl. Marsden said in a few years we would forget many of the horrors we witnessed on Okinawa, but we said we would always remember them. How could I ever forget when Terry and I were pinned down in a foxhole on the southern end of the island. It was raining and we lay in a foot of mud. Suddenly there came a banzai charge. We could hear them yelling above the splattering of the rain. Terry poked his head up, grabbed his M-1, took aim and pulled the trigger. Nothing happened! His M1 misfired. It was the mud. He called for my rifle and I handed it to him; it too misfired. I thought we were doomed, and then I saw Terry leap from our foxhole. He grabbed his entrenching tool, and began swinging it like a baseball bat. He knocked over a soldier with one blow, but he didn't stop. Like a mad man, he hammered down on the man with crushing blows, until he beat him to death. It was bizarre, like a Class B movie. I could see him silhouetted against the night's sky, rain falling all about, flares going off all around, the sound of rifles firing. He fell back into the foxhole, shaking like a dog after it had been given a bath. When the rain stopped and the banzai charge was over, we climbed out of our foxhole, and there in the ditch was not a Japanese solider but a young boy, perhaps eleven or twelve. He was stone dead.

Now, only a few months later in Tsingtao, I hardly

remembered the incident. One does forget, and I would probably have forgotten it altogether hadn't it been for Terry bringing it up one night when several of us were drinking beer at the EM Club in town. I never thought the nightmare would have haunted Terry but it had. There were other such memories that slowly began to fade, and in years to come they would be gone. Still, there were some images, memories of Tsingtao mostly, that I was sure we could never forget. Whittington spoke of one image he will remember always. It was early morning at the Strand.

"Our squad bay was in the front room on the third floor," he said. "Because it was the only tall building around, you could see for great distances. There was a public park about 400 yards away, and the ocean was beyond that. One cold, frosty morning, I had grabbed a can of pineapple juice from the windowsill—one from the batch the guys had swiped from a warehouse at the docks while on guard duty—and went out on the verandah. I spotted some elderly Chinese men, in fedora hats and dark overcoats, practicing Chinese exercises. The trees in the park were stark and bare. As the men exhaled, their breath came out white and hovered in the still air. They moved in slow motion, with deliberate animation. I was transfixed by the subtle beauty of it all. While I was watching, a "honey-cart" that had just visited our outdoor head went by. That beautiful image of those men in the park, as fine as a painting by a great master, vanished, and was replaced by the one of the honey cart. Both images will always be there."

Mrs. Djung and her daughters Mae and Rose had their friends for dinner at least once a week, but I was not invited to dine with them a second time. Sometimes I would help the servants in the kitchen prepare *djow-dzes*, cutting the dough in squares and getting myself covered in flour, while Mrs. Djung did the supervising. We would practice speaking Chinese and it was fun, but when the guests were about to arrive she would usher me out of the house and send me back to the base. I really wanted to be a part of the family but try as I did I was not accepted. I felt I had green hair and three eyes and was an alien out of Flash Gordon. Nevertheless, I still strived for their approval. I made the mistake, however, of asking Mae one time if she wanted to come to a movie on the base. There was a good John Wayne movie playing that everyone was talking about. She was polite and said she didn't care for John Wayne and suggested instead I take a girl from one of the bars that I frequented. It was difficult for me to explain that some of the girls were really quite nice. They didn't go around sleeping with every GI that came along. In fact, some girls didn't sleep with the Americans at all. They worked hard supporting their families—mothers, fathers, brothers and sisters, and the grandparents—and a few were even putting themselves through school. That's what the girls told us and there was no reason not to believe them. I spoke to empty ears at the Djung house.

I often spoke to Mrs. Djung about my friend Stevenson. "He's really a smart guy," I said. "He has a year of college, and when his China tour is up, he's going to finish college and then get a commission. He wants to be a Marine officer." It was true, Stevenson did plan to go back to college, and secretly he wanted to get a commission, but he couldn't go around the squad bay bragging to everyone that he was going to be an officer one day. He did mention it once and the guys laughed him out of the room. "You an officer, ha, ha, ha, you gotta be kidding!" We all knew Marine officers were special stuff, the stuff that you are born with. You just didn't decide out of the blue you wanted to be one.

"He sounds like a very nice boy," Mrs. Djung said. I had her where I wanted her. Now all I had to do was appeal to her emotions.

"He is very nice," I said. "He's very interested in my Chinese lessons. He studies too, on his own. He always asks me about you. He misses home a lot."

"Well, then you must bring your friend one day. He can

come for dinner."

"I will tell him," I said.

When I did tell Stevenson he was delighted. I told Mrs. Djung and she set the dinner date for the coming Friday night. The spit shine on Stevenson's shoes never looked brighter, nor the crease on his trousers sharper. He wore his barracks hat, refusing to loan it to me, and bought Mrs. Djung a box of chocolates at the PX. I had class with Mrs. Djung that day until five, but she had given me written assignments to prepare while she and her daughters labored in the kitchen with the cooks. I told her that Stevenson liked *djow-dzes* and they made a platter of them a mountain high. Once when I peeked into the kitchen to ask her a question about my lesson, I saw tons of food. This was certainly going to be a big banquet. I was hoping Dr. Fenn would be one of the guests. I'd like to pit him against Stevenson. Five o'clock came and no sooner had I closed my book than the doorbell rang. It was Stevenson, right on time.

I was truly impressed with Stevenson. He was the perfect gentleman, gracious in every way. And he completely baffled me, or was he masquerading? No, I was seeing a side of him I never knew. Like a boxer who had been preparing himself for a long time, he entered the ring. "I saw a copy of Lin Yu-tang in a bookstore in town," he said before dinner when we were seated in the study. "Do you agree with his philosophy?"

He threw the first punch but Rose countered quickly. "If you are talking about his *From Pagan to Christian,* we can hardly agree," she spoke up, "We are Buddhists in this family."

"Oh, I am not questioning his beliefs or disbeliefs," Stevenson said, getting himself into a corner and I wondered how he was going to get out of it. "When we came to China, I thought I might find the answer." He was sparring now and it was working.

"And what is that?" Rose asked, ready for the next jab.

"How Dr. Lin viewed the West," he said avoiding a clinch. "Western culture sees nature in the terms of control and exploitation. But for the Chinese, it is the source of all harmony and balance. Isn't that what you call the *yin* and the *yang*."

Bravo! Stevenson had won the first round. He had the Djungs waiting for his next move.

"So few of you foreigners understand *yin* and *yang*," Mrs. Djung said.

At that moment, Bea Ling, the amah, announced that dinner was ready. The others hadn't arrived. I thought perhaps they must have already been seated and were waiting in the dining room but when we entered the room the table was set for five. There were no others coming. Mrs. Djung was keeping us isolated from her friends. I was terribly disappointed but not for long. The food was served, and it was good. Course after course arrived, and the *djow-dzes* came in two heaping platters. We did our best but couldn't finish them.

After dinner the conversation resumed. Perhaps it was best that no other guests were invited. Rose and Stevenson were back in the ring. Stevenson didn't see it coming but she was about to land the finishing blow when she asked him about his studying Chinese.

"Yes," he said, "I wish I had time to study like Stephens here, but I have to work in the office late in the day."

"But then, how do you learn Chinese?" she asked.

"From my Chinese friends," he said. "They teach me." Without hesitation, and with great pride, he began speaking Chinese, the colloquial Chinese he learned from the street and from the taxi dancers in town. It was his destruction. Mrs. Djung choked, as if something had lodged in her throat and she lost her capacity to breathe. Rose, who was sitting next to her, slapped her on the back and handed her a napkin. Mae turned crimson red, and for a moment I thought she might become ill too. It didn't help when I chuckled, for poor Stevenson had no idea what he was saying. Some Chinese curse words when translated into English are mere names of animals, but when spoken in Chinese in certain phrases they can be very foul in meaning.

I was still laughing when we got back to the Strand. What came as a complete surprise was that Mrs. Djung invited Stevenson for dinner again. No one could deny, he was gracious, schooled in every charm, and he was thoughtful too, especially when he went bearing gifts from the PX. He was invited back again and again.

Ever since I began studying Chinese, Roger wanted to take me to a Sing-Song cabaret. "Good way learn Chinese," he said. The Saturday after we had dinner at the Djungs, Stevenson and I conceded and Roger took us to a cabaret. I guess I was expecting something like the Follies in Paris, with dancing girls kicking their legs above their heads. We soon learned a Sing-Song cabaret is nothing like that. There were no women kicking their feet up high. In fact, the only woman was a lone singer on stage. The audience was made up solely of Chinese men in long robes who sat at tables about the size of postage stamps drinking tea and eating sunflower seeds. I hoped we'd sit far in the back but Roger lead us to a table right in the first row in front of a raised dais which served as the stage. We could not have gotten any closer without sitting on the stage.

We were the only Westerners, and felt very much out of place, until the Chinese bowed when they saw us and gave smiles of approval. Stevenson gave a deep bow from the waist, holding his barracks hat across the chest.

I couldn't make out if the songstress was pretty or not. She wore a long, white silk dress with a high collar, and she was so heavily made-up it seemed that if she smiled her face would crack. Her lips were painted fiery red like rose buds, and her face was so white with powder she didn't look real. Her hair shone in the light, and she had bangs that reached down and covered her eyebrows. She stood in front of a microphone that was so outdated the only place you see them is in silent movies. Two musicians sat slightly behind her on high stools. They were playing fiddles of sorts. One instrument had half a dozen strings; the other only two. "The one with more stlings call *qin* in Chinese," Roger explained. I had never seen him so excited. He was actually bouncing up and down on his seat as he tried to explain it all to us. "Vely old, most old in China. Other call *erhu*, two-stling. I teach you how play." We had to calm him down.

Behind the singer and the two-piece orchestra stood an old man wearing a worn western suit coat much too small for him. In each hand he held a huge brass cymbal which he brought crashing together making an ear-shattering noise that vibrated across the room and rebounded off the walls like cannon fire. When the clanging stopped, the fiddlers began playing in tones so high and so shrill they gave the same effect as running fingernails over a glass plane.

After short pauses, the songstress would begin. No one but the Chinese trained from youth can sing with such startling high soprano voices. How totally alien to foreign ears. Although her voice was high, extraordinarily high, it was not shrill. It remained at the same high pitch level without vibrato or variation. Each time she paused, the musician with the cymbals would clang them together several times, and the fiddlers would begin their duet. At other times the songstress would continue with her singing, higher and higher, and then the two fiddlers and the musician with the cymbals would all try to out "noise" one another. One might expect the audience to be elated, to applaud with enthusiasm, but they didn't. They remained dispassionate, unmoved, without apparent feeling. They continued drinking tea and splitting sunflower seeds with their teeth, and showed no emotion or indication that they either liked or disliked the music. What they lacked, Roger made up for in enthusiasm. Even out in the street, after we had left the cabaret, he sang in high soprano, like the woman on the stage, for all in the street to hear. Stevenson and I picked up the beat trying to imitate him. Everyone on the street who saw and heard us must have thought we were drunk. We were drunk, but not from alcohol.

After the Sing-Song cabaret, Roger insisted we visit a few

of the more popular bordellos in town. "You learn more, like in school, but only lookie see," he said. We then became sunflower seed eaters and tea drinkers, sitting with strange women in incense-filled rooms, making small talk and holding conversations we never would have had at the Djungs. Once again Roger became our teacher. "Girls come from country when maybe ten years old," he said and introduced us to Sue-Lee. She was incredibly shy, especially for a girl in her trade, and she couldn't have been over fourteen. "You furstay Chinese people, boy Number One, no girl Number One. Pay mama-papa money for girl. Like shoes, like hat, you buy girl. She work fur other girl, wash, empty pot. She get fourteen, she now sleep wid man. You first time sleep girl, pay ten dolla mecan money. No one dollar. Maybe twenty dolla girl Number One." One dollar for short time; one and a half dollars for a long time, meaning an hour. Virgins went for ten dollars, or twenty if they were pretty.

We left Sue-Lee standing in the room, with the mamasan yelling obscenities at us, and went to another house. Every bordello we visited had four floors with open balconies that faced a courtyard. When a customer entered the courtyard, hundreds of girls, those who were not occupied, appeared at the railing waving and shouting. You felt like a matador standing in the center of a bullring, looking up at an audience cheering you.

"Buying and selling humans, do you agree?" Stevenson asked as we took seats in another room and ordered more tea. I couldn't answer him and Roger didn't quite understand.

The girls here were even younger than at the first place. The mamasan wanted to know if we wanted a virgin, a young girl that just came in from up north. We declined, and she asked if we wanted instead a well-trained and experienced girl. As the girls came and went, Roger continued his conversation.

"I tell you this China now. Me no can change," he replied.

"And what is their future?" I asked.

"Their future is now. You alive, that is enough. This is China, under Generalisimo, remember?"

There were many questions we wanted to ask, but Roger's English was limited, and my Chinese was not much better. Roger did manage to get his point across. He was a gad about town, a real Oriental playboy, but he was also very careful. He let it be known that the female companionship that GIs sought in bordellos was a risky undertaking in China. We were warned there were plenty of girls but there was also plenty of venereal diseases. Before the bordellos were put out-of-bounds by the Provost Marshall, every bordello had a pro station run by the U.S. military. When the bordellos closed, pro stations were set up at entrances to camps, and every Marine who returned drunk had to take a pro, whether he indulged or not. It was a messy business. The men had to insert a small tube-like object into the end of their penis and squirt in a dark brown liquid that looked like dye, and which burned terribly. He then had to rub over his entire private parts a white cream that played hell with skivvy drawers. It was the price one had to pay for love in the Orient.

"It's better than getting bullhead clap," Terry testified at one of our bull sessions. "The medics stick a tube up your dick all the way into your bladder. Then they turn a small knob that allows small knives to extend out the sides of the tube. The tube is withdrawn with a twist and a pull, opening up the tract." Terry laughed aloud. "You can hear the screams clean out of the sickbay and all over the compound when this happens."

"How do you know, Terry?" Chandler asked.

"That's what they tell me," he replied.

It was a fact, everyone who played around with the ladies was worried about bullhead clap, yet no one really knew what it was. There were all kinds of scuttlebutt going around, that guys who had it when they returned to the States were sent off somewhere never to be heard from or seen again. Of course, no one knew where that "somewhere" was located. Nobody really believed it, but they all talked about it.

There was a sign above the door in the sickbay that added to everyone's worry: "We treat sick liver, ulcerated stomach, splintered spleen, high blood pressure, weak heart, shattered nerves, diabetes, Bright's disease, beriberi, rheumatism, insomnia, arteriosclerosis, piles, fistula, chronic dysentery, and constipation, but we have no cure for bullhead clap."

Roger was really a phenomenon. If it wasn't a Sing-Song cabaret or whorehouse he introduced us to, it was a medicine show or a sidewalk story teller. The medicine shows were fun to watch. Performers could do amazing feats of strength, like picking up weighted concrete blocks with their teeth. Mean while, their partners ran around selling snake oil guaranteed to cure everything from heart ailments to arthritis. It was touted that it could stop heart burn, that it killed pain for tooth, that it was good for sprains and strains, that it prevented impotency, and that it could stop falling hair.

The storytellers were master showmen. They sat on dark street corners, and under the glow of a flickering oil lamp, they told tales of daring feats and gallant acts of heroism. They kept their audience, sitting huddled around them, mesmerized, dwelling in a magic world of wonder. I had a difficult time understanding the Chinese they spoke, but it didn't matter. The drama was captivating enough. Roger was worse than anyone and no help when it came to translating. He was too involved. His eyes were as wide open as the youngest tot in the audience, and his jaw hung lower than anyone else's. It was like an Italian opera and you didn't have to know the language to enjoy it.

Roger had answers for most everything. When I asked him about Lin Yu-tang and mentioned my discussion about him with the Djungs, he had an answer. "Your flend, Djungs, they no likie him. Him go China to Melika. Him born Fukien. Now him live California. Him think no likie Chinese. Him think same same him papa, missionary man." He was right. When I looked up Lin Yu-tang in the library, I learned his father was a

Presbyterian minister, and like his father, he was a devoted Christian. I wanted to read more about Lin Yu-tang but the library had only reference material and none of his books. I wrote home to my sister and asked her to send a couple of his books.

I never did understand why Roger hung around us so much, especially when he was openly snubbed and ridiculed by the other Marines, but he always took it without malice or complaint. We thought maybe he was just thick skinned and didn't know any better, but he was sensitive to many things. One thing for certain, he was truly concerned about Ming-Lee and me. "She na'lice girl," he assured me.

"I like her very much," I said. It was a confession I didn't care to make publicly. "Marines are not supposed to say they are in love."

"You speakie only weak man know love?" Roger replied.

"For Marines, yes, only weak men fall in love."

I was saying words but idle words, words that I didn't mean. We often says things we don't mean. It's another way of saving face. Mrs. Murray often tried to explain what face means to the Chinese. "You must understand," she often said, "you do not want to make the Chinese lose face."

The word face is misleading, and I soon learned very few of us Westerners fully comprehend its meaning. When the Chinese speak of face, it's not "faces" they mean. They are concerned with a psychological and not a physiological entity. We can all admire a pretty Oriental face, with those beautiful almond eyes, but its their physiological face that we have a hard time understanding. Marines have face, but it's not quite the same. Many men who lost their lives in battle on Okinawa lost their lives because they didn't want to lose face in front of their buddies. They charged machinegun nests, not because they wanted to be heroes, but because they wanted to prove to their buddies they weren't afraid. It's more of a question of honor. The man who is slapped in the face and does not offer a challenge to a duel is losing "honor," but in the Chinese sense he is not losing "face." On the other hand, the unruly son of a Chinese general who goes to a Sing-Song cabaret and is insulted by a singer, and returns to order the arrest of the Sing-Song girl, then has the cabaret closed down, is getting "face," but we would hardly say that he is gaining "honor."

Marines want to be heroes, but only among their buddies. They come back from liberty, bragging that they beat up a couple swabbies, or they decked a queer who looked at them sideways. Maybe they say they met this big-titted blonde driving a convertible who stopped to pick them up and she had a case of booze in the trunk, and they went to her place and screwed all night. They wouldn't dare say they went to Hollywood and had coffee and donuts at the USO and waited a couple hours to make a free call home. They talked about their girls back home, but that was different. No one ever dared belittle another guy's girl back home, not even in jest. And a Marine never admitted to the weakness of love. How do I explain this to Roger? "Yea, Roger, you're right," I said. "Me likie Ming-Lee."

Love for China Marines came at a price. Jerry Ruker was in love, and he was a decent fellow. He could get away with things no one else could. Officers and staff NCOs had room boys and barbers come to their quarters. Ruker was the only non-NCO who had a private barber come to his room at the Strand every morning, just a few minutes before reveille. He had his own private rickshaw boy wait for him at the gate. He sent out his shoes to have them polished, and he had a private tailor who not only kept his uniforms trim but also tailored his shirts and even his skivvies as well. For some reason the other Marines respected his ways and he was not the subject of their wrath of jokes. In a way, he was everyone's hero.

At the Prime Club, Ruker was King. He drank good Kentucky Bourbon. He was the only guy I knew who had his own private stash, a bottle the bartender kept behind the bar for him. And women adored Ruker. He was a gentleman to them all, and to Jenny he was a saint. If ever a code of chivalry existed in the Orient, it was displayed when Ruker was with his girl. Had he been able to walk the street with her, and come to a puddle of water, you could be sure he'd take off his field jacket and throw it down for her to walk upon. But then you never walked with your Chinese girl in public.

Ruker and Jenny were in love, and anyone would know there was something special between them when he entered the Prime Club. The instant Jenny saw him, no matter who she was with or what she was doing, she dropped everything and went running toward him with her arms open, and he picked her up and swung her around the room with her feet a yard above the floor. He may have been troubled when he saw her sitting with paying customers, but he never let on that it bothered him. He smiled through it all. It wasn't an easy thing to do. We all wished we had enough money to have the girl we liked sit with us all night, but no one had that much money, except maybe a couple high-rolling blackmarketeers and the White Russian con artists. The women were marvelous in pacifying their boyfriends.

For a West Virginia backwoods boy, Ruker was a magnificent dancer, and he taught Jenny everything he knew. When the two of them did the tango, everyone on the dance floor stopped to watch them. He was always jolly and happy, and he made those with him feel the same. "Oh, I love this country," he would say, and then add: "The women too, of course." He did have his competition though. Billy Stompano, an Italian pretty-boy from LA was one. He wore his uniform like a zoot-suiter did. When he got into a club, he took off his tie and unbuttoned his shirt down to the waist. He had a heavy gold cross on a gold chain hanging around his neck. He carried a comb in his back pocket and was forever combing his hair. No one liked Stompano, but they did like Ruker.

Ruker was the only guy I knew who slept with a girl from the Prime Club. I refused to believe it when I first heard it, but in private he confirmed that he was living with Jenny. The management had fixed up a spare room for him and Jenny above the club and he had moved in with everything but his sea bag. He spent several nights a week with her in their love nest, as he called it. It was almost like they were married. It was clever how he did it. Had he been a civilian and put his mind to business, he would have been a millionaire. At the Strand he managed to get assigned as laundry clerk. He had a room on the ground floor where Marines brought their laundry every morning. He had them fill out laundry slips which he signed and gave back to them, and at 10:00 every morning the Chinese came and picked up the laundry. He never lost as much as a sock or a skivvy drawer. He knew not to cause a disturbance or have any disagreements. No one had complaints. He convinced the Exec that he should have a gate pass, to supervise the laundry business, so the troops don't get ripped off. "Good thinking," the Exec said and signed his pass. He made it known it was his duty to go to the gooks to be sure they were using proper soap and hot water and not beating the laundry to death on a pile of rocks. When he was seen coming in the gate in the morning, a half hour before reveille, he was lauded for getting up so early and making sure the chinks were on the ball. No one knew he was out all night with Jenny and was just getting in.

But Ruker was no fool. He realized he was at a dead-end. Life was to be lived for the moment, and he accepted this without any feeling of self pride. "We have to take from life what we can," he told Jenny. He never denied to her that he would have to leave her one day. "I am in hell when I think about it," he told me once, "but this is the way it is. We live in two different worlds."

With Hecklinger it was something else, cool-handed Heckinger, the guy with an answer for everything. He had fallen in love with a Chinese girl and he wasn't any better for it. "I never thought it would happen, not with a slant-eyed slope head," he said. "I always knew you can't squat with your spurs on, but I did anyway."

Heckinger was a cowboy philosopher who had a saying

for just about anything, but he never talked much about himself, until we were pinned down in a foxhole for two days and two nights on Okinawa. A foxhole is like a confession box in church. You begin telling things you never would outside. He was a cowboy, proud of it, and he even had the bowed legs to prove it. The only thing, he told me the second night, he didn't know the ass-end of a horse from its head. He was an undertaker's assistant. The rumor that went around was that his old man was killed busting a bronco when Hecklinger was six years old. In truth the old man was a bulldozer operator for an oil company and he died when the machine turned over on him, leaving behind a wife and three kids. At seven Hecklinger ended up in a home and at nine he was adopted by an undertaker and his wife in Oklahoma City. "I'd never be in the Marine Corps hadn't the judge given me an option," he said.

"Why's that, Stretch?" I asked. We called him Stretch. He was about six four, skinny as hell, and the other rumor was he was hung like a stallion.

"I reckon I had this bitch and she ditched me, fur no reason. She just upped and said she didn't wanta screw me no more. So I read about this creep artist who cut off his ear and gives it to his whore, so I think it was a good idea. But not to cut off my ear. We had a cadaver come in and I cut off his prick and mailed it to her. She panicked and called the cops and I went to jail. 'Military service or to prison,' the judge said. What the hell, the Marines sounded good. So here I am getting my ass blown off for sump'ton stupid."

"This isn't actually any genius idea you have now," I said when he told me about his Chinese girlfriend. I was having a hard time believing what I was hearing.

"Hey, I know what you are thinking, but this is different," he said. I thought we were back in the foxhole confessional box on Okinawa again.

"But she's a whore," I said, taking a chance that he wouldn't lay a haymaker on me. He was a street fighter and capable of doing it. I then realized he was too troubled emotionally to be aggressive. He wanted sympathy.

"Come on, don't say that," he said sadly. I knew what was coming was not going to be easy. "I wanta take ya'll to meet her."

I wasn't keen on meeting her, that is, until I realized the magnitude of his involvement. "I'm tired," he confessed. "I hate this shit Marine Corps. I never wanted to be in it in the first place. I don't wanta go back to pumping dead corpses with formaldehyde. This woman ain't no different than me I tell yea. Hey, buddy, think about it. We call them sluts and bad mouth all these whores in Ping-Pong Willies, a thousand assholes under one roof, and we say every chink woman has her price and they are all available for a price. That's a crock! And what about all these White Russian broads, they brag that they were cousins of the Tsar. Bull shit! They were kicked out of Russia and had no place to go. What about them? White Russian women get twice as much as a chink for a screw, and that's the difference with them. So what do we do, we screw them all; we give our dollars; and we go back to the barracks and call them all worthless sons of bitches. Are we any better? Come on, are we any better than them?"

It was dark when we set out to meet Hecklinger's Chinese girlfriend. She lived deep in a poor section of town, where the streets were even too narrow for rickshaws. The pavement was cobblestone, rough and irregular; no street was straight for more than a dozen yards. They all twisted and turned, ran uphill for a couple yards and down hill the next. The buildings had slits for windows and like the doors they were locked shut. The walls were damp and if you touched them your hand came away soiled. The cobblestones were slick with grime and filth. "Don't talk too loud and make noise," Hecklinger warned. "Someone might open a window and dump a piss pot on us." We had to be careful as we trudged along; we slipped with every step we took. When we chanced to see someone in a darkened corridor, they vanished suddenly without a trace. I ended up looking behind me as much as I did where we were going. But Hecklinger knew his way. He made turns and rounded bends that completely befuddled me. At last we came to a door. He knocked a secret knock and the door creaked open. An old lady all in black with bound feet stood there. She smiled a toothless grin and bid us enter.

Presently the girl appeared. If I were to see her in the daylight I would not recognize her. The room where we sat, and drank tea, was as dark as the streets outside. I tried conversing with her in Chinese but she would only giggle. Conversation was impossible. Hecklinger in his pidgin English got his message across and they seemed to have no difficulty understanding one another. Hecklinger had obviously spent much of his time in her company. Here was an example of a case that I had heard so much about. A family sells the services of their daughter, and as is the custom, a young brother goes through the streets pimping for her. "Hey, Joe, you want my sister, clean girl." Like everyone else I thought it was a promotional gimmick, but I could see now it was no gimmick. The girl was real, and so was her brother that we met. I gathered Hecklinger was supporting the entire family. The brother, he told me later, lay around with little to do anymore.

Hecklinger wandered off into a back room with her and an hour passed, and then another. Still he didn't appear. I had to get back to the Strand by 2200 or be put on report. I don't know how I managed, but I found my way through the maze of alleys, caught a rickshaw and was back at the Strand just as the bugler was blowing taps.

In 1946, trying to maintain a romance with a Chinese woman was near impossible. Any serious relationship had to be clandestine. Let it be known that a Marine entertained the idea of marrying a Chinese woman and he was on the next boat back Stateside. There was no law forbidding it, but the unwritten law was strictly adhered to. The church in town also worked with the authorities. They reported any attempts by Marines or sailors to marry.

Roger knew my feelings for Ming-Lee and he suggested that I rent a room in town and that we move in. I was beginning to think it might be a good idea. We were clearing 50 dollars a month on a Pfc.'s pay, and I made a couple of extra bucks from black-marketing PX goods. Cigarettes were ten cents a pack; I could get a quarter. I wouldn't have to hang out at the Prime Club so much, and that would save money. I decided to talk it over with Stevenson. I went to meet him in his office where we could talk, making sure Col. Roston and the Exec had left for the day. He was sitting behind his deck puffing away on a Chesterfield. Before I could say a word, I knew something was wong. It was written all across his face. "Looks like I won't be seeing you again," he said.

I didn't expect this. He was leaving. What terrible news it is when you hear that a buddy is leaving. It can be devastating. Often it's harder to take than when you leave home. Good buddies are forever. But Stevenson hadn't even hinted that he was leaving. He must have known.

"Holy shit! You can't go just like that," I said. "What the hell, you could have said something."

He looked at me in the strangest way, like I had lost my marbles. He got up from his chair and walked around to the front of the desk. He put his hand on my shoulder. "Hey, buddy," he said. "It's not me. It's you who is leaving."

Chapter 9

LAST TRAIN TO PEKING

I didn't have to wait until the next morning to have Col. Roston break the news to me. Stevenson told me without the need to wait. I figured it had to do with my meddling in the affairs of all the guys and their Chinese dolls. Maybe the colonel knew about Ming-Lee and me, that I planned to move in with her. Could I be on the next boat home? I wasn't afraid to face the truth, that I was keen on a Chinese girl, but what about her, Ming-Lee? Would she understand that this wasn't my doing? That's the first thing I said to Stevenson: "What about Ming-Lee?"

"She can join you," he said.

"How in the hell can she join me? How do I get her to America? You know the rules."

"Who said America?"

"You did."

"I didn't say anything about America. You didn't give me a chance to say anything."

"Okay, let's start from the beginning. I am going someplace. So where am I going?"

"You're going to Peking."

"Peking!"

"Yea, Peking. The colonel is sending you and two others from Fox Company to Chinese language school in Peking. A special six-month course at University of Peking, sponsored by the Nationalist Government. They are taking three guys from every outfit, and you have been selected. You'll be detached from Fox Company and put on TDY."

Col. Roston confirmed the appointment the next morning. "You will wear Chinese clothes, and you will have your own rice bowl," he said with a smirk while shaking my hand. He returned to his seat behind the desk, with the American flag to one side and the Chinese nationalist flag on the other, and became serious again. He mentioned the directive from Fleet Marines. "Aside from you," he said, "Cpl. Gilbert from Easy Company has been chosen. Maybe you can recommend someone from Fox Company." He saw me glancing around. "Not Whittington. He's got so many points he should have gone home a long time ago. And not Stevenson. I can see the two of you running around Peking. Besides, we need him here. Pick somebody else, and be prepared to leave before the week is up. You'll fly to Tientsin and take the train from there to Peking." He then dismissed me. He may have been smiling but I didn't wait long enough to make certain. You never knew about your COs. You thought they didn't care but they did. Sometimes.

Not one single Marine, not a one, wanted to go to Peking, especially to go to school to study Chinese. Part of their reasoning was due to a directive that came down from Fleet Marine Headquarters. It was disturbing news. On April 1st 1946, the 6th Marine Division was officially disbanded. The 29th Mariners became Baker Company, 1st Battalion, 3rd Marine Brigade. It didn't mean much to the new recruit replacements who were joining the 29th in droves, but for the old timers who fought with the regiment since Guadalcanal and Cape Gloucester and survived Okinawa, the news didn't come with any great joy. Even more disheartening was the order that we had 30 days to remove 6th Division patches from our uniforms and replace them with 4th Division patches. That was the worst possible thing they could have done to us. Headquarters could have told us we were being absorbed by the US Army and it would have had less effect than telling us we had to give up our 6th Division patches.

No one wanted to go to Peking knowing that when they returned there would no longer be the 29th Marines. I felt much the same, but I had my orders, and I was getting desperate. I had to go, and I had to take two men with me. Cpl. Gilbert from Easy Company had already been chosen, and now another Marine from Fox Company had to volunteer. I knew it was hopeless to recruit Hecklinger. With his woman problem, he was only a step away from going over the hill as it was. Col. Roston wouldn't let Stevenson go, as he was needed to run the office, and he knew we'd get into trouble if we went together. Ruker was tied up in the laundry room and wouldn't want to jeopardize his position. Kyle couldn't stay awake long enough to make up his mind. Terry thought I was crazy even to mention it to him. "Go back to school!" he stammered. "I couldn't get through the sixth grade." That left Smitty, Chandler and Melanowski. I thought both Smitty and Chandler would be good mates for six months, but Melanowksi was out of the question. He had never even opened a book let alone read one. But Smitty and Chandler flatly refused. I told them they didn't have a choice. Colonel's orders. One of them had to volunteer.

"I hate the gooks so why do I want to study their stupid language," Smitty said and rolled up his sleeve. He gently kissed the Hawaiian girl tattooed on his forearm, as he always did when he was frustrated or under pressure. Chandler made some lame excuse about needing reading glasses. When I said he could have his eyes checked in two days, he complained about his arthritis. When I questioned him further, he didn't even know what arthritis was. "It just sounds good," he said. I didn't even bother to ask Melanowski.

"I'll tell you what," Chandler finally said. "Since one of the three of us has to go, I say we draw cards." They agreed and they drew cards. Melanowski drew the top card. He would be going with Gilbert and me to Peking.

"Well, old gold bricker, we'll be waiting here for you when you get back," Stevenson said when I went to his office to say good-bye. "Hell, six months is no time," he added and then handed me a package that just arrived in the mail. It was from my sister. She had mailed me three Lin Yu-tang books: *The Importance of Learning, The Importance of Understanding* and *From Pagan to Christian.* I was delighted.

"When I finish reading these volumes," I said, "I will be able to stand up to Rose Djung."

"When you finish reading them," he replied, "you won't want to."

Sammy checked out a 4x4 and drove Gilbert, Melanowski and me, along with Ming-Lee and Little Lew, to the airport. I felt terrible about leaving. Things were going well for me in Tsingtao. Ming-Lee was terribly sad but she cheered up when I made her promise she would come visit me in Peking. Little Lew was all tears. "I'm not leaving forever," I explained to him. "I'll bring you back a present. What would you like?"

"Only you," he cried and started to turn away. I reached out and grabbed him and pulled him close to me. Try as I did, I couldn't hold back my own tears.

"Lew, listen to me. Everything will be alright," I said. "The guys will take care of you." He wouldn't stop crying and my heart went out to him. I thought of him in that sewer, and now only a couple of months later he was a changed boy with rosy cheeks and hope at last. When Ming-Lee saw the tears in both our eyes, she too began to weep.

"You better get out of here," Sammy said, "or you'll see me bawling too." I left them standing at the edge of the terminal building, not daring to look back.

My terrible anguish about leaving my friends passed when I climbed aboard the DC-6 and saw for the first time the inside of an aircraft. I had not flown before and I looked forward to this moment. Back in 1946 not many people had the experience of flying. When one wanted to travel across America they took a train. When they traveled across oceans, they went by steamer: three days across the US by train; five days from New York to London by boat; three weeks from San Francisco to Manila and Hong Kong by slow boat. That song "A Slow Boat to China or Maybe Siam" was only too fitting. For us, two hours from Tsingtao to Tientsin by a DC-3 Gooney Bird wasn't bad either.

The pilot, a young 1st lieutenant flyboy with a MAG-3 patch on his flight jacket, instructed us to make sure our seat belts were secured and then reminded us that lifejackets were under our seats. He added we would fly at 5,000 feet and would follow the Yellow Sea to avoid flying at a higher altitude to clear the Loh Shan Mountains. He didn't say it, but I imagined he didn't want a repeat of the three spy planes that went down in bad weather on the north shore of the peninsula. I could envision Fox Company coming to look for us.

We strapped ourselves into bucket seats with our backs to the bulkhead. Gilbert was all smiles while Melanowski had the look of uncertainty in his eyes. The co-pilot closed the door, swung a bar down into place and locked it. He yanked twice to make certain the door was secure. He paid no attention to Melanowski who sarcastically asked if the captain thought we might try jumping out. Ignoring him the co-pilot walked to the front of the aircraft, disappeared behind another door, and the three of us were alone. The propellers began to rotate, painfully, the port side first, then the starboard, coughing and spewing out smoke as they labored to come to life. Once they began turning in unison, the pilot revved them up. The old bird began to vibrate and shake, and the noise grew so loud I could no longer hear Melanowksi complaining. We began rolling down the runway, turned and stopped. The plane jolted as the pilot applied the breaks and held them. I didn't think the noise could grow any louder, but it did as the pilot revved to full throttle. He then released the brakes, and we went rolling down the mesh-laid landing field. It seemed we would never lift off the ground. Breaking all rules, I unfastened my seat belt and stood up to look out the tiny oval window above our heads. Gilbert followed suit. We watched until the clouds obliterated our view and the ground below disappeared. Even the wing and starboard engine, only yards away, melted into the white void, and the air in the cabin turned frightfully cold. We reached for blankets stuffed behind our seats, and spent the next two hours shivering and wondering it we would ever reach our destination. There was one advantage with the unending loud noise—we couldn't hear Melanowski beating his gums.

I had never been to St. Louis, but I had seen enough movies to know I'd like the place. When I saw Tientsin, I thought I had arrived in St. Louis. It was a displaced modern Western city transplanted to the Orient. High rises, glass-fronted shops, wide avenues, restaurants and at night bright lights, not at all what one might expect for China. I had seen Broadway and 42nd Street when I got out of boot camp while on my way home on furlough, and the main drag though Tientsin was much like Broadway and 42nd Street. No wonder China Marines bragged about Tientsin duty. That night a couple of Marines from the garrison showed the three of us around town. We found it so enjoyable I hoped we could spend a few days more, but we had a rendezvous at 0600 at the rail station the following morning.

The worst duty in China, and certainly the most dangerous, was train guard duty. The coal shipments guarded by the 1st Marine Division were vital to the Chinese people. Gen. Wedemeyer pointed out that it was a military necessity that at least 100,000 tons of coal reach Shanghai every month, and his orders to IIIAC were to ensure that this coal reached its destination. Without coal shipments Shanghai would collapse. The average Marine standing his turn on guard, huddling against the biting winter wind that blew down from the Gobi Desert, was not aware of this, but his superiors were, and they lived under the constant pressure of that knowledge.

The communists were regularly sabotaging rail lines and firing on Marine-guarded trains. At Chinwangtao, Marines clashed regularly with the communists. What was so crazy about it all was that many of these communist partisans had risked their lives time and again to rescue American flyers from the Japanese. On Guam I had met crews of B-29's who had bailed out on their return from bombing Japan and had been smuggled to safety by villagers who were now held to be enemies. In this very same area communists now sniped at Marine trains, and Marines shelled villages in retaliation. While both sides avoided open warfare, the area of intermittent conflict was spreading as IIIAC expanded its hold on key cities and vital routes of communication.

The night before when we toured the town, I met a couple of off-duty train guards in the Cherry Club. They weren't too happy guarding trains and envied us in Tsingtao where it was peaceful and quiet. Without thought, I mentioned we were in China to repatriate the Japanese and nothing more. "Don't give me that bullshit," one Marine yelled and for a minute I thought he might get up and take a swing at me. "Marines are in North China to support Chiang's regime. They said we were coming to evacuate the Japanese from China, and so we did. They shipped all those little yellow bastards back in a couple of months."

The second Marine butted in. "Do we go home?" he asked. "Hell, no! No sooner do the Japs began to leave, when we hear the Russians are coming."

"Yea, the Russians," the first Marine sounded out. "We have to stick around to counter the Russian troops in Manchuria or they'd take over China. Then they announced that we are remaining indefinitely to guard supply lines from coal mines to the coast. That, too, is bullshit. Everybody knows this ain't so. We are here to protect and defend Chiang K'ai-shek. The Kuomintang knows this! Chiang K'ai-shek knows this! Who doesn't know it? The American people don't!"

After the next round of beers, they both mellowed out and agreed Tientsin was good duty. "Hell, it's better than selling cars in Pittsburgh," the first Marine said.

"Or working in the friggn' steel mills," the other Marine added. They were both from the Pittsburgh area.

On the way to our train compartment the next morning, I watched two Marine guards take their positions on top of a boxcar. The doors were barred and locked. Their positions on top of the cars didn't look very comfortable. I asked one Marine where he was from, the first thing a Marine asks when he meets another Marine. He said he was from Detroit. "I thought Detroit was cold," he said, "but shit, this is colder than a witch's tit, coldest I've ever been in all my gawd damn life. We sleep in our clothes and still can't keep warm." He told how one time he drank putrid water to make himself sick so he could go to sickbay where it was warm, and where he could get some decent food. Marine guards on the run to Peking had their own compartment with bunks and a wood stove to keep warm. At midpoint between Tientsin and Peking the northbound train made rendezvous with the southbound train, and here guards changed trains and returned to their home base. They had a sign hanging on the outside of their compartment: THE GOBI EXPRESS.

Our conductor, a nervous and excitable little old man in a thread-bare uniform, led us through throngs of pushing and shouting people to our compartment. When we saw the people attempting to funnel up the steps and through the doorway, we never thought we would make it. This obviously was not the time to be polite and courteous. We shouldered our seabags and hit the line like Notre Dame linebackers do when charging Army at their championship football games. Our conductor was the referee. Somehow he got ahead through the crowd and we could see his hand waving frantically above the heads of the people, summoning us to follow. Unlike most trains, this one had a long hallway that ran the length of one side of the compartment. Every inch of hallway was jam-packed with passengers trying to find their compartments. They carried loads of luggage; their friends helping them carried loads of luggage; their coolies following behind them carried loads of luggage. Once they were inside their compartments, others outside on the platform passed to them more loads of luggage through the windows. Where all the luggage was going to be stored was a mystery.

Our four-berth compartment was jammed with passengers, all waving tickets at our conductor. Again this was time for action. We had to block and run scrimmage, and push everyone out the door. We tipped our conductor with a dollar note and locked ourselves in. We threw our seabags on the top bunk and sat down on the lower bunk.

The coal-burning train to Peking could hardly be called an express. In better times it could make the run in less than a day, but not now. It stopped for one reason or another every few miles. Some of the stops lasted an hour or more. At one unexpected stop we saw two Marine guards run past our window with their weapons drawn. A half-hour later we saw them returning and threw open our window and asked what the delay was all about. "One of our tanks guarding the line ahead ran over a Chinese man on a donkey cart," one Marine said.

"What happened? we asked.

"He killed them both," he answered and went on his way. We learned later the tank commander had to pay a fine of $10 for the man and $20 for the donkey.

The train to Peking was one of those ancient conveyances that must have served the US Marines before us during the Boxer Rebellion. The coal-burning engine huffed and puffed and sent out belches of steam and messy black soot. It left Tientsin and reached out for the outer edges of the great Gobi Desert, possibly along the same route Genghis Khan had taken with his hundred thousand mounted horsemen when he conquered Peking.

We watched the great empty landscape of China, arid and

dust-swept, pass in slow motion beyond our window. The earth was brown, all brown without color. Farmlands were flat with the houses low to the ground and surrounded by mud walls. Burial mounds of hard earth dominated much of the landscape. The mounds seemed to be endless. The sun, only a mellow disc in the sky, lay low on the horizon, without giving warmth, and played hide-and-seek behind the mounds. The motion of the train was hypnotic. The click-idy-clack, click-idy-clack was mesmerizing. It was easy to fall into a reverie. I found myself thinking less about working with my father in his electrical shop and more of Ming-Lee and what we would do when she joined me in Peking. Maybe she would even stay with me and not go back to Tsingtao. It was a very nice thought to dwell upon.

When I tired of looking out the window, I turned to reading Lin Yu-tang's *The Importance of Understanding.* I read for a while, drifted into thought, and then returned to reading. The book had more meaning for me while rumbling across a barren Chinese countryside than it would have had I been reading it back home. I thought about the author giving up China to live in America. Those Chinese I talked to believed he was a traitor. I was giving up America to live in China. This was the lot of all China Marines. Were we giving up more than we were gaining? Back home did they consider us traitors?

We didn't move, we crawled across the wasteland, and by the next morning, after endless stops, I grew weary of reading. I left the compartment to walk along the hallway to exercise my limbs. I opened the door that lead to the next car and came upon an open area between the cars. A steel ladder led to the roof. I climbed the ladder and found I could sit on the roof with comfort, with my legs dangling over the side. I had a splendid unobstructed view. Since we were moving slowly, there was not a great deal of wind.

For the next few hours I sat there, studying the unattainable horizon. The tracks before us unrolled like a black ribbon upon an endless waste, and behind us we left a finger of smoke that lingered motionless in the lacquered sky. I became dust-covered—my eyelashes, my hair, my clothing. Then I saw it.

First I saw the dust, a sky of dust, and then the outer walls. It was Peking. The great city loomed up like a picture in a child's storybook. Peking, the mighty and ancient capital of Cathay. What a magnificent sight.

It seemed like forever for us to close the distance; there was something so strange about it all. There appeared to be nothing else except a city surrounded by a wall. There was no hint of what might be beyond that wall. It was, if anything, a bit frightening.

The track led into an arched opening, with barely enough room for the train to slip through, and certainly not enough for me sitting on top of the car. I leaped down on the platform between the cars, but to my horror the conductor had locked the door. I couldn't get back in! I climbed back up the ladder and lay flat on the roof, and at that instant we entered the tunnel. I was suddenly in a black void, enveloped in a cloud of acrid smoke, choking and gasping for air. We emerged from the tunnel with me coughing and covered with black soot.

But in another fleeting moment I forgot my discomfort. It was like an explosion. A new and fascinating world opened up before me, strange and unbelievable. Everything caught my attention. I wanted to stop the train then and there, as though once we passed it might disappear and be gone forever.

As we edged deeper into the city, I could hear the sounds, even above the roar of the train, and I could even catch the smells. Rickshaw and pedicab drivers shouted warnings as they padded along, vendors clicked wooden blocks to gain attention, wood-burning trucks tooted their horns and there was the general clamor of an excited city.

Still coughing and covered with soot, I made my way down the ladder to find the door open. But getting back to the compartment was a chore. The narrow hallway was again crammed with people, this time attempting to make a quick exit when the train reached the station. I pushed my way through the crowd, like the quarterback at Notre Dame, and eventually got back to the compartment where I found Melanowski and Gilbert impatiently waiting. They were angry and started shouting at me, but their anger quickly passed when they got a better look at me. They broke into laughter. "Look at you!" Melanowski shrieked flopping back into his seat.

"What in the hell happened to you?" Gilbert asked. "You look like a West Virginia coal miner."

I explained what had happened, cursing the conductor who locked the door, but not really minding, and then looked down the front of my uniform. I was a mess, covered with black soot and grime. I looked in the mirror above the wash basin. The wind had tangled my hair and it stuck out in every direction. My eyes still stung from the smoke, and they watered with tears, and as the tears ran down my cheeks, they streaked my face. I was in no condition to report to Marine headquarters looking the way I did. I would have to stop somewhere and clean up first.

We waited until the car emptied, then slung our seabags over our shoulders and stepped out on to the platform. Upon seeing us emerge, a gang of coolies wanting to help us materialized out of nowhere, and then came the beggars and street urchins. Coming through the crowd was a Marine gunny sergeant, waving a brown envelope above his shoulder, and shouting angrily for the crowd to get out of his way. When they saw him, they cleared a path. He stopped short, looked at me, and said, "Marine, you look like shit."

The gunny was from 5th Marine Headquarters quartered in the old British Legation. He was under orders to pick us up and take us to the University of Peking where we had to register. It was Saturday afternoon when we arrived, and the gunny explained that the headquarters office was closed. The university was providing quarters and all we needed to do was check in at headquarters every Saturday morning. "You have until next Saturday," he said. "I'll log you in." We thanked him and I apologized for my appearance, blaming it on the conductor for locking me out. He softened his tone a bit, even smiled, and was not as gruff as he was at first. He said we could stop at a bathhouse on our way to the university and I could clean up. He had a 4x4 and a driver waiting for us outside the station.

We drove to a bathhouse, similar to the one Stevenson and I visited in Tsingtao, and I felt better after a good scrub down. I came out clean shaven and smelling of fufu perfume, with my uniform cleaned and pressed, and my shoes shined. The whole operation took less than an hour. I wished I had Stevenson's barracks hat to make it complete but he wouldn't loan it to me. The others were waiting and we took off in the 4x4 through the streets of Peking.

What excitement to be driving for the first time through this great Oriental city, one of the greatest capital cities of the world. Suddenly the gunny took on another role. He began pointing out all the sights, telling us to look here one moment, and over there the next. He was quite knowledgeable about the history of Peking and took delight in telling us about the city. "The wall around the city, over there to our left, it's 4,000 years old," he said as we drove along the western section of the city. Indeed, it was a magnificent wall. "It surrounds the whole city, and within the walls are some four and a half million people." He had the driver stop so we could see the wall better. "There are four main gates," he continued, "but they couldn't keep out Genghis Khan. It was called Chungtu in the 12th century when he arrived with 100,000 mounted horsemen and stormed the place. It was his grandson, Kublai Khan, who rebuilt her and changed the name to Cambulac —The Great Capital."

The gunny, self-made historian turned guide, insisted we drive through Tiananmen Square. "Here you will feel the might of China," he said, and he was right. We could almost feel the strength of China by looking out over this vast empty square which seemed to radiate power. He had the driver take us to the southern end of the square and here we stopped. "Look at that, look, look," he shouted, pointing to three marble bridges that crossed a narrow moat. On the other side was a high-walled building with huge gates. Adorning the wall was a grand poster of Generalissimo Chiang K'ai-shek. "This is the Forbidden City," the gunny shouted, standing up in the front seat of the Jeep and spreading wide both his arms as if embracing the whole of Peking. His excitement was infectious, and like laughter in a schoolroom, it spread to us. We felt the full glory and the excitement of being in Peking. Even Melanowski agreed, "It is nice."

We made one more stop, The Temple of Heaven, and then the gunny delivered us to the University of Peking. He handed me a brown envelope with our orders and wished us good luck. We had only known him for a few hours and yet we felt we were losing a good friend. "I'll look you guys up," he said, and we knew he felt the same. The Marine Corps can do that to you. We were sad to say goodbye, and ten minutes later we regretted leaving the gunny and his world behind. The head counselor of the university was waiting for us. He wasn't anything like the gunny.

Dr. Siang Wren, head counselor, could have been Dracula reincarnated. He had a pockmarked face and was well past middle age, but he carried himself erect as a board standing upright. He wore a dark robe that fitted high around his neck and extended down to his shoes. You got the feeling that if he tried to walk he would trip. He had pince-nez glasses perched on the very end of his nose. He kept his hands tucked into his wide sleeves and when he greeted us, he bowed slightly, keeping his gaze firmly fixed on us all the time. He did not offer to shake hands, and we found ourselves bowing too. He did it naturally; we did it awkwardly like the three stooges did in the movies. We knew at once Dr. Wren was a man who demanded respect.

"I will address you gentlemen in your own language," he

said quietly in an English Oxford accent. "But this will be the last time we speak in English."

"But we don't speak Chinese," Melanowski interrupted.

Dr. Wren didn't like to be interrupted. "That is why you are here," he snapped. You could suddenly see flames in his eyes, enough to burn a hole in Melanowski. But Melanowski was not about to be intimidated by an emaciated, arrogant Chinese professor.

"I am here because they sent me here, sir" he fired back, putting much emphasis on sir.

Dr. Wren would not concede. "Yes, you are here to study Chinese," he said, "and we shall teach you Chinese." He removed his right hand from his sleeve and raising a finger to his lips, he continued. "You are a guest of the Chinese National Government. You will be given Chinese clothes to wear, a slate to write upon and books for your studies." He took the brown manila envelope that I had given him and opened it. He read the contents very carefully. This was worse than standing at attention in front of Col. Roston while being reprimanded for coming in late from liberty. He then scrutinized the three of us, starting at the tops of our heads, then down to our shoes and back to our faces. He had an uncanny ability of making us feel the size of toy puppets, and all he had to do was pull the strings to make us act as he wanted. I waited but he didn't pull the strings. "You will address me, and all your professors and all your teachers, as '*syan-sheng.*' Syan-sheng means sir. You will be given Chinese names." He studied the records again. "Why do you want to study Chinese?" he asked looking at me.

I was confused with the question and didn't know quite how to answer. I was tempted to answer him in Chinese but I thought it best not to. I didn't care to leave myself wide open for harsh criticism that he most likely would reign upon me. "Well," I said stumbling for words, "I guess, I mean, I mean I like China. I want to know how to speak to the people."

"You like China?" he questioned.

"Yes, I like China."

"Your last name we can translate into Hsi. You are Hsi Syan-sheng. You understand?" I nodded. Dr. Wren continued: "You say you like China. How much do you like China?"

"Very much," I replied.

"You say very much. The verb 'to like' in Chinese is '*huan*.' To like very much is '*huan loh*.' Your Chinese name is Hsi Huan Loh. Repeat it."

"Hsi Huan Loh," I repeated, pronouncing slowly each word. It was an easy name to pronounce and I rather liked it.

"Very well. Again, what is your name?" Dr. Wren asked.

"Hsi Huan Loh," I said proudly.

"No," the professor snapped. "When asked your name you will reply, '*Wada bee sheng shir Hsi Huan Loh*.' 'My humble name is Shi Huan Loh.' When you ask an elder his name, you must ask for his '*gwei sheng*,' his honorable name. Now you understand." That was one of the first things that Mrs. Murray taught me, but it was best I didn't tell him that I knew. I didn't want him to end up losing face.

I could see the anguish on Melanowski's face. I knew at once this was not what he had in mind when he agreed to study the language. It was not the easy duty he thought it would be. To him, Dr. Wren was another Col. Roston, and he didn't like Col. Roston. But I was finding the situation quite the opposite. It was like a game, and I liked games when they were a competition. The good doctor was simply playing a game. I felt this until he made his next announcement, and then I wondered if I too might be wrong. There was no winning this game. Dr. Wren announced that each of us would be given separate quarters, and that meant not only separate rooms but we would be located in separate buildings as well. He gave each of us a piece of paper with a name and an address. Mine read Hostel No. 3, 253 Da Shao Lao Road.

I didn't have a chance to talk things over with the other two, or even to say goodbye to them. Dr. Wren made certain of that. We were suddenly being ushered out of his office by his assistants. He had made arrangements for pedicabs to take each of us to our quarters. Our last instructions from Dr. Wren were that classes start at 0700 sharp on Monday morning. Before I knew what had happened, my two friends, my Marine Corps buddies, were gone and I was alone.

My pedicab driver placed my seabag on the seat next to me and I settled back for a new experience—riding a pedicab in Peking. Unlike two-wheeled rickshaws that are pulled by coolies who position themselves between two shafts, pedicabs are three-wheel bicycles that are peddled by drivers who sit in front. Passengers sit behind them in the rear. Pedicabs seem more humane than rickshaws but it's still grueling work. I remember Roger telling me how the rickshaw business began. "Not Chinese like everyone think," he said. According to him, the rickshaw was invented in Japan in the 1860s; the American Baptist missionaries called it *jinrikisha,* which means 'man-powered cart.' Its popularity spread from Japan to China and to most countries of Asia. For almost fifty years the style of the rickshaw was little altered. Then came the two-wheeled bicycle and a revolution in the transportation business in the Far East. The bicycle principle was added to the rickshaw, and every city in the Orient, it seemed, made its own version of the tricycle-rickshaw, now called the 'pedicab.' Roger disliked the use of rickshaws. He often said the rickshaw was an invention of the imperialists to enslave the Chinese. Shanghai had more rickshaws than any other city in China, some 50,000. "Shanghai much much foreigner people, now you savvy why," he said. I disagreed with Roger. Nevertheless, I rather liked rickshaws, but then I am not Chinese. Pedicabs were not popular in Tsingtao because of the hills.

Hostel No. 3 was located in a quiet residential section of the city. It was a grand old stone building with high ceiling hallways and long corridors. It was probably fashionable around the turn of the century. The receptionists at the front desk were waiting and handed me my key—Room 249. The room boy, a young lad about fifteen named Bon Yee, took the key, whisked my seabag from me and bid me follow him. There was no elevator and we walked up carpeted steps to the second floor. Yee opened the door, stepped aside and let me enter. It was the most depressing sight I had ever looked upon. To one side was a single bed with a lumpy quilted covering of different shaped patches sewed one over top the other, and across the room against the wall was a washstand with a porcelain basin and pitcher with rabbit-ear handles next to it. There was no water faucet and no plumbing, only a bucket under the washstand for collecting water. There was but one light, a naked bulb suspended from the ceiling. The light switch was a dangling cord that you had to pull to turn the light on or off. The window was the worst thing about the room. Although it was large with glass panes, it was so yellow and stained with age that very little light entered the room, and what did made the room appear even more dreary. I don't think the window opened, and if it did, rags stuffed around the window would fall out. The rag across the sill was brown with dust. The whole room in fact was dust-covered.

Yee placed my seabag on the floor, and then explained that the communal WC was down the hall. He smiled proudly as he pulled the cord to show that the light worked and pointed to a towel hanging by the washstand. I could see that he was pleased to show me the room, and rather than disappoint him I nodded my approval. He beamed even more. By his standards, of course, I was getting five-star accommodation. But no sooner had he left than I realized something else about the room. It was unheated. I took my coat off and had to put it on again after only a few minutes.

On my table next to the bed, I placed my three Lin Yu-tang books, the *Dowager Empress,* the old *Spoken Chinese* text from Guam and my most recent acquisition, a history of the city, titled *Peking*. I laid down on the bed, my mind wandering, and studied the room, my new home for the months to come.

I was following a crack across the ceiling when there came a knock at the door. It was Yee again. He was carting a bundle of clothes. He laid them piece by piece on the bed: heavy-duty wool sweaters, two of them; two pair of Chinese trousers, the wrap around kind that require a belt or sash to hold them up; a quilted parka with enormous pockets; a muffler as long as I was tall with a golden dragon spitting out fire embroidered along one edge; and a pair of soft-leather boots with fur lining. I was surprised that they fit, although a bit snug. The most prized possession was a fore-and-aft lambskin hat. I would be well clothed, thanks to the Chinese Nationalist Government, and thanks to the US Government for giving lend-lease to Chiang K'ai-shek so that he had the money to spend. I didn't really know which government to thank, so I thanked Yee and decided to let him sort it out. As he was leaving he said dinner was at 20:00.

In my resplendent new wardrobe I marched into the dining room, and immediately wanted to do an about face and leave. There was not another white face in the room. The steward saw me, came running, and as he escorted me to my table, everyone stopped eating and heads turned to see who this foreigner, this foreign devil, might be. I was on parade. I felt ridiculous, even stupid, in my dress and wished I had stayed in uniform. It was the most uncomfortable feeling I had ever had, and my thoughts went to poor Melanowski. He had to be in torture, about the same time, or else he was very hungry.

Servants in much worn white jackets loafed around with napkins over their arms. There were more servants than diners. Two rows of four-bladed fans hung from the ceiling in long shafts, but none were turning. Everything about the place was shabby, the tablecloths and napkins, the chipped plates and the cutlery with no two pieces the same, and yet, there was a pride that the Chinese displayed that couldn't be denied. It was almost humorous, and could have been a comedy had they not been so serious. Everything they did was done in earnest seriousness. They performed well, as if they were in the Court of the Queen of England and the dinner guests were all dukes and duchesses. The food was western, or an attempt to be western. It was awful.

I finished my dinner and lingered over a cigarette, and then another one. I dreaded returning to my room, to the cold and the loneliness, and considered taking a walk but then I remembered the weather. I returned to my room, climbed into bed, and tried to read, but with the light bulb directly overhead shining down in my eyes, it was impossible. My first duty the next day would be to buy an extension. I yanked on the cord and the light went out. I pulled the cover over my head, and with the fur parka over the top of the bed, and with my trousers, shirt and socks on, I still froze. I thought I would never get used to the cold.

The light filtered through the window the next morning and I awoke slowly, wondering if this was real or was I dreaming. I even imagined someone was in the room, but when I heard the shuffling I knew it was not imagination. I turned to find Yee standing by the washstand. He was placing a bowl with a lid on top on the table. I hadn't noticed but he had already placed hot bricks at the foot of the bed. When he saw me stir, he said breakfast was being served in the dining room.

With my fur parka draped over my shoulders, I put my feet on the warm bricks and the cold didn't seem so bad. I went to the wash stand assuming the bowl with hot water was for shaving, but when I removed the top, I saw tea leaves floating on the top. I returned to the bed, sat down and while drinking my tea, I read some from *Peking*. The more I read about Genghis Khan, the more I was fascinated with this man, a Tartar invader from Mongolia. He and his heirs ruled China for several hundred years. I was anxious to read how they were expelled from China but if I didn't hurry breakfast would be over. It wouldn't have mattered much had I missed it. No fruit juice; no bacon and eggs; no toast and butter. Not even coffee, only tea. Instead we had congee, a thick rice soup with a few vegetables floating on top, and more tea. Life was taking on many changes for me, and I found it all rather amusing.

I had the day all to myself. I didn't feel like reading, but what would I do? In the Marines we were always surrounded with buddies and were never alone. This was different. If I knew where Melanowski and Gilbert were, I could meet up with them. But, of course, I didn't know. I wouldn't mind even putting up with Melanowski's grumbling. I tried to imagine what Stevenson would be doing in Tsingtao. He was one guy who wouldn't be bored. He was probably taking Judy to a movie on the base. Maybe Roger was taking Judy to the base to meet Stevenson. What would we do without Roger? No more thinking about Tsingtao; I decided to go for a walk. I bundled up in my parka and put on my leather fur-lined boots and made my way to Tiananmen Square by following the map in my *Peking* book. The wind came sharp, and even with my parka pulled up tightly around my neck the cold still got through.

A few snow flurries filled the air, and when I looked out over the square there was not a soul to be seen. How remarkable, I thought. Here I was standing in front of one of the world's best-known landmarks and I had it all to myself, completely. No Genghis and a hundred thousand Tartar horsemen raping and pillaging, no US Marines in the Boxer Rebellion defending the foreign legations, no Dowager Empress leaving the Forbidden City for her last time, no Japanese conquerors riding white stallions as I had seen in *LIFE*, no more Generalissimo Chiang K'ai-shek and his parade of warlords and their troops showing their strength to the Eighth Route Regulars. The only echo now was my leather boots on the cobblestones of empty Tiananmen Square. How alone could I possibly be?

I missed lunch, not that I wasn't hungry, but I didn't want to go to a restaurant alone and have everyone stare at me. I didn't want to try to hold a conversation in my limited Chinese either. I went back to my room, and to keep warm I climbed into bed. I began reading *Peking*. Now and then I looked up at my Chinese clothing hanging on hooks behind the door. Little by little it began to sink in. I was now a bonafide student in Peking. And for the first time in my life I was alone; I mean really alone. But there was always Monday morning, my first class, and I'd be meeting students. I didn't sleep much that night, and it wasn't only because of the cold.

Chapter 10

WE DO EVERYTHING BACKWARDS

Monday morning at last, and my first day of school. I quit school in the 9th grade because I hated school. I hated verbs and adjectives and who cared what the Amendments to the Constitution were. What good would the history of Ancient Greece and Rome do me if I was going to work in an electrical goods shop with my father. If I could add and subtract why did I need algebra and geometry? So I quit school and soon after joined the Marines because I wanted to get away, far, far away. I was far away now, about as far as I could go, but the irony was I was back in school. And what was so strange about it all was that I was looking forward to it.

It was Monday morning, and again I was aware that someone was in my room. As I suspected it was Bon Yee, the room boy. Like the day before, he had placed warm bricks at the foot of my bed. Peeking out from the top of my blankets I watched him go over to the washstand and place a bowl of hot tea on the counter. When he saw that I was awake, he reminded me breakfast was ready. Why protest? This was obviously going to be the routine.

I really didn't like someone entering my room when I was still asleep, but on the other hand the warm bricks at my feet and the bowl of tea did make a difference. I scrambled out of bed, and with my feet on the bricks and my cover wrapped around me I drank my tea. This too I could see was going to become a habit. Hot tea and not hot coffee in the morning. Outside my window the wind howled, and with the wind came dust from the Gobi Desert. Dust began to collect on the windowsill and some seeped in under the pane. It took courage to dress. I didn't bother with my wrap-around-Chinese trousers and instead put on my winter greens, and over this went the heavy woolen sweater they had given me. The fur-lined boots were a blessing. It was miserable shaving in frigid water, and it brought back to mind when Marsden had me shave under my bunk at the Strand. Could this be Marsden's revenge?

The dining room was not much of an improvement over my room; it wasn't any warmer. I didn't get as many stares as I did the day before and I felt more comfortable. I ate my bowl of congee in silence, slipped into my quilted jacket that smelled like a dead goat, and went out into the street. My spirits were lifted when I found my pedicab driver waiting for me. That solved one worry, finding my way to the university.

The university was a grey-stone building with a long winding pathway that led to the main entrance. It was the toughest walk I ever had to make. My only salvation was hope that I would run into Melanowski and Gilbert, and perhaps some of the other Marines in the program, but the only white faces I encountered were a couple of women, and I assumed they were White Russians.

The corridor inside the building was a mad scramble of confused students. I expected someone to blow a whistle and it would all end, but no whistle blew and no bell rang. Where could Melanowski and Gilbert be? I then saw a face I recognized, Dr. Wren. I managed to push through the crowd to reach him. "Dr. Wren, Dr. Wren," I called.

Dr. Wren turned when he heard his name called. As I approached, he stood firm, and with a calm but stern voice, he said in quiet Mandarin, "Are you addressing me?"

"Yes, sir, I am," I replied in Mandarin, surprised that the words came so easily.

"Then, guest of my country," he said sarcastically, "do not

address me in English." I understood completely what he said, but I did not appreciate it. I was trying to form the words to answer him, and at the same time wondered if I told him to go to hell and walked out could I be court martialed, when to my complete surprise he took me by the arm and led me down the corridor to a classroom. He dropped my arm, pointed to the room and without a further word was gone. I stepped through the door and entered another world. I cursed and asked myself why did I ever volunteer to study Chinese? I didn't like this one bit. Would my teacher be another miserable old bastard like Dr. Wren?

Relief came when I saw a half dozen other white faces already in their seats, and judging by their haircuts they too were Marines. Before I could say a word of greeting, one man put his fingers up to his lips. "*Ni shi hao ma?*" he said, and it was immediately apparent he and the others were already indoctrinated. We were only allowed to speak to one another in Chinese, as Dr. Wren had warned. The professor stood at the head of the class in the front of the room, and he seemed pleased. He was a young man, with a pleasant smile, and I liked him from the start. This wasn't going to be too bad, and I hoped I wouldn't be wrong.

"*Qing, ni gaosu tamen, ni shi hao,*" the teacher said to me—"Tell them how are you."

And so on this cold winter morning in Peking my study of Chinese began. There were eight Marines and several other non-Chinese in my class, all eager to learn the language. At the end of the class each Marine disappeared while I was talking to the teacher and it wasn't until the second day we were able to converse, in Chinese of course. Marines came from Tiensin and Shanghai. There were two more language classes of foreign students, and I surmised that Melanowski and Gilbert were in these.

Aside from spoken Chinese, we had to learn writing as well. By learning characters it also helped with the spoken word. I soon discovered what made Chinese calligraphy particularly interesting was the composition in these characters. Chinese characters are formed from the oldest, originally pictographic, elements. When I recognized the character for water, I could easily see when another stroke was added to that same character, it would then change the meaning but it would still be related in some way to water—ice, beverage, snow and the likes. In my room one night I began copying characters for practice, and the next day proudly showed them to my teacher, and discovered they were all wrong. I learned strokes must be delicately balanced against each other and must be made in a precise manner. It wasn't as easy as I thought.

Aside from two hours of Chinese language classes each day, I was required to attend other classes—Chinese history and Chinese literature. The idea was that the more I was exposed to spoken Chinese the quicker I would learn the language. Students in these classes were of mixed nationalities, including a very pretty White Russian girl I saw sauntering around the class rooms. But most of the students were Chinese, male and female, and to them their studies were a serious matter. The majority were in their late teens, but a few were in their middle and late 20s. Su Fung was 26. She was rather plain, with thick glasses, and very bright. She was from Shanghai and sat next to me in my literature class. Her friend Mae Chu was 25. We broke the rule about speaking only in Chinese during a break when we were in the courtyard.

Both Su Fung and Mae Chu spoke very good English and I was able to gain a lot from our friendship. Both girls' parents were teachers. They spoke English but they were very naive, as most Chinese students were. I tried joking with them but that proved to be impossible. In our literature class we were studying Chinese poetry and under discussion was T'ao Yuan-ming, a poet from the 4th century. I had to admit I had never heard of him. "You mean you never heard of him?" Su Fung said. "He has had a tremendous impact on generations of Chinese poetry and fiction. He was one of China's most beloved poets."

"No," I repeated, "I haven't heard of him." I don't know how they expected me to know about a Chinese poet from the 4th century. "Have you heard of Robert Frost?" I asked in my defense. I didn't know much about Robert Frost, except that he was a famous American poet.

"Oh. Robert Frost, yes—'The Mending Wall.' T'ao Yuan-ming was before his time, of course, but his poems on beauty and awareness of nature have been compared to those of Robert Frost." Without intending to do it, Su Fung called my bluff. I was more careful in my discussion with them the next time.

I knew nothing about T'ao Yuan-ming, but that was soon to change. In our next literature class we began reading "Peach Blossom Spring." I didn't understand all the words but the sounds and rhythms were melodic, especially when the teacher read the poem in Mandarin Chinese. Of all Chinese dialects, Mandarin is the most beautiful. Maybe the Chinese could never in a thousand years develop an atomic bomb within the scope of their language, but they could write beautiful poetry. Su Fung sat next to me in class and translated some of the lines, and when I went back to my room at night I read "Peach Blossom Spring" from a translation I borrowed from the library. The story was beautiful and it captured my imagination. I kept imagining Peach Blossom Valley where the action took place, and even pictured myself coming back one day and searching for a lost valley. In the poem, T'ao describes how a fisherman sailing along an uncharted stream comes upon a radiantly beautiful peach orchard where, "Falling petals fluttered in colored profusion." Entranced by the orchard's loveliness, the fisherman explored further and found a narrow passage in a mountain cliff. He entered the passage and suddenly emerged into a land of beauty and mystery, an idyllic community where no one grows old.

This was an early version of Shangri-La. I went to the library and checked out James Hilton's *Lost Horizon* and spent the whole night in my room, under a cover, reading it. Dawn was breaking when I finished. Back in class we continued with "Peach Blossom Spring." The villagers were surprised by the fisherman's arrival but were pleased to converse with him. They tell him that their ancestors fled tyrants centuries before; and they have been hidden from the world of wars and suffering and know nothing of the outside world; nor do they wish to rejoin it. The fisherman is treated by the farmers as an honored guest, and is feasted with all the fruits of their harvest and their finest wine.

When the fisherman describes to them the violent and turbulent world he comes from, they shake their heads and sigh. For several days, he lives among them, spellbound by their good will and guileless ways. He watches in admiration, as the people follow neither kings nor calendars but only the natural rhythm of nature. He senses a happiness and contentment among the villagers that does not exist in the outside.

Excited by his discovery, the fisherman requests permission to leave. The villagers allow him to go, asking that he not spread word of their existence. The fisherman leaves, but despite his promise, he carefully marks his route and reports what he saw to officials. The officials quickly enlist others to return with him but to his amazement his markings have mysteriously disappeared and, try as he might, the fisherman can never again find Peach Blossom Spring. All subsequent attempts to find the valley have ended in failure. If I could convince Stevenson, we could get a Jeep and look for Peach Blossom Spring. I couldn't wait until I saw him to tell him about my plan.

We all need dreams, and that was mine. In the mean time, aside from formal classes, we had to attend Chinese functions three evenings a week. We had many choices—Chinese films, Sing-Song cabarets, teahouses, or Chinese operas. I went to my first movie with Su Fung, Mae Chu and two of their male friends.

The Chinese films were dreadful and it took real

perseverance to sit through them for two or three hours. Actors overacted and overdramatized. When they cried, it wasn't simple tears they shed; it was wailing and hollering and falling to the floor, and rolling into a ball in a fetal position, and pounding the floor with closed fists. Actors didn't walk; they floated. They didn't die simple deaths; they stretched the agony into twenty-minute scenes in which actors and actresses miraculously came to life only to die again, and not once or twice, but perhaps a half dozen times. Staging was totally without ingenuity. Two actors talking and shot close up may have an open vista for a background, with a snow-capped mountain range in the far distance, and in the next shot they are in the studio and the background is a white sheet on a wall. To make things worse, the director didn't bother to have the creases taken out of the sheet.

The Sing-Song cabaret I didn't mind, for my friend Roger in Tsingtao had taught me the finer intricacies of the show. Still, they were enjoyable only for the first ten minutes. Like in Tsingtao, the singers were always women accompanied by classical Chinese music, which was mainly one-string violins and gongs. The female vocalists were highly skilled. The audience, always well dressed, sat around tiny tables drinking pots of tea, eating sunflower seeds. After several sessions I was still unable to understand a single word they sang, but I did develop a liking for tea and a dislike for sunflower seeds.

Chinese students at the university were not friendly. They looked upon foreigners with suspicion. Aside from Su Fung and Mae Chu I was able to befriend a few older male students. Chinese women for the most part kept their ground and were unapproachable. I had the feeling they wanted to be friendly, but they appeared too afraid to do so. As a result, they became defensive, and even vindictive. I tried to be nice to them but always felt slighted. Nevertheless, they were lovely, and very feminine. I loved their narrow bodies and slender limbs. Their hands were fine and delicate. Asian women had charm, but the most striking thing about them was their eyes. When a

Western man falls in love with an Asian woman, I think it's because of their eyes. I never tired of looking at their eyes. Ming-Lee had lovely eyes. They were as striking as any Oriental eyes that I had seen. It was the first thing I noticed about her.

When my Chinese became more proficient I was able to engage in more conversations with the students, and at these times women could be drawn into the circle. They became more argumentative than the men. I could feel a revolution brewing in all of them. One Chinese woman student who irked me was Lee Ann. She had a chip on her shoulder and was ready to attack me for the most trivial thing. Her English was excellent, for she grew up in London where her parents were in the Chinese foreign service. When the war ended, they returned to Peking. She obviously didn't want to be in Peking, but now that she was, she defended her position vehemently. She was a cad, a snob, and what we in the Marines call "a spoiled brat." Nevertheless I liked her. I liked her for her arrogance, and with her I knew where I stood, at the opposite pole. I could depend upon her being straightforward. You may not like them, but these are the most dependable people, no beating around the bush with them.

Lee Ann was a revolutionary at heart, but the country was still run by the Kuomingtan, and one had to be cautious. Chinese women, who for centuries groaned under the weight of the male-dominated Confucian doctrine, nurtured promises that generated from the revolutionary movement. I couldn't escape Lee Ann's wrath on this subject. She was quick to bring up British colonial relationships with China, especially with Chinese women. The Opium Wars were hashed and rehashed every chance she found to bring them up. It took a great deal of effort for me, burning the midnight oil, reading up on the subject, to prepare myself to meet her head-on the next day. Her pet peeve regarded the employment contracts British males had to sign before they took up their new posts in the Far East. Essentially these contracts stated that British men were not allowed to marry Chinese women, nor were they allowed to have Chinese women living with them. They could not even take Chinese women as guests into their messes. Lee Ann constantly reminded me about the sign at the entrance of the Bund in Shanghai, the promenade where all the foreigners gathered before the war, which read: CHINESE AND DOGS NOT ALLOWED.

Not all the students were as sophisticated as Lee Ann. To most of them I was a novelty. If I had rolled up my sleeves for any reason, they wanted to touch the hair on my arms. Often, when they thought I wasn't looking, they made funny gestures with their fingers, indicating my long nose, and would laugh about it. With these students, conversations were usually a waste of time. I learned nothing from them,

I never tired of sitting in the teahouses conversing with them. Once they got to know me, they besieged me with endless questions. At first I thought they were being facetious, but I soon realized they were dead serious. One student asked, "In the West, why do you do everything backwards?"

"Backwards! Like what?" I asked.

"You read a book from the wrong end first."

I couldn't argue this point. Chinese were writing books long before the Egyptians were using cuneiform. Which then was the right way to begin a book? I had to pass. To have said otherwise I would have made a fool of myself. The front of a book to us is the back of the book to them.

Another student asked: "How can you tell one foreigner from another? You all look alike."

So all Westerners look alike. That was interesting. How many times has it been said in the West that all Asians look alike? Before I came to China, I couldn't tell Chinese apart from Japanese. Now I could. It was queer to find myself on the opposite side of the fence.

There were other questions I couldn't answer either, like why do we put titles—Mr., Miss, and Mrs.— before names rather than after them, and why do we make excuses when we really mean no? "My father has a shop," one girl said, "and every time a foreigner comes in and admires something, and then changes his mind, he says, 'I'll be back.' Why does he have to lie and say he'll be back when he doesn't mean it." I never thought about it before, and I couldn't answer her.

Often times such simple questions provoked deep thought. When I returned to my room and was alone I pondered over them. I began feeling empty inside. Were they, perhaps, not right? Why were we so different in the West? The more I got to know the Chinese, the more I came to realize that our thought patterns are not alike. When using deductive reasoning, we don't come to the same conclusions, not from a universal to a particular. Was this what Mrs. Djung was talking about when I was more interested in stuffing myself with *djow-dzes* than listening to their reasoning? Maybe I was being misled by Lin Yu-tang. At the library I began arming myself with both Chinese and Western philosophy books and these I would devour at night. Reading these books did not make life for me any easier, only more complicated. I desperately wanted to know the Chinese mind, but I soon realized to know their minds, I would have to cast away Western thoughts and ideas and think only like they do. The question was how to do that, but I would need more time than I had to find the answer. I found myself, when I was alone in my room and confused, standing in front of the mirror, slanting my eyes with my fingers, wondering why I had to look so different and be so different from everyone else. Was this what it meant by being in the minority.

Not all the students were Chinese. Some came from Kazakhstan and Uzbekistan, and from Tibet and Mongolia; others from Turkmenistan and Assam, and from many places I had never heard before. They came from faraway exotic lands, all speaking their strange tongues and dialects, bringing with them their customs and habits. They too were here to study Mandarin Chinese.

There were a few Europeans, mostly White Russians. They were the easiest to recognize, as they stood out from everyone else. I enjoyed watching them, for I had never seen an ethnic group quite like them before. They were outcasts in China, and yet they gave the appearance of having a social status far above anyone else. In Tsingtao they owned and operated bars and restaurants and had all sorts of clothing shops. There was a bordello that boasted having all White Russian women, six of them. Other than what I saw of them, I knew little about them. I saw them around the university but didn't think of them one way or another, until in my history class I took notice of one of the fairest women I had seen in all my stay in China. She was White Russian, and there was no mistaking about that. Who was she?

It was about my second week in class that I first saw her. It was probably because she sat in the rear, and when the class ended she was out the door before anyone else. On this particular day, at the end of the class, she had to bring a paper to the teacher in front of the room. She had to pass right by my desk. Her beauty was startling. She had the whitest skin I had ever seen on a human being. There's the expression, "as white as snow," but she was whiter than that.

She was elegant. She could make a man gasp. She wore high leather boots, almost up to her knees, and had draped over her shoulders a fine coat with thick fur around the collar and fur on the fringe at the bottom. She had a matching fur muffler, which hung from a cord around her neck. She laid the paper on the desk, said nothing to the teacher, and as she walked past to leave the room she put on a big fur hat. Her movements were graceful and deliberate. That image of her lingered long after she had gone. I couldn't get her out of my mind. The next day I went to class early and took a seat farther towards the back, but she did not show that day. Once or twice after that I got fleeting glimpses of her but could never get close to begin a conversation. I was determined to meet her.

On the morning of my first Saturday in Peking I was

preparing to go to George Company at the British Legation to check in when the gunny sergeant who first brought me to Hostel No. 3 appeared in the lobby. I didn't even know his name, and then remembered he didn't tell me. "Today's a holiday and the office is closed," he said. "Thought I'd come and check you in and save you a trip." I was excited to see him, and had many questions to ask. He had a bottle of White Horse and asked if we could go into the restaurant and drink there. He saw me looking at the bottle. "Don't worry," he said, "real stuff." The Scotch was the first booze I had had in weeks. It tasted great and after two drinks my head was floating.

Melanowski and Gilbert were doing fine, he said. Both were still in school, staying in another hostel. We could all meet up next Saturday and he would show us the town. He asked if there was anything I needed, and as he was leaving he said, "Good reports about you. Keep it up."

The following Saturday he kept his word. When I went to check in, he was waiting. Gilbert was there too. Melanowski had checked in but was gone. The gunny took us to lunch in the mess hall, my first American meal, and that evening we went with a couple of other Marines to Wagonlits Hotel for an evening meal. We then did the town. Bars, dance halls, cabarets—it wasn't much different than Tsingtao. I could sense that Gilbert was not much into it, and neither was I. We made excuses and bowed out early. The gunny offered to drive us back to our quarters but we insisted we could take pedicabs.

We each called our own pedicab, and as I was climbing into mine, Gilbert said, "Melanowski is in some kind of trouble. He's missed more classes than he's gone to. It has something to do with some girl."

"He'll get over it," I said

"Not him," he replied. "He's been talking about deserting."

This was serious. I told Gilbert I would talk to him. We parted company, agreeing to meet next Saturday. On my way home I wondered about the Russian girl. Who was she?

I decided to cable Ming-Lee to ask her to come to Peking.

Chapter 11

THAT WHITE RUSSIAN WOMAN

L ife in Peking wasn't all studies. I did much wandering around town on my own. Anyone who liked walls would have loved Peking. We lived behind walls. There was the massive, 12-meter thick outer wall that everyone had to pass through when they entered the city. Then there was a second wall which enclosed the Tartar City, and within that a third wall around the Imperial City. And in the very center of all these walls was another wall; it enclosed the grandest site of them all—Forbidden City.

There were still other walls, like the Whispering Wall of China, a true masterpiece of masonry. You could stand with your ear to the wall and talk to a friend a half mile away. Well, almost. A place I liked to visit was the Temple of Heaven, and it too had a wall around it. In the very center of the marble courtyard was a circular stone and when you stood there, you could hear your own echo while no one else could.

At the university, however, things were not going well with my history and literature classes. The idea behind my attending these classes was not so much for me to study Chinese history and literature as it was for me to practice speaking Chinese. When students in these classes learned that I spoke English, they were very anxious to converse with me. It was the only chance they had to practice their English. As a result, they were learning English and I wasn't practicing my Chinese. There weren't many foreigners who spoke Chinese, other than the White Russians, and that was only because of necessity. French used to be the international language, and now it was English. I tried to reason why few Americans speak foreign languages, and the only reason I could come up with was Americans and Englishmen simply refuse to be bothered with another tongue. And why should they? Everyone else is determined to speak English. I guess we can just blame it on laziness.

Nevertheless, I was enjoying meeting all the Chinese students and conversing with them. However, I had to know where to draw the line. Some students wanted to argue and debate issues, and with them I had to be careful. They knew more about politics, governments and economic systems, but I was learning. The more time I spent in Peking, the better equipped I would be to meet with Mrs. Djung and her daughters. In the mean time, students wanted to debate with me and arguments erupted, like the time I mentioned that I had explored the *hutongs* by myself.

To the students, the *hutongs* were a forbidden area. I didn't agree. The fact was in less than a month of living within the walls of Peking, I had learned my way around the city along Hattaman Street and gradually I had spread out into the maze of these back alleys called *hutongs*. "You can't go into the *hutongs* alone," Su Fung said to me when she heard that I had been there. The other students agreed.

"Why, 'cause I'll get lost?" I asked.

"No, because it's unsafe. The *hutongs* are Peking's underworld. Anything can happen."

Like all Chinese, Su Fung and most other students had their opinions, but none of them had been to the *hutongs*. "You are voicing only what you have heard," I said. "Why don't you come with me and see for yourelf?"

This is where the argument started. "Why do you want to go to the *hutongs*?" they asked.

Like Mallory, when asked why he wanted to climb Mt. Everest, I replied, "Because it's there."

The students could not accept my premise— because it's there. "That's the trouble with you Americans, you want to be the first to do something because no one else has done it. What is your purpose?"

"Because we are adventurers. We like to explore."

"The Chinese were the first explorers. You must have heard of Admiral Cheng Ho?"

I was traveling on a narrow ledge. I couldn't admit I knew little about their great naval hero. I said I would take up the discussion later, and hurried back to Hostel No. 3 to my history books. I hastily looked up in the index "explorations," "fleets," "China Seas." Under "fleets" there was an interesting note. In 1907, US President Teddy Roosevelt sent his "Great White Fleet" around the world in a display of American might. It seems even back then they wanted to impress the Japanese. And what a fleet that was—sixteen battle ships, and 14,000 crewmembers. Wow! The fleet visited every important port in the Pacific and Southeast Asia, from Manila to Singapore and then on to Ceylon and India. Even in World War II there was not another fleet like it on the high seas.

I then came to "Chinese fleets." There was his name, sure enough, Admiral Cheng Ho. In 1407, some 500 years before Teddy Roosevelt's time, he set out from Canton with 62 ships and 37,000 men. He had aboard his command ship the daughter of the Emperor of China, and her 500 handmaidens, to be presented to the Sultan of Malacca for her hand in marriage. It mentioned that Admiral Cheng Ho was a Three-Jeweled Eunuch. No wonder he had everything below his belt cut off. With 500 young virgins aboard his ship, the Emperor didn't want to take chances. That was what you call service to the Emperor.

"Yeah, I know all about Cheng Ho," I remarked to the literature class the next day during break. "But remember, he was on an expedition for trade, backed by a rich and powerful government. I am talking about individual adventurers." I wanted to make some wise comment about the admiral being castrated but didn't know how defensive they might be about their cultural heritage. There were in Peking many eunuchs still alive, living within the walls of the Forbidden City. Like the subject of bound feet, this was a sore spot with students.

They would hardly agree with me. They kept pounding away with questions, and it was times like this that I wished I had Stevenson helping me out. They wanted to know why Westerners wanted to scale the peaks of the tallest mountains in the world and dive to the deepest depths of the seas. Why Westerners set off in small boats to sail around the world. It wasn't that they were ignorant of the facts. They knew about Joshua Slocum, the first man to sail alone around the world, and they even knew the name of his tiny boat *Spray*.

But I was making some progress. "Okay," Su Fung said. "I'll go to the *hutongs* with you, won't we Mae Chu?"

It was bitter cold the Sunday morning we set out. The biting wind swept down from the Gobi and brought clouds of dust which made the day as dark as twilight. But this didn't matter I explained; even in a dust storm we couldn't get lost. There was always a wall to follow. The only traffic we had to avoid were bicycles and pedestrians. The girls were amazed. No, they were charmed. This was their town and they knew nothing about the *hutongs*. What excitement for them to walk through these crooked, narrow streets and meandering alleys that had no order or direction. We discovered a maze of narrow lanes, with timeworn doors, sagging lintels, shutters hanging on bent hinges, with light filtering down in shades of yellow. The shops were tiny, cubbyholes in walls. Food stalls had counters with space for only three or four stools. The food they served was inviting, freshly-made *djow-dzes* and noodles rolled and cut before our very eyes. The delicious smells were wild and daring, and we couldn't resist a bowl of noodles here and a sweetmeat there. Where was the horror of the *hutongs* that everyone talked about? Here was the heart and soul of the city. Indeed, what horror was this, little old ladies, sitting by the wayside warming themselves in the sun that managed to break through the clouds. What harm were they, the old women of Peking, in somber dark clothing, with gold teeth that flashed when they smiled, bouncing their grandchildren and their great grandchildren on their knees. Some of these older women had bound feet. I found myself sitting with them, talking to them. They laughed and threw up their arms when I spoke Chinese to them. "This foreign devil speaks our language," one *lao taitai* said and they all picked it up and joined in the laughter. It was the funniest thing she could have said. Su Fung and Mae Chu were astounded at my audacity, and I was happy that I could be showing them another side of Peking.

Before the week was out I went to Hostel No. 1 to find Melanowski but he was out for the evening. When I got back to my place, the gunny sergeant from George Company was there waiting for me. He announced he was arranging a field trip with beer and barbecue to the Great Wall the coming Sunday and had a couple Motor Pool vehicles lined up. Did I want to go? Did I ever. I had wanted to see the Great Wall ever since I heard my Uncle George talking about it back on the farm in Pennsylvania. He and my father were putting up a stone wall, and they argued about how much manpower it would take to construct a wall two thousand miles long. After our trip Sunday, I could write home and tell them all about the Great Wall. "We have plenty of room," the gunny said, snapping me back to the present. "Bring along some of your student friends."

At school the next day I passed word around that the Marines from George Company were having a picnic Sunday at the Great Wall, and anyone who wanted to go was invited. No one accepted the offer. I had a feeling a few of the girls might have wanted to go, but custom kept them from accepting. It wouldn't be proper for a Chinese girl from a good university to be seen driving around in an open vehicle with a bunch of foreign men, especially Marines. They all knew and envied the foreign community with their fine parties at the embassies and legations, the parties where everyone dressed in their best and danced the night through to the music of 15-piece orchestras. They knew about the champagne that flowed and the gourmet food that was served, and they longed to be part of the fun, but they could not accept any invitations. I hated to disappoint the gunny. I had the feeling he only invited me because I knew a lot of female students at the university, but it did little good by my "just" knowing them. I was feeling rather glum, sitting at my desk in class with my nose in my books when a hand tapped me on the shoulder. "I would like to go," the voice said. I looked up and couldn't believe my eyes. My pulse missed a couple beats. It was the Russian girl. "I would like to go," she repeated, "if you still have room."

I had planned exactly what I would say to her if we met. I would be suave, charming in every way, and I would say clever things that would make her laugh, and she would tell me that I was very amusing, not at all like the other men she knew in Peking. What came from my lips was nothing like this. "Yea, sure," I grunted, "Yea, I guess we have room." I mumbled. When she wanted to know where we should meet, I said we would meet her in front of the university Sunday morning at eight. She thanked me, and then lingered for a moment. I was numb for words. She said good-bye and left. I wanted to yell after her as she was leaving the room, to say something nice, but it was too late. I cursed myself. I could face a banzai charge but not a pretty girl. Thank goodness none of the guys were around.

I didn't see her in class the rest of the week and wondered if she would even turn up on Sunday. I went to George Company to check in on Saturday morning and there they were, Melanowski and Gilbert. "Boy, am I glad to see you guys," I said. I mentioned the coming picnic and Gilbert was keen on going but Melanowski had other plans.

"I heard about your plans," I said. "You've got a girl."

"Yea, and I don't want any shit from you," he said, and without waiting for my response he continued his tirade. "I wanta marry her. So don't give me any crap, not from you nor from nobody. I wanna marry her."

"Hey, buddy, hold on," I said and backed off. He was hot under the collar and with his temper there was no telling what he might do. I got him off to the side, away from the Company office. He was talking loud and didn't care who heard him. "Hey, Ski, this is me, remember, your buddy," I began. "Now what are you talking about? Do you know?"

"Hell yea, I know what I am talking about. What do you think, that I'm crazy too?"

"I don't think anything like that, and you know it. But you can't get married when you are in the Marine Corps and you know that."

"I'm getting out," he said.

"You can't get out. You know damn well you can't get a discharge here. You have to go back to the States for that."

"Who said anything about a discharge?"

"What are you talking about? If it's what I'm thinking, I don't even want to hear it."

"Well, I'll tell you anyway. I'm getting out and I'm going to marry that girl."

"You are saying you'll desert."

"Call it anything you want."

"They can shoot you for that."

"They have to catch me first."

He was far worse than I had thought. It was impossible to reason with him in his present state of mind. The best I could do was listen to him. He explained the girl that he was in love with was half-French and half-Chinese. She started working for Mamma Georgia six months before Melanowski met her. He wanted me to meet her and to talk to Mamma Georgia. He wanted to take me there right away. I agreed, but first I had to find the gunny and tell him we had to pick up someone at the university at eight the next morning. "A great looking Russian girl," I boasted. He beamed. I then set out with Melanowski to Mamma Georgia's place.

After we were away from headquarters and walking for a few minutes, I attempted to appeal to his senses once again.

"Look, she's different I told you," he quickly said.

"For gawd's sake, Ski, how many times have I heard that, 'she's different.' They are all different." I expected him to fire back at me in a tirade of four-letter words, but he didn't. The fact that he didn't made me realize something was not the same. Melanowski was one guy who couldn't speak without using the four-letter "F" word. It was his vocabulary, his seven parts of speech; it was his nouns and his pronouns, his adjectives and his adverbs. He interjected his thoughts with the "F" word. Had he been a religious man, he could not have said his prayers without using the "F" word.

As we walked along toward Mamma Georgia's, every now and then I'd glance over at him. I couldn't help it but I felt sorry for him. It was that same kind of pathetic sorrow you felt when a favorite hunting dog gets lame and you know he wouldn't get better. Melanowski should be back in Minnesota, I thought, and not in a back alley in Peking. He was a mill worker, not a pursuer of Chinese women 12,000 miles away from the mills. He was out of place, a big clumsy kid, with big hands and big feet. His father had emigrated from Poland and settled in Minnesota. Like his father, he was a steelworker. His idea of success was overtime at the mill. To be prosperous meant to have a potbelly. He didn't mind the Polack jokes tossed his way. You might say, he even encouraged them. The jokes made him the center of attention, which he liked. Everyone riffled him, and ridiculed him, and yet they all liked him at the same time. Finally, I asked him, "Who's this Mamma George?"

"Hey," he said, stopped and placed a hand on my shoulder. "You'll like her."

"How do you know that?"

"You know Mamma Georgia, don't you?" he said.

"No, why should I know her?"

"Holy hell," he said. "I thought everyone knowed Mamma Georgia." It took him a bit of hemming and hawing but he finally told me about Mamma Georgia. I was dumbfounded. Shocked, in fact. Mamma Georgia was a black woman, and she ran a whorehouse. Before he told me who she was, I thought she might be a dance hall owner or maybe a barkeeper, but not the madam of a whorehouse. And who was this girl he was in love with? Certainly not her partner. I wished I hadn't agreed to go with him to meet her.

He tried to explain the best he could, in the mildest manner possible, all about Mamma Georgia. He said she had been a nanny for the two daughters of Col. Willard Scott and his wife Beatrice. The Scotts arrived in China just before the outbreak of the Boxer Rebellion in 1908. I read all about the Boxer Rebellion in the book I got at the library on Guam. Around the turn of the century, Tsu Hsi, the Empress Dowager of the Ch'ing Dynasty, was hoping to close China to foreigners. America wanted an "Open Door" policy in China that would guarantee equal trading rights for all and prevent one nation from discriminating against another within its sphere. A secret society, which foreigners called "Boxers," refused to cooperate and in the early months of 1900, thousands of Boxers roamed the countryside. They attacked Christian missions, slaughtering foreign missionaries and Chinese converts. Then they moved toward the cities, attracting more and more followers as they came.

In Peking, foreign diplomats, their families and staff, lived in a compound just outside the Forbidden City's walls in the heart of the city. Working together, they threw up hasty defenses, and with a small force of military personnel, they faced some 20,000 Boxers on a rampage. For almost two months, the foreigners withstood fierce attacks and bombardment. Things began to look hopeless. Seventy-six defenders lay dead, and many more were wounded. Ammunition, food, and medical supplies were almost gone.

An international relief force of soldiers and sailors from eight countries was summoned but they did little good. The United States, eager to rescue its ministers and American personnel, sent a contingent of 2,500 US Marines to the rescue. The Marines landed at Tientsin and fought their way to Peking and defeated the Boxers. Col. Scott, his wife and daughters, and their black nanny from Georgia, where among those whom the Marines saved.

Evidently Mrs. Scott was a gregarious Southern woman who spent her time socializing, and in the restricted society that Peking had to offer, this meant endless hours at the officers' club with the other officers' wives. And like most of the other women, she was heavy on the bottle. Taking pride in being from the state of Georgia, she favored Mint Juleps. As a result of her socializing, she, of course, neglected her home life, but Mamma Georgia took care of things at home, plus a few other things. That's about all that Melanowski knew. "If you want to know more, you'll have to ask her yourself," he said. I doubted she would ever tell me the complete story, but I thought I would try. It had to be interesting.

Mamma Georgia's place stood out from all the other buildings on the street. It was the only wooden structure, and badly in need of repair. It appeared never to have been painted. Melanowski began making excuses as he pulled a ring attached to a cord that hung from the door. "Mamma Georgia said if she fixes up the place, they'd raise the rent," he said.

I listened but I couldn't hear any sound from beyond the door. Melanowski pulled the cord the second time. "Perhaps no one's home," I remarked.

"They're home," he assured me.

Sure enough, there came the sound of wooden clogs, and the door opened partly. Through the crack, I could see a girl standing there, a mere child not yet in her teens. The sight was sickening. Young girls working as chamber maids in whorehouses. What could be more disgusting? Melanowski saw the look on my face. "Mamma Georgia adopted her," he said.

Yea, sure, I thought. Same old story, but I kept my thoughts to myself.

I was quite surprised that the small courtyard was rather clean and tidy, with plants in dragon-carved urns along the walkway. Nor did the place have that discomforting odor that the bordellos like Ping-Pong Willies in Tsingtao had.

The girl led us to another inner door and stepped aside. Melanowski took over and led the way down a long hallway with a white tiled floor to a reception room at the end. Here was Mamma Georgia, seated in a polished, hardwood Empress' chair. With her hands crossed over her protruding belly, she sat there like a grand lady of the Chinese court preparing to pass judgment. She attempted to get up, but I bade her to remain seated, and it was probably well that I did. She was so heavy-set I doubted she could even stand, and if she did, it would have to be with great effort. In a heavy Southern black accent she asked me to be seated. She called for a servant girl to bring us tea, and even when she spoke Chinese, there was no mistaking she was from the Deep South. How the Chinese understood her was beyond me. I thanked her and sat down. I was really curious now and wondered how I would approach the question about her past.

"I understand you worked for a Marine colonel," I began, cautiously.

"I shu did," she replied, "and he shu wuz a hard-up somna-beech." She began laughing. Her laugh was gruff, hardened no doubt from years of smoking cheap Chinese cigarettes, which I saw on the table next to her. She had to wipe the tears from her eyes before she could continue. It was evident from the start she was going to enjoy telling me her story, probably the same one she told over and over to every Marine and sailor who came to her establishment. She poured me tea and said, "I knowd you come ta talk at me, an I knowd you ain't commin to get laid."

"You're right, Mamma George," I said. "I'm leaving that up to my friend here." With that she burst into laughter again and I had to wait until she dried her eyes once more before I could continue. "How long did you work for the colonel?"

"Until hiz misses done fired me when she catched us."

"Caught you what?" I asked.

"You sur is a young fellar who don't know nottin much. Fur bein his lover, dat's what."

It was too hard to believe. As I sat there in the room listening to Mamma Georgia, I could not imagine her as the lover of a Marine colonel, or the lover of anyone for that matter. She had grown grossly fat over the years. And in all probability she hadn't bathed in years. She certainly didn't hesitate to talk about her past, as sordid as it was. "Ah used to be quite sexy when Ah wuz fo'teen an f'teen," she explained.

"You mean the colonel was banging you when you were fourteen?" I asked.

"Wuz he evah! Ah wuz the bes' lay he evah had. He use ta come git a nooner ever' day, while hiz wife wuz boozin' it up at da club."

She stopped talking often, coughing and laughing at the same time. She'd stop coughing when she lit a cigarette, and then she'd continue the conversation. I found myself laughing too, also into tears.

"How long did this go on with the colonel?" I asked.

"Til one aftahnoon when da kernel's wife come back a da house. She wuz already drunk as the Lord, too many Mints for lunch, and come draggin' da kernel's driver wif her up a da bedroom. He wuz a frightened, pimpil-faced lil bastud. Don't know what da hell she ever seed in him. Dey wuz haf undress by da time they enter da room, an' der we wuz, buck-ass neked on da floor. Da kernel had dis crazy idea dat if we doodit on da floor—not on da bed—den it wun't madder for sum reason. Ah didn't mind. Ah didn't have ta make up da bed. It wuz one of dem ole poster beds da kermel wife shipped all da way fum At-lanta. Come on oxen carts most da way fum Tientsin."

"Okay, okay, Mamma Georgia," I pleaded, "never mind

the poster bed, what happened then?"

"Da kernel 'sploded. Dat poor frigg'n private, standin' der, ready ta take out his pekker. Beatrice—da's da kernel's wife— she begin defendin' him. 'What you expect!' she screamed, 'you wid da nanny.' Der won't much da kernel could do 'bout da driver. He made corporal a cupple month latah, and den go transferred."

"And you, Mamma Georgia, what happened to you?"

"Ah had ta go, bu Ah won't gonna go back to Jawja. Da kernel fix me all up wif da room. He nevah do me afta dat."

"Never?"

"Nevah. Had too meny white boys do'in' me aftah dat. Dos Suttern white boys couldn't get da black stuff back home, so dey come heah."

Mamma Georgia went on to tell me how she later opened her own house and managed to remain in China, as an oppressed black woman during the Japanese occupation. "Da Japs wan' white wimmen," she said, "an' der wur enuf white Russian wimmen 'round ta set up a gud bizness."

Mamma Georgia liked Melanowski; I could see she mothered him. It wasn't all business with her and him. She knew he was falling for Monique, and if things got too serious, she might lose one of her best money earners. But she also had a soft spot for Monique. I gathered this when she came into the room and we were introduced. I was shocked. She was beautiful, with all the fine features of an Oriental lass combined with the best qualities of her French father. I had the feeling that if Melanowski carried her off, it would be a Godsend. But I guess deep down Mamma Georgia knew that would never happen, unless he stayed in China, and that was another kettle of worms.

I knew, of course, that Melanowski was already entertaining this crazy idea. I stayed to have dinner with them, and after the meal he mentioned about getting a job with UNRA, but when I pointed out he had no engineering background or technical skills, he thought about working for one of the other foreign companies. "Come on, Ski," I insisted, "once you start talking like that, they'll ship your ass right back to the States. No one gets a discharge here."

"You have to help me," he said when I was leaving. I made him promise he'd attend class and we would try to work things out. I caught a pedicab back to Hostel No. 3, and was so deep in thought, wondering how this was all this going to end, that the driver had to shake me twice to tell me we had arrived.

The clerk at the desk handed me my room key and a telegram from Tsingtao. I waited until I got in my room to open it. It was from Ming-Lee. She was making plans to come to Peking for a visit and was very excited. I was hoping now that the Russian girl wouldn't show up on Sunday morning. The last thing I wanted was complications like the other guys had. Probably the next thing I would hear was that Stevenson was planning on getting married. Maybe even Ruker. That's what happens when they send Marines to foreign lands. The women fall in love with them. I remembered the pat phrase Ruker threw out every time someone asked him about his love life. He would sound out: "I am handsome, strong, good looking, easy to get along with, a good dancer, boxer, swimmer, track man, weight lifter, a Marine, and all the women like me. What do you expect?" Sometimes I think he actually believed it. That's what the Marine Corps taught us anyway. We were the best. But we were also learning we were vulnerable.

Chapter 12

THE MISSING MAN

The moment I stepped out of the Jeep at Badaling and saw the Great Wall of China looming up before me, I thought about my father and my Uncle George. For two years they had been constructing a stone wall back home on our farm, and with all their effort and time spent it was no more than a 100 feet along. And here was a wall, 3,000 miles long, and not three feet high but 30 feet high, and 25 feet wide. I couldn't help wondering how the Chinese had done it. Every stone that went into that wall on the farm back home was placed there with an argument. "What are you doing? That doesn't fit there," followed by, "It's better than the one you have." How many centuries would it have taken my father and my uncle to build the Great Wall of China?

I only wished they could have been with me, but then maybe it wasn't such a good idea. They would have argued why the wall went up that hill to the left and not to the right where it appeared to be less hilly. I could hear them, "That's why they put it there where it is, for defense."

When we arrived in our caravan at 0800 at the university that Sunday morning, I was very pleased to see the Russian girl waiting for us. My doubts were quickly forgotten. She looked radiant, in her high boots and coat that fell just below her knees. She carried her fur muff and wore a huge black-fur hat. Gunny was seated behind the driver's wheel of the leading

4x4 weapons carrier, and the moment he saw her, he motioned for her to sit in front. She slid in next to him. She introduced herself. "My name is Katarina," she said in her Russian accent, just like they speak in the movies. She pronounced it Kat-tar-rina. It sounded great the way she said it.

"Kat-tar-rina," Gunny said, mimicking her. "I'm Gunny Wesley." I knew the gunny all these months and it was the first time that I'd heard his name. We simply called him "the gunny from George Company." Names in the Marines are never important when referring to staff NCO's. Sometimes the names we gave them couldn't be spoken in polite company.

I slid into the front seat next to Katarina. Gilbert and two other Marines sat behind. We immediately caught the full aroma of her perfume. The air became saturated with the scent, strong and overpowering. Gunny Wesley wasted no time commenting on its fragrance. "That's great perfume," he said, and in the same breath he wanted to know its name, where she got it and was it her favorite perfume. He was trying hard to win her favor and he was succeeding. He kept the conversation lively for the next three hours, cracking jokes and making small talk, until we reached Badaling.

We parked the vehicles, with one Marine left behind to guard, while Gilbert, the other Marines and I ran ahead and climbed the ramparts to the first tower. Gunny followed up the rear helping Katarina along by holding her arm. The wind blew strong and it was bitter cold, but it was invigorating. We waited for Gunny and Katarina to catch up, and then Gunny gave us a dissertation on the wall and its construction. He continued to baffle me with how much he knew about Chinese history. He was knowledgeable, and sometimes witty. "The Chinese wanted to keep out the Tartars," he said, "so they built this wall 30 feet high, 25 feet wide, and 3,000 miles long. Now they want to keep out the white man, who conquered them in two opium wars, so they created an ideology, and called it communism."

We found protection from the wind below the first tower,

and here Gunny had the Marines set up the picnic area. They spread out the food and opened an ice chest containing cold beer. While they were setting up, Gunny told us more about the wall, how 300,000 soldiers labored to build the wall for twenty years during the Qin Dynasty. "They also used donkeys to carry baskets of lime up the mountains, and bricks were tied to the horns of goats, which they lured up the mountains."

It was a fun day at the Great Wall of China, but I had to admit I was rather perturbed that Gunny had taken over Katarina and had monopolized her completely from the moment he saw her that morning until he took her home that night. I was even more upset that he dropped me off at my hostel first. He was pulling rank, but in a way I couldn't blame him. I had been rather innocuous and had little to contribute to the party. I rationalized my behavior by remembering that Ming-Lee was coming to Peking and I didn't want to butterfly around. But on Monday in my classroom the situation changed. Katarina was cheerful and sat down next to me. She had never done that before.

"You should have come with us," she said, placing her hand on my arm. "We went dancing at the Tivoli."

Why was she telling me this? I acknowledged that I heard her and let it pass. But she continued.

"Gunny's quite a charmer," she said. "He's fun."

"You like him then?"

"As a friend, yes."

"I think he likes you."

"Yes, I could feel that. That's why I had to be careful."

"Careful," I replied. I wanted to say something about her going dancing with him but held back.

"Yes, I didn't want to give him a wrong impression." The teacher entered the room and she returned to her seat in the rear, but before leaving she asked to have coffee after school. I agreed, but without Gunny I said under my breath.

Katarina took me to a Russian bakery off Hattaman Street. The delightful smell of baked bread greeted us before we even saw the shop. In the bay window facing the street were shelves with loaves of bread and rolls, sprinkled with white powder, stacked one atop another. As we pushed open the door a bell above the door went ting-a-ling announcing our arrival. An attendant came running and greeted us. Along one wall were four postage-stamp size tables. We draped out coats over the backs of our chairs and warmed our hands over a charcoal brazier that the attendant hastily placed before us. The attendant was a huge Russian woman. She was dressed all in white, with a white apron and a white babushka covering her hair. Bits of gray hair showed beneath. She and Katarina spoke together in Russian. It was obvious they knew one another.

"She does a good business," Katarina said after the woman went to get our coffee.

"I didn't think Chinese would like Western bread," I replied.

"Do you know how many Russians there are in Peking?" she asked, raising her voice.

"I have no idea."

"What do you know about the Russians?" I could see she was defensive about her lot as a White Russian.

"That they beat the Germans, that Stalin is in charge, and they want all of Manchuria," I replied.

"You see, you think all Russians are the same. We Russians in China are Belorussians, or as you call us, White Russians." I didn't care to have a lecture, especially when I knew nothing of the subject. I often wondered about all the White Russians I saw in Tsingtao but never delved deeper into their past, until now. I had more reading coming up while burning the midnight oil. We changed the subject to the Americans living in Peking. After the second coffee we parted, each taking a pedicab our own way, with an agreement to have coffee together later in the week. I had a feeling she didn't want it to end but I had things to do, like checking out a book on Russian history from the library.

When I was studying with Mrs. Murray, I couldn't quite understand why she was so concerned about the Russians taking over Port Arthur in Manchuria when the war ended—weren't they our allies—but I began to understand as I read my history. The agony of the White Russians began in 1918 when the revolutionary Bolsheviks put a bullet into the head of the Tzar Nicholas II and then into his wife, their five children and the family dog, thus ending the reign of the Romanovs. The Boyars, the landed gentry, the aristocracy—all White Russians—were forced to flee from their mother Russia. But since the new government had made peace with the Kaiser in the West, they had to turn to the East—to China.

The White Russians, although they never integrated fully into Chinese society, made China their home for the next thirty years, but now the Red flag was casting a shadow of doom upon them. In the beginning, however, when they first fled from Russia, they were received with open arms in China. Among their ranks were many well-trained military officers who held positions in the Chinese army as instructors while others obtained fairly high ranks. Many became government servants, advisors and teachers.

"You did well in China," I said to Katarina the next time we sat down to coffee.

"You mean our parents did. The second generation, my generation, doesn't have the schooling nor the training as our people did before us. We had to shift, and began opening up restaurants, bars and clubs."

"You can never go back to Russia?" I asked.

"Never. If Chairman Mao takes over in China, this time there is no place to go."

My relationship with Katarina became warmer each time we met, almost without my being aware of it. We met just about every day now after class, and if we didn't have coffee and the weather permitted, we went for long walks. Sometimes we took short bus trips. We enjoyed visiting the Imperial Summer Palace and went several times. Within the palace was a lake, and upon the still waters was a magnificent boat, constructed of solid marble. Naturally, it didn't float. I remember reading the story aboard the *USS Napa*, from the book I got from the library on Guam. It told how in 1911 when the Empress of China was hounded by her advisers to build a powerful navy, she obliged them. She sank, literally, the entire treasure's purse into a marble boat.

The first time we held hands was crossing a street, and soon we began walking arm in arm—to keep warm, we said. Since we were both foreigners, the Chinese did not frown upon our actions. In fact, the Chinese hardly even noticed us. As we drank coffee and tea, and walked through the parks, Katarina spoke a great deal about the plight of White Russians in China. When I learned she was three years older than I was—she was going on 21—I was a bit disappointed, but after a while that didn't matter. I liked her company even if she was older.

There was a bit of the daredevil in Katarina which I liked. I remember one time I was at Forbidden City with Su Fung and we saw a few old men sitting on a bench in front of the temple sunning themselves. I asked who they were and she said they were the last of the court eunuchs. "You mean some of them are still alive?" I asked in astonishment. Immediately my curiosity was aroused.

"There are many, many," she explained. "I remember hearing only recently about one old man who lives behind the walls. His name is Sun Yaoting."

"I would love to meet him," I said. "Can't we go and find him?"

"That would be impossible," she snapped. "Eunuchs are from the past. The practice was outlawed. I am sorry that I even mentioned it to you."

With Katarina it was the opposite. When we were visiting the Forbidden City I casually mentioned that the old men out front were eunuchs. She was as surprised as I the first time I heard it. I then remembered the old man that Sui Ying mentioned. I even remembered his name—Sun Yaoting.

"Let's see if we can find him," she suggested.

"I would like nothing better," I said. "When do you want to go?"

"Now, right now," she replied.

At a cluttered tiny office in the rear of the temple we approached a shaven-headed monk writing in a ledger with a quill which he dipped into a cup of black ink. I asked in my best Mandarin where we might find Sun Yaoting. He didn't answer, nor did he even bother to look up from his desk. "He's a eunuch," Katarina said, and upon hearing a female voice, the monk looked up.

"I know who he is," he said after studying us for a moment, "and you are not the first to ask about him." I thought for sure he would ask why we wanted to see the eunuch but he didn't. He willingly told us the room number and pointed out the direction. Katarina insisted that we go back out into the street to where we saw vendors selling their wares. One vendor was roasting chestnuts over a brazier. She bought a bag of roasted nuts and we returned to the temple. As we started down the corridor looking for his room number above the doors, I told Katarina what I knew about eunuchs from the *Dowager Empress* that I had read aboard the *USS Napa*, the same stories I had told the guys when we were under the lifeboat. "You know it's a pretty bloody operation," I said. "They use a round knife and with one whack they cut everything off." I remembered some of the details and told her that at the end of the Ming Dynasty there were more than 70,000 eunuchs in the palace, possibly 100,000 throughout the empire. When China banned eunuchs in 1912, there were only 470 left. "That was only 35 years ago, and some of them must be alive today."

We found Sun Yaoting's room and knocked. The door creaked open and there in the dim light, clad in a saffron-colored robe, stood a wrinkled old man. I told him we would like to talk to him, and when Katarina handed him the bag of chestnuts, he bid us to enter.

The room was sparse, more like a cell, with only a cot for

a bed, a small writing table and a single chair. The walls were whitewashed and a musty dampness permeated the room. The only air came from a small barred window high up on the outer wall. Katarina and I sat on the edge of the cot. There was a long moment of silence, and finally I asked if he minded us intruding. I explained I had never met a eunuch before. This amused him and he smiled, causing his face to wrinkle even more; he seemed to take pleasure that we had singled him out. "Yes, I was ten when I became a servant to the emperor," he said in Mandarin. His voice was high-pitched and not like any I had heard before. It was almost comical and had the circumstance been different, I could have chuckled. But he was serious.

"And what year was that?" I asked.

He didn't answer questions directly, but replied in a way that made it sound like he was programmed what to say. I guess he had a long time to think them out. "My father did it himself using only hot chili sauce as a local anesthetic," he said. "I remember quite well him taking a curved knife to my genitals and with one whack they were gone, penis, testicles, all gone. All to make me eligible for service in the Forbidden City, home of the Imperial family."

As a eunuch he was trusted to enter the inner courtyards of the palace, where the women of the imperial family and harem lived. Other men, including officials, military guards and even the emperor's male relatives, were often required to leave the palace grounds at night.

"And what year was it that you had the operation?" I asked again.

"I received 20 yuan a month salary, which was a lot of money in those days, and had to do very little for it." I then asked what was court life like, changing the subject. "One year after my operation, the republican revolution came and ended the empire."

I knew the revolution came in 1911. Quick calculation and I placed him at 45 or 46. I couldn't believe it. My father was about the same age and he was filled with life, even planning on starting an electrical appliance and repair shop when I got out of the Corps. I tried hard to picture this withered old man at 45, housed in a simple room at the rear of an old Buddhist temple, a far cry from the days when he lived in splendor in the Imperial Place.

Sun Yaoting went on to tell his story and I had no need to interrupt him again. He explained that after the revolution and when the Empress was exiled, he served with the court of the last emperor Pu Yi for eight years. He waited upon Empress Wang Rong, Pu Yi's wife. He told how some eunuchs before the revolution had great power and wealth, and they lived freely among the concubines, not only dining with them but bathing with them as well. Sun believed he was heading for great things, too, except that the revolution suddenly changed the rules. It all ended in 1924 when Feng Yuxlang, the converted Christian warlord, who baptized his army with a fire hose, threw the former emperor and everyone else out of the palace.

Surprisingly Sun Yaoting had no regrets about his being forced to become a eunuch. He explained that traditionally a eunuch preserved his genitals in a jar to insure that they would eventually be buried with him, in the belief that this would guarantee his reincarnation as a "full" man. He kept his family jewels not in a jar but in a small leather bag around his neck. Maybe he was still a eunuch, dedicated to the cause, but I watched him eyeing Katarina seated in his room, with her legs exposed. The spirit was still there. I tried to imagine this 45-year old man, as a young boy, living in a Chinese harem, maybe sitting in a bathing pool with a bevy of young naked Chinese dolls. There was so much more I wanted to ask him, but some things are best left to the imagination.

Katarina was also helpful in the *hutongs*. In the afternoons when it was warm, I saw old Chinese women sitting on benches in front of their mud houses. They kept themselves busy conversing with other women. Gossiping, no doubt. Many of these women had bound feet and I was curious about this ancient Chinese tradition. I had seen a few old women in Tsingtao with bound feet, including the old woman who sold her services the first night in the compound when we arrived. Katarina didn't mind sitting down with the women and talking with them, something my Chinese student friends would never do. One old lady, with only a few of her teeth left, and those were stained black, explained the process to us. "When a young girl's feet are being bound, the pain is something terrible," she said. "Their skin is inflamed and the flesh decomposes, smeared with blood. At this time they moan and cry, and can neither eat in daytime nor sleep at night for the pain, and they develop all kinds of sickness."

"Why would any girl submit to this kind of torture?" I asked.

Through her rotted teeth she smiled and said, "To make us look beautiful. Girls cannot be beautiful without small feet!"

"Of course," I said and she beamed. A strange custom indeed. Chinese men once regarded girls who had disfigured feet and walked with a kind of tortured gait as beautiful!

I enjoyed listening to the many stories Katarina had to tell. She told how her mother, three aunts, and grandparents escaped from Russia and fled to Manchuria in 1915. They had a small family farm in Harbin, Manchuria. They left Manchuria around 1930 and leased the farm to another White Russian family. The family traveled from Harbin to Shanghai aboard a coastal steamship. She was eight years old at the time.

"Why did you leave Manchuria?" I asked. "A farm doesn't sound too bad."

"The farm was not like your American farms. We had three or four milk cows, chickens and ducks, but no crops. Why did we leave? The Japanese had Manchuria then."

She told how they were little more than prisoners under the Japanese, and she had horror stories about how the Japanese conducted human experiments on the Russians living there. I asked about her father; he had died in the revolution. In

Shanghai her mother met a China Marine and they married in 1931. The following year she gave birth to a son at St. Mary's Catholic Hospital. Until Pearl Harbor, the family lived together in a three-bedroom apartment. "It was a quite huge apartment in the French Concession, at Route Vallon, a block off Avenue Joffre," Katarina said. "They called them 'key' apartments. A person put up a large amount of cash as a down payment and made a lease for ten years. But we never had ten years."

Despite her stepfather being an American, Shanghai for expatriate White Russians was not easy. Life for them was uncertain. Her aunts worked in candy stores, bakeries and small upscale clothing and fur stores. "We called the clothing shops salons. Many White Russian women were seamstresses and hairdressers."

"What happened then?" I asked.

"The Marines left Shanghai before Pearl Harbor. They knew something was coming. There was tension and a lot of Japanese army on the streets. My mother and stepfather were married but their marriage was unauthorized. They kept the apartment but he had to live at the Marine barracks. One night my stepfather and two Marines stopped by, and they spent all night burning papers in the fireplace. When Pearl Harbor broke out the Japanese confiscated all radios and the British and American men and women were sent to camps at Pootung and Lunghwa. My mother and brother were able to flee on an American ship. Wives of American Servicemen and their dependents who were caught, with the help of the Red Cross, were detained in a camp. The camp, since it was all wives and small children, was not all that bad as compared to the camps that the British and American civilians were in."

Katarina spoke about her aunts with great affection. "They were very beautiful women. At the time of our arrival in Shanghai they were in their late twenties or very early thirties. They were very kind to their mother and to each other and to me and my little brother, as well as their elderly grandparents. Their warmth, I believe, came from their joining each other for survival; being stateless is very frightening. Before the war my middle aunt saw quite often a very successful film producer who asked her to marry him and go to the United States. She did not even consider this possibility as she had fallen very much in love with an American sailor. The film producer left for America after asking again and receiving another refusal. The sailor did not return. My aunt believes he did not survive the war, but of course it could be that he just chose to not return."

She told me about her other aunts. "My oldest aunt fell in love and went steadily with an officer in the Flying Tigers, however, he left for home and left her due to the fact that he had a wife at home. Both my aunts are still in Shanghai. They said they would stay even if the Communists take over. They are tired of running. My grandma just went back to Manchuria to try to locate her sons who went from Manchuria to fight the Germans. She feels with her age that she will be safe. But we haven't heard. I came to Peking to further my studies. I want to be more than a seamstress."

It was understandable why I had a warm feeling for Katarina. When you got to know the White Russians you felt sorry for them. I recall one Sunday afternoon visiting the Thieves Market near Hattaman Street. I was at one street-side shop studying the vast assortment of pocket watches the shopkeeper had. I was contemplating buying one that gave not only the time of day but the phases of the moon as well, when a voice in English came from behind. "Sir, sir," it said. "Can you help?" I knew immediately it was not an Asian voice. I turned to see towering over me a giant of a man, perhaps six five or six. It was cold and he wore a long tattered military overcoat. I first noticed his hands, swathed in dirty bandages. I raised my eyes and there stood a White Russian man whom I would guess was in his early thirties. His eyes were the bluest eyes I had ever seen. His hair was blonde and long and shabby. I then saw it, the left side of his face. I stood back aghast, dumfounded. The flesh on the side of his face was eaten with leprosy. My first reaction was to mutter some stupid words. "No thank you," I said and turned to my pocket watches. But the sight of that face remained, and when I turned he was vanishing in the crowd down an alley.

China had millions of lepers. They were everywhere. Just before I saw the White Russian I saw another man, Chinese, in rags being led by a boy holding on to a stick. His face was completely gone, and his teeth showed like that of a skeleton. He was eating rice that some charitable person had placed in his bowl, and he was using his hand to hold the rice in his mouth. His hand was lacking fingers. It was a terrible sight, but what I had just experienced with the White Russian was far more moving. I questioned my own thoughts. Was not a leper, a leper? Did it matter who it was? I suddenly realized we were foreigners in an alien land. It bothered us to see other foreigners suffering and helpless. We foreigners could never be Chinese. We would always remain white people to them and to each other. I could understand my empathy now towards Katarina. I did like Ming-Lee, very much, but it was Katarina that I felt sorry for. Was this being prejudiced? I hardly knew the meaning of the word, but I was aware that the feeling I had for Katarina was different. Suddenly I couldn't wait until I saw Ming-Lee again. What was taking her so long to arrange her trip to Peking?

One Saturday morning I went to George Company to check in, and the duty clerk informed me that I had made corporal. That called for a celebration, but before I could give it more thought, he informed me that Gunny Wesley wanted to see me. He said his orders were explicit, that I was to meet the gunny in his staff quarters as soon as I arrived. He then gave me directions how to get there. I was certain Gunny was going to confront me about Katarina. He was very keen on her that Sunday. Katarina told me he had called her several times but each time she had rebuffed him. It was a month or more now that I had been seeing her regularly. Gunny knew about us.

I found his room and knocked. A minute passed before he opened the door. When he did, he stepped to one side to let me enter. On a low table in the center of the room were papers in disarray with a briefcase and a few books placed on top of them. Standing in front of the table was a young lieutenant who rose to his feet when I entered. The delay in opening the door had obviously been due to their covering up the papers. I needed only one glance at the officer to know he was another G-2 gumshoe. "Lt. Barker from G-2," Gunny said. I was right.

What kind of trouble was I in now? Was Katarina a spy, a Soviet spy? Maybe it was Melanowski. He had defected. But what did Gunny have to do with all this? Was he under fire too, or was he part of these snoops? All kinds of thoughts raced through my head. When Lt. Barker said I could call him Henry I didn't like the way it was going. Enlisted men don't call officers by their first names.

"I'm from Washington," Barker said. "I'm here to investigate a matter and maybe you can help." I breathed a bit easier. "First, let me ask, you know the students, is there any indication of unrest?"

"Unrest, I don't know what you mean. What is it you exactly want from me?" I asked bluntly and to the point. I hated these surreptitious approaches.

"What the students are talking about. We feel an uprising is coming."

"The students are always uprising about something or someone. They don't like Americans if that is what you mean."

"Do they ever talk about the Marines and our duties here?" the man from G-2 asked.

"Always. They want to know why we are guarding ourselves from them," I replied.

"That's all?" he asked, disappointed.

"We talk mostly about the American way of life verses the Chinese. We talk about writers and poets," I replied. "But they are always critical of our way of government."

"What do you tell them?" Gunny asked. All he had to do

was ask that one question and I knew immediately his duties with George Company Headquarters were not simply to act as liaison between a couple American students and company headquarters. He was far too bright and knowledgeable for that. I did wonder about his reasons for my inviting students to the picnic. He wanted to get to know them, and now I knew it wasn't that he just wanted to meet girls. He wasn't a girl chaser. But what was he?

"Did anyone ever mention anything about Marines guarding the trains?" the lieutenant asked.

"You mean the coal trains?" I asked. The lieutenant nodded and I continued. "I don't remember any such discussion." I wondered what the students had to do with train guards.

"That's a relief," Lt. Barker said to Gunny.

"What's a relief?" I asked.

The two men looked at each other. "He might as well know," Gunny said to the man from G-2. "He might be able to tell us if the students are aware." He then turned to face me. "Coal is being shipped from Peking to Chingwantao near the harbor of Tiensin. It's shipped in closed compartments. Marine guards take over guarding the trains once the boxcars are outside the city. The only problem is, is it really coal shipments we are guarding? The boxcars are sealed and locked shut when we get them."

"If it's not coal, what is it?" I asked.

"Loot," Lt. Barker spoke up. "Chiang K'ai-shek is looting the city, stripping its treasures and sending them all to Formosa."

This wasn't anything new, and I told them so. Train guards knew the difference between open coal cars and sealed boxcars. The only thing that puzzled me now was Formosa, an island off the southern coast of China. One of the students I knew was from Formosa. It was a mountainous island with some aborigine tribes and nothing more. It had nine automobiles and not a hundred miles of paved roads. The Portuguese discovered the island 400 years ago and called it Formosa, or

Beautiful Island. The Japanese took it over and now the Nationalist Chinese had it back. The rumor we had was that Chiang K'ai-shek was withdrawing from the mainland and regrouping on the island to prepare for an invasion of the mainland. But this was only rumor.

"Guards know it, but do the Chinese people know it? Do the Communists know it?" Gunny asked, more of a statement than a question.

"They are pretty stupid if they don't," I replied.

"You're right, but if they find out and acknowledge it, it's going to get a lot of Marines killed. At Chingwantao the train arrived from Peking the other day and the guards woke up the next morning and found the Commies had their artillery trained on them. They were given 36 hours to pack up and get out. The Commies are sure to stop all the trains now. If what Chiang is doing gets known, it can erupt into an international incident."

"The students haven't mentioned it yet," I said again.

"They will sooner or later. We are abetting a thief, a criminal. He is not only fleecing the American government but we are helping him steal from his own people. There's a good reason for calling Chiang K'ai-shek by his name Cash My Check. Madam Chiang addresses a joint session of congress and wooes Americans into giving them more money."

"There's something else," Gunny said. "There's another investigation going on."

"Did you ever hear of the name *Sinathropus Pekinensis*?" Lt. Barker butted in.

"Can't say I have," I said. What did they expect? I had a couple months of schooling, and that was only Chinese, and maybe I read a few books, and yet they were treating me like a scholar. How was I to know what sinta pepis—I couldn't even pronounce it—was?

"*Sinathropus Pekinensis* is also known as Peking Man."

That, of course, I knew—Peking Man. Everyone at the university talked about the discovery. The Anthropology

Department had been deeply involved in the project. I told them that I had heard about the Peking Man, but there wasn't much more I could tell them.

"What about a U.S. Marine named Gerald Valentine?" Gunny asked.

"Again, negative. Never heard of him," I replied.

"Valentine was rescued from a Japanese POW camp near here in September 1945. We got him out just before the Russians came. He returned home, was discharged, and the next thing we know he is in London, lodged somewhere near Russell Square. He had changed his name, and he wants two million dollars."

I was intrigued now. I accepted a cigarette Lt. Barker handed me and listened to his story. According to him, the discovery of the fossil bones of Peking Man was the most important discovery to the 20th century. The fossils were uncovered in a limestone hill near Peking in l926. The hill, in fact, contained the largest collection of prehistoric fossils ever discovered, the fragments of more than 40 skeletons. The number and variety of the bones would have made it possible to reconstruct how Peking Man must have looked, and could provide an important link in man's evolution. But now they were gone.

For fifteen years anthropologists flocked to Peking to study the bones. Then in 1941, as Japanese troops advanced on Peking, the bones were handed over to the commander of the US Marine garrison, Detachment D, at the United States Embassy, packed in military footlockers, and prepared for shipment to the United States for safekeeping.

But within hours, before the footlockers could be moved, Pearl Harbor was bombed and Japan and the U.S. were at war. The Marines surrendered to the Japanese and went off to POW camps and the footlockers with their priceless contents disappeared. The Marines were released from POW camps in 1945, and among them was Valentine.

"The whereabouts of Valentine is unknown," Lt. Barker

said, "but if he could be found, one of the most intriguing anthropological mysteries of our age could be solved." He waited for me to say something, but there was nothing I could say. "There's more than money involved, however," he continued. "This is becoming a major factor in furthering the growing rift between Red China and the United States."

"The Chinese believe that the US has taken the bones and for some reason will not give them back," Gunny said. "Washington is anxious to prove that this is not so."

"What does this have to do with me?" I asked. I had already been adding things up in my mind. Marines become involved in intrigue every place they go. The old song is so right, "from the halls of Montezuma to the shores of Tripoli" they fought off revolutions and gained republics for the dispossessed. They battled in places like Nicaragua, and they came to China to protect Americans during the Boxer Rebellion, and became involved in a revolution and helped found a republic. We came to guard coal trains and ammunition dumps and find we are searching for old bones and helping a new warlord steal his country's treasures. We Marines complain constantly, and we love it.

"I don't know what we can find, but I have been instructed to go take a look at the site, a kind of unofficial report. I need an interpreter, and a Chinese might think we are up to something evil. We have elected you to come along."

"I'm still in school," I said. I really didn't care if I missed classes, but I was concerned about Ming-Lee. She could arrive any day and I had to be in Peking when she arrived.

"Two or three days, five at the most, and that's all," Gunny said. "We will follow along the Great Wall and then turn to the southeast to reach Zhoukoudian Township."

The Great Wall again! How could I not go? I accepted. We would leave the following morning. No time to waste. I went back to my hostel to pack, and at the deck I found a package from Tsingtao. It was from Stevenson. I hastily opened it. Inside, neatly folded, was a green skivvy shirt, the standard

GI issue undershirt. I wondered what it was all about until I lifted it up, and there on both sleeves were sewn two corporal chevrons. A green skivvy shirt with two dress corporal chevrons. I would keep that shirt forever. I called Bon Yee up to my room and gave him my uniform to have chevrons sewed on it too, including my khaki shirt. I only wore the uniform on weekends when I checked in, but now I felt like wearing it to school. But that wouldn't do. Only a few students knew I was in the Marines and it was best to keep it that way. It's a proud day when a Marine makes corporal but I had to keep my pride to myself.

Gunny was at the front door to pick me up the next morning at 0600. He had the Jeep with jerry cans filled with fuel, an ice chest with beer and food he brought from the company mess. A corporal driver from Motor Pool sat behind the driver's wheel. "This is Joe," Gunny said and we set out to find the trail of the bones of the missing man.

Gunny sat up front with Joe. Once we passed through the city wall gate and the last guards, both U.S. Marines and Nationalist soldiers, Gunny opened the pack he kept at his feet and took out three .45s in their holsters and three duty belts. He gave Joe and me each a weapon. We would be traveling into communist-held territory, but fortunately the reports were that there were no troops in the area. "Just to be safe," Gunny said. I had a hard time concentrating on what he was saying while trying to enjoy the journey. I did find it exciting to be on the move again, with a new adventure ahead. I wished we could continue driving, right on into Tibet. But there are no roads to Tibet, I heard.

Nevertheless, Gunny talked on. He explained a few more things about Valentine. The former Marine was an amateur anthropologist, and he alone, among the Marines in charge of the bones, knew their value. Did he take them with him into the Japanese POW camp, succeed in keeping them throughout his imprisonment, and then take them to London after the war? Why did he change his name?

Gunny told me of another report made by Dr. Franz Weidenreich. The professor had left Germany because of the radical policies of the Nazi regime, and in 1935 he was appointed as visiting professor of anatomy at the Peking Union Medical College. As relations between China and Japan deteriorated, he decided he had better move the fossils from Peking to prevent them from falling into the hands of the Japanese. He left Peking, taking much of his material with him. According to him, after he left, the bones were packed in locker boxes in November, 1941, and arrangements were made for the US Marine Corps to take them when they left Peking for the United States. That was all he could report.

"You are not getting bored?" Gunny asked after he had been ranting for more than two hours, but before I could answer he continued. "The Pope is involved too."

"The Pope! What does the Pope have to do with the missing bones?" I asked.

"Well, I'll tell you. It seems the Pope died and arrived at the pearly gates," he said.

Joe and I both laughed. "Okay," I said, "the Pope arrived at the pearly gates. Then what happened?"

"Now this is serious," Gunny said. "He arrived and the guard said, 'There must be some mistake. You're not on the manifest.' 'Do you know who I am?' the Pope demanded. 'I've been in the service of the Lord for sixty years' 'Yea, you say you are the Pope but I don't know. I'll tell you what. It's late and you can sleep here in the guard shack for the night. The place is full so there's only a top bunk left.' There wasn't much the Pope could do, so he found a top bunk and tried to get some sleep. When dawn came there was a hell of a racket outside, and when he looked out there was a Marine gunny sergeant riding in a bright yellow convertible. In his right hand he clutched a bottle of Bourbon, and sitting next to him was this luscious blonde. The Pope rushed up to the guard and said, 'What this all about? I am the Pope and I get a top bunk to sleep in, and this guy gets all this attention. I did sixty years of good work for the Lord, and I demand to know what this is all about.' 'I'll tell you,' the guard said. 'We get a Pope up here every 40 or 50 years. This is the first time we ever got a Marine Corps Gunny Sergeant.'"

By late afternoon we had reached Dragon Bones Hill in Zhoukoudian Township. The drive is less than 50 miles but we drove almost 200 following along the Great Wall. Unfortunately we couldn't get near the wall, as there were no roads, not even trails, but nevertheless it was always in the far distance for us to see. I vowed I would one day return and hike the length of that wall.

The Zhoukoudian site was screened by rolling mountains and ridges on the northwest and adjoined a vast fertile land to the southwest under a boundless blue sky. The Zhoukou River rushed down the mountain valley and zigzagged its way south and emptied into the Glass River.

All work on the excavations had stopped years before. Mud and clay walls on the open pits had collapsed into piles of rubble. Our report said that Dragon Bones Hill was formed by limestone in the Ordovician period. It rises nearly 300 feet above the Zhoukou River. Since 1926, 23 fossils and cultural relics have been found within a relatively small area. It is estimated that Peking Man lived in a big cave on the northern slope of the Dragon Bones Hill about 500,000-600,000 years ago.

The first complete skull of Peking Man was discovered in 1926. Bone fossils of over forty individuals of different ages and sex, some one hundred thousand pieces of stone instruments and a large number of animal fossils, were unearthed in the same area. It was interesting poking around in the ashes but other than that, there was little that we could report. We camped that night on Dragon Bone Hill, under a star-filled sky, with a sliver of a moon on the horizon. We felt affinity with our early ancestors who must have sat on the same spot a half a million years before. And most likely they too looked up at the same stars and the same moon and wondered what it was all about. We lingered at the site the next morning, and by nightfall were back in Peking. As I laid in my bunk that night in Hostel No. 3, I wondered how great it must be to be an anthropologist. A year before, that thought would never have entered my mind.

And so it was back to my studies. The students were becoming more outspoken with each passing day. When we first arrived in China, we were welcomed with open arms; we were their liberators. Now our presence was more like their conquerors. Students clamored that new traditions had to replace old traditions. They no longer revered or respected the West. They now insisted it was the Chinese who were the great technological innovators and not the Westerners. "The West stole from China," Lee Ann, the antagonist, argued with me. "That's why in the 15th century we isolated ourselves from the rest of the world. We saw that our true interests lay inside our own borders. It was you in the West that had the compulsive desire to invade other people's space, and have refused to accept your own limits."

Lee Ann shouted that we Western barbarians have a grim look about ourselves; we keep ourselves untidy, have an unpleasant smell, are liars and are arrogant. We conquer countries by fraud and force, ingratiate ourselves in a friendly way, and then oppress the masses. At the heart of our conduct is violence.

The Spanish, Dutch, Portuguese, British, French and later the Americans, all came bearing Chinese inventions, gun powder, the magnetic compass, the stern rudder. We came not just to sell, but to impose, our goods, our ideas, our religion, and our will. We set up great trading colonies, lorded over them from grand mansions, paid for by illicit trade in goods like opium.

"For more than a century white men have looked down on the peoples of Asia," Su Fung said, "classifying us in the status of second-class human beings. You think you won the war. The Japanese won the war. They have driven the white man from his lofty status. The struggle is not over. China today has almost succeeded in freeing herself from the yoke of the foreigner."

It was getting too heavy. How had they developed all this hatred? It was their new ideology. "The Chinese will free themselves from the white man, a fight that China has already started. Tomorrow the peasants of Asian dominated countries will be fighting against their own native overlords for a share in the new freedom that the struggle of all has brought."

The revolution was coming. There was no stopping it. Katarina above all began to feel the agony of change. She found herself becoming isolated from the few Chinese friends she had. "I cannot stay any longer in north China," she said one day when we were having coffee.

"What about your school?" I asked. She grew quiet. She had thoughts she wasn't about to share with me.

I finally had a telegram from Ming-Lee. She announced that she would be arriving by train over the weekend. I immediately began to make plans, but it was awkward. Do I invite her to stay with me in my room, or do we move into a hotel? Maybe this was being presumptuous. I didn't even know if she planned to share a bed with me. The very thought made me a nervous wreck. The first question was solved when I learned that I was not allowed to take women to my room. The next question, that of a hotel, would have to wait until she arrived and we would play it by ear, so to speak. Now I had to tell Katarina. I had told her before about Ming-Lee, and admitted we had never been lovers. She listened with interest but had no comments to make. But now when I told her Ming-Lee was coming to Peking, I saw a side of her I didn't know existed before.

"A Chinese girl," she cried. "How could you? How could you do this? I've listened to you all these months. What fulfillment can a Chinese girl give you?"

She refused to listen to what I had to say and in anger stormed out of the coffee shop. Was I misunderstanding women? Did I not realize she had feelings for me? I suddenly found myself torn between two worlds, between two women. Okinawa was easier.

That evening I went to Mamma Georgia's and learned that Melanowski and Monique had a room together in the back of the compound. I expected to find Melanowski morose but he was quite happy. He even admitted he was finally learning Chinese. "What happens when we go back to Tsingtao?" I asked.

"Monique will come with me," he replied. It sounded so simple. Maybe it was, and it was I who was making an issue of things.

The train station in Peking was a nightmare. Attendants had to use force to control the masses. They did their utmost to squeeze passengers into the compartments. They showed no mercy for women or kids. They were brutal, and the people fought back. It appeared hopeless. I didn't think I would ever find Ming-Lee in the crowd, especially after I waited for one train after another to arrive from the coast. Doubts began to take over. My mind was blanking out. I tried to picture her face but I couldn't remember it. What was happening?

It was Ming-Lee who saw me first. How could I ever have forgotten that lovely face, those beautiful eyes, that wonderful smile? We didn't think about customs or traditions, or what people might say. When I saw her coming toward me, and she saw me, we threw ourselves into each other's arms. "Roger booked us a room in a Chinese hotel where we can both stay," she said. That was one problem solved. We found the hotel, and for two days we didn't come out of our room. We had our meals brought in; I never knew love with an Asian girl could be so grand. I also discovered streetcars do not run sideways. Some things, I learned, do come naturally.

Ming-Lee had friends she had to look up so I was able to

spend a few days in class. At night we did the clubs at the bases around town and we had most of our meals at Wagonlits. Unlike in Tsingtao, we were not worried about appearing together in public; we took pedicabs and traveled together from place to place. But we did have other concerns. Tensions were running high in the capital. Rumors had it that Nationalist forces were beginning to yield control of the North to the Chinese Communists. Some even said the Nationalists were considering a "polite surrender." General Fu Tso-yi, the Nationalist commander, was attempting to negotiate a separate peace for Northern China. Meanwhile in the Nationalist capital of Nanking, Generalissimo Chiang K'ai-shek, who had been fighting the Communists for more than twenty years, announced that he was considering retiring as president of China with the hope that his departure would bring an end to the hostilities. We figured it was another of his ploys. Whatever happened, Mao Tse-tung was prepared to take control.

No one knew which way to turn. Tsingtao was still the stronghold of north China, but how long that would last was anyone's guess. My classes were starting to get me down. I was tired of arguing with pseudo-intellectual students and I felt my mind was being twisted and turned by problems I could not solve. I no longer looked in the mirror and wondered why I didn't look Chinese. Instead I put on my uniform and stared at myself, glad that I was a Marine.

I knew that my time in Peking was about up. Ming-Lee had been with me in the city nearly three weeks and we decided it was best that she return to Tsingtao. She could look for a room for us to rent. I was waiting in my room for her to phone when a knock came at the door. It couldn't be her, and the only other person who came to my room was Bon Yee. I slid out of my warm bed and in my skivvy drawers I partly opened the door. Katarina stood there. I was startled and reached for a towel to wrap around myself.

"How did you get in?" I asked.

"Very simple. They told me your room number and pointed

out the direction."

"But women aren't allowed," I said. "They said that was the rule."

"Not everyone's rule. Aren't you going to ask me in?"

"Yes, yes, I'm sorry, come in," I mumbled and stepped aside. "But I don't understand. I was instructed no women were allowed."

"No women," she said. "They mean no Chinese women. I am a white woman, a White Russian, you remember?"

I didn't have time to answer. She came to me and threw her arms around my neck. "I can't bear it any longer," she sighed. "I want you. I need you." I could feel my pulse quicken. She reached down and took the towel from around my waist and threw it over the back of the chair. She took off her coat and placed it too on the chair. Without taking her eyes from me, staring straight at me, she took off her boots and stockings, removed her dress and inner garments, and stood there in front of me completely naked. I could only look upon her Vargas-girl body in disbelief. Her skin was flawless, and absolutely white. Her breasts were firm; her waist thin. She stood there, letting my eyes and thoughts feast upon her. She held her garments in her hand, and then slowly turned to place them on the chair.

She saw something that made her gasp. She jumped back as if she was confronted by a demon with fangs about to pounce at her. She clasped her hands over her mouth. The door to my closet was open.

"What is it?" I called and leaped toward her.

"Your uniform!" she cried.

"My uniform," I replied, "what about it?" I saw my uniform that Yee had hung carefully on a hanger, along with my shirt. The chevrons were exactly as I told him to sew them on. "What's wrong with that?"

"The stripes! You are only a corporal," she stammered.

"What's wrong with that?" I said, completely confused.

"I thought you were a captain."

"A captain! What made you think that? I never told you I was a captain," I said

"They call you captain," she cried.

"Who?" I asked.

"All the guys, Gilbert, the others," she replied.

I suddenly remembered. They did call me captain—Captain Mitty. The guys started calling me Captian Mitty after we had seen the movie, "The Secret Life of Walter Mitty" starring Danny Kaye and Virginia May. I started acting out the lines: "We're going through. Damn, the pounding is increasing, listen—ta-pocketa-pocketa-pocketa-pocketa-pocketa." Sometimes I'd say, "Never mind, it's only a broken arm," like Captain Mitty did when he stood at the helm of a ship in a storm. The guys would laugh, and soon they began calling me Captain Mitty. Before long they dropped the Mitty part. When Katarina told me this, I had to laugh. I tried to explain who Captain Mitty was and how it all started. She wouldn't listen.

She quickly began to dress, her skirt, her blouse, finally her shoes and stocking. "I don't know what you are thinking," I pleaded, "but I didn't know you thought I was an officer."

"You don't understand. You don't know what it is to be homeless. I don't mean just poor. I mean without a country."

"What does this have to do with me being a corporal? Does that change how I feel about you."

"Yes, for me it does!"

"That's the only reason you went out with me, because you thought I was an officer?" I asked.

"Yes, because you had promise," she replied.

"I didn't promise you anything," I insisted.

"Not that kind of promise," she fired back.

"What kind then?" I asked earnestly.

"The promise of a future."

"Like what? Like getting married."

The anger in me flared up. All the time she was using me, like a pawn. I was her pawn, her checkmate, her ticket to get out of China. She had absolutely no feeling. She was cold and calculating. She had deceived me completely.

"My mother married a Marine, and he couldn't even live in the same house. He had to sneak back to base every night. My aunt fell in love with a sailor. She could have had a Hollywood executive but she gave in to a sailor, and he sailed away and never came back. They say he died in the war, but he probably had a wife in America. My other aunt fell in love with a Flying Tiger pilot, and it turned out he was married. I swore I would never let this happen to me. You can't give me what I want." At that she grabbed her coat and fur hat and muff and rushed out of the door, slamming it behind her.

I slipped into my clothes as fast as I could, not even bothering to put on my shoes, and ran down the steps to the lobby. By the time I got there she was gone. I rushed up to the desk. "Where did the girl go?" I asked.

"She go half hour before," the receptionist said.

"A half hour ago!" I shouted. "What girl you talking about?"

"Chinese girl who come from Tsingtao," he said.

"She came here and was waiting?" I asked.

"Same, same," he replied stoically.

"What did you tell her?" I demanded.

"Me talkie her she was no allowed here," he answered. "Me say you cannot come down. You in room with Russian girl flend."

I reached out and grabbed him by his collar, shook him, and sent him flying back against the wall. "You little gook bastard," I shouted and ran back up the stairs to my room. I dressed as quickly as I could, but it wasn't quick enough. When I got to the hotel, Ming-Lee had checked out and was gone. She had to be heading back to Tsingtao, I thought. I caught a pedicab and had the poor fellow peddle as fast as he could to the train station, just in time to see the train departing for Tiensin. Ming-Lee was gone.

Chapter 13

RETURN TO TSINGTAO

One Thursday afternoon, what we feared would happen one day, did happen. Orders came from the Fleet Marine Force Headquarters that all US Marines studying the Chinese language at the University of Peking had to return to their duty stations immediately. Gunny Wesley came to my hostel to inform me that at 0700 the following Monday morning we had to muster at George Company for further transportation to the airport where we would board a C-47 for Tsingtao.

"Things are not looking good," Gunny explained over coffee in the restaurant. "Mao's forces have overrun Manchuria, and the losses have been disastrous. It seems the communists have obliterated twelve Nationalist army divisions west of the key city of Mukden." He went on to tell me in certain terms that government troops were trying to escape from the area by sea. Some had reached Yingkow, the port on the Gulf of Liaotung which was still being held by the Nationalists, but a large number of Chiang's troops were bottled up in Hulutao on the western shore of the gulf. "It doesn't look good," he said again.

He was saddened that the communist's success in Manchuria made the Nationalist troops in Northern China much more vulnerable. It meant that Chiang had lost Manchuria's coalmines and much of her heavy industry to the communists. The civil war was getting out of control, and the safety of the Marines and military personnel in Peking was in jeopardy. The Marines alone could not take up arms against the entire Chinese communist forces. I thanked the gunny for the information; he had turned out to be a great pal and I wondered if I would ever see him again.

I hardly had time to say goodbye to everyone at the university. I was touched when Su Fung and Mae Chu burst into tears at the news of my parting. Even arrogant Lee Ann confessed she was sorry to see me go, and would you believe, Dr. Wren was there to shake my hand and wish me good fortune. But the biggest surprise was the celebration Saturday night at Mamma Georgia's place. Fifty people must have been invited, maybe more, and Mamma Georgia cut no costs and made sure the booze was plentiful; it was the real stuff right from the officers' mess. Her girls, decked out in their finery, looked grand. They could have matched any Philadelphia mainline society debutantes at their coming-out party. They looked absolutely ravishing, and hadn't anyone known their vocation, they might have been taken for proper young ladies. When I arrived I thought this was a going-away party solely for Melanowski, but I soon learned it was for Monique as well. She too was going to Tsingtao, by train. She and Melanowski planned to meet once she arrived. I was completely in the dark and had no idea what they were planning but thought it best not to ask. I would find out the facts in due course. Nevertheless, I couldn't believe Mamma Georgia was not only letting Monique go, but it was with her blessing. It wasn't until we were aboard the C-47 en route to Tsingtao that Melanowski told me the full story.

"Gunny Wesley is helping me," he said.

"Helping you what?" I asked, straining hard to hear what he had to say against the roar of the engines.

"Gunny told me how I can get my discharge in China," he said, and in bits and pieces I gathered he had applied for a position with UNRA. If I was hearing right, he felt that he would be accepted. "Once I am out of the Crops and have secured my job, Monique and me can get married." Was I going deaf? Was the roar of the engines altering what I was hearing? I was truly baffled at his next remark. "I have you to thank," he said.

"Me, what did I have to do with it?"

"If you hadn't convinced me to come to Peking, it would not have happened," he said.

"You mean you wouldn't have met Monique," I replied. "Is that what you mean?"

"That too, but my studying Chinese is what got me the job with UNRA."

I didn't know if I should be pleased or feel at fault. The last thing in this world I ever thought was that Melanowski would become a linguist and remain in China. I wanted to ask him if this is what Monique wanted. I wanted to tell him about Katarina, that she was looking for a ticket to the States, and might Monique be the same, but we began to make our final approach and would soon be in Tsingtao.

It was a wonderful sight to watch Tsingtao unfold beneath us as we dropped down out of the clouds in our C-47. I think at that moment, upon seeing Tsingtao, I realized then that we were truly China Marines. We were coming home, not home to San Diego or LA, or Peoria or Charleston, but home to Tsingtao. I strained hard to see out the window, and finally unstrapped myself from my bucket seat and stood up to get a better view. The others soon followed and we all stood now staring out the windows. First to come in view were the miles of beaches with many coves and white sand that caught the morning rays of sun. Then came the city and the vast harbor with endless ships at anchor. There were the junks, fleets of them, and the rusted, unkept freighters at the docks, and among this vast floating panorama were the ships of the American Seventh Fleet anchored in the roads. What a sight that was! The fleet was in! There would be a wild time in the old town tonight, that was for sure. Bars and cabarets would be bursting at the seams. I couldn't wait until I got to the Prime Club. I pictured myself charging through the front door and seeing Ming-Lee there. I didn't care if she was sitting at a table with other Marines or even sailors. I would grab hold of her and tell her how it was all a mistake. It didn't matter how she would react. Angry at first, certainly, but I would make her understand. I had some hard convincing to do, but she would listen. I would make her listen.

I was hoping Sammy would be there at the airfield to pick us up but it was another driver from motor pool who came to get us. Nevertheless, he was affable and swung through town to give us a tour before taking us to the university where we had to report in. I had been away only eight months but I could see that many changes had taken place. The city was progressing; it wasn't the dilapidated city that greeted us when we arrived nearly two years before. The streets were cleaner, the shops brighter and there were more vehicles. Gone were the waving and cheering crowds that had greeted us as when we first arrived, but that didn't really matter. The people knew we were their liberators.

Everything this time was familiar, every street, every turn. The twin towered church stood above the city as it always had, and there were the bathhouses down the street that Stevenson and I had visited, but they were now out-of-bounds. The bars and restaurants that lined the route along the drive up the hill to the university were still there, but their names stood out bigger and the fronts were newly painted. The only disappointment was the disbandment of the 29th Marines; troops no longer occupied the Strand Hotel. I would miss that place, but I had no complaint about being quartered in the university. This too was soft living.

There to meet us in the Fox Company office was Stevenson and Whittington. They wanted to hear all about Peking, but each time we began telling them, they interrupted us with their own stories of what was happening in Tsingtao. Lt. Brandmire busted two more guys. Col. Roston finally left. There's a new dancehall that opened and it's better than the Prime Club and Ciro's. Some places are charging a buck and a half for a bottle of Hubba Hubba these days. And that new bunch of green troops that arrived are real pussies. They were like a couple of Chinese *lao furen* trying to out talk one another. Finally Stevenson led me out of the office and to a room on the second floor facing the main gate. "I saved this room for you," he said. There were two bunks in the room and he saw me looking at the second one. "Another surprise," he announced, and before he could say more, Little Lew bounded into the room. I couldn't believe my eyes. He was at least a foot taller, and he had made corporal. He was proud of his stripes. Big tears rolled down his cheeks. He was so choked up he could hardly speak, and I wasn't much better. I no longer needed to get down on my knees to put my arms around him. He stood well above my waist. He had lost his Chinese accent. In fact, he talked like a New Englander. He had been palling around with Chandler that was for sure.

With Little Lew swinging on my arm we went down to the ground floor to the laundry room to see Ruker. He had moved his bunk into the room and fixed up the place. On all the walls he had put up posters of Vargas girls in various stages of undress. He had a stuffed leather easychair with an inlaid pearl table to one side, and upon it a reading lamp made from coral. "Uh, uh," Ruker said when Little Lew came into the room, and it was the signal for Lew to cover his eyes with one hand. "Atta boy," Ruker said. Like a blind man feeling his way with an extended arm, but peeking through his fingers, Little Lew made his way to the easychair and threw himself down. Ruker smiled like a beaming father.

The Marines were quite content with their facilities at the university. They had everything they needed—a gym with weights and basketball court, a big well-stocked PX with Planters Peanuts and Clark Bars, movie hall, library and study room, and a barbershop with real barber chairs. No one needed to go off base if they didn't care to, and many didn't.

Back in my room, before I could unpack, all the old squad came to welcome me back. "You came just in time," Smitty said. "We've having a party for Whittington. He's shipping back to the States next week."

The going-away party for Whittington was held at the EM Club in town. The guys thought of everything, including Little Lew. So that he wouldn't feel left out, they arranged for a kid's movie night at the movie hall. I wanted to go immediately to the Prime Club to see Ming-Lee but I didn't have a choice. The new CO arranged for a ten-wheeler to bus us down to the EM Club. There was one problem, however. No one remembered to tell Whittington; he didn't show up for his own surprise party.

The EM Club was roaring by the time we arrived. The whole building was vibrating like one of those machines that overweight people use when they want to lose weight. A couple of extra paddy wagons were parked outside. Burly Shore Patrolmen waited in the vehicles for calls which were certain to come. The Seventh Fleet was in Tsingtao and the US Navy had taken over the EM Club. Ming-Lee would have to wait a bit longer for me.

There wasn't an empty table in the place, but we were able to double up with some guys from Easy Company. We scouted around and stole chairs from sailors' tables when they got up to order more beer or go to the head. An hour after the club had opened its doors, the bar ran out of cold beer. Two hours later it ran out of beer altogether. They turned to selling hard stuff, gin and rye whisky. That's when the trouble began. Stevenson, Ruker and I were able to sneak out, leaving Chandler, Hecklinger, Terry and Smitty behind. It wasn't until we got back to the university that night that we learned Chandler was in the hospital.

The story we heard was that our squad suspected the club would run out of beer so they bought up a couple of cases and stacked them under their table. When the beer ran out, sailors at the next table wanted to buy some from our guys but they refused. Tension began building and remarks like "jarhead" and "leatherhead" verses "swab jockey" and "deck ape" began to fly back and forth. Chandler went to dance with Buxom Bonnie, the navy Chief's daughter from Shore Patrol, when all hell broke out. Chandler heard a rumble coming from the direction of his table and saw that a fight had erupted between the Marines and sailors. It was getting serious. Two sailors had grabbed Smitty and started shoving him out of the second story window. There was little Hecklinger and Terry could do to help him; four or five sailors were holding them back with chairs and threatening to beat them over the head with them. Chandler didn't hesitate; he charged like an enraged bull to help Smitty and knocked the sailors back. The next thing Chandler knew, one sailor broke a coke bottle and came at him swinging. He struck at Chandler and slashed him across the face, tearing off half his nose. Fortunately a big Navy SP stepped in and laid the sailor's head open with his billy club. Both men were taken to the hospital and the medics sewed Chandler's nose back on. Stevenson, Ruker and I knew none of this, of course, when we arrived at the Prime Club.

For days I had been thinking about this moment, how I was going to arrive at the Prime Club, and now it was becoming reality. When the girls saw Ruker they dropped whatever they were doing and came running. Even those who were at tables with customers came running too. Judy saw Stevenson and rushed up to greet him with outstretched arms. Everyone came, happy as larks, everyone but Ming-Lee. She was nowhere to be seen. When things quieted down, I asked Judy where she was. She didn't answer.

It was a hang fire, like when you pull the trigger and nothing happens. No, it was worse. It was like one of those new grenades that didn't pop. The Corps introduced them during the last days of fighting on Okinawa. Marines had discovered that when the Japs heard the pops from our grenades, they would count the seconds, and if they had enough time they would pick them up and lob them back at us. So the engineers developed the pop-less grenade, but they didn't tell us about them. Terry was the first to discover it. He picked up a grenade, pulled the pin and when it didn't pop he just looked at it. Disgusted that it might be a dud, he casually tossed it aside. It exploded less than a dozen yards away, and fortunately didn't kill anyone. Was this another dud? When I asked Judy again about Ming-Lee, she looked at Stevenson and then at me. " She's gone," she said sheepishly. "I think maybe you know."

"Gone," I repeated. The grenade exploded. "What do you mean gone?"

"She go Shanghai. She no come back to Prime Club. She go live in Shanghai."

My world came to an end. I didn't feel like partying anymore that night. I had one drink of Hubba Hubba with the boys, made a flimsy excuse about having the runs and went back to the university. In the rickshaw I concluded that I had to find Roger. He might know something about Ming-Lee. The only problem was that when I had asked about Roger, no one had seen him in a couple of months. I had never been to the hotel where he lived but I did have a letter from him tucked away in my seabag, and it did have a return address on the envelope. I'd go see him on my next liberty. He would help me find Ming-Lee. I felt a little better.

There were some mighty sore heads the next morning and I was glad that I had stopped partying when I did. We had a new company commander, a 30-day wonder major who had replaced Col. Roston. He called me into his office, and as I stood at rigid attention he gave me my assignment. I could see he was going to be a miserable bastard. You would think these new officers would be pleased to have seasoned combat Marines under their command but it was usually the opposite. They didn't like troops having more experience than they had. So I got my assignment. I would be attached to the MP Battalion, and would be carrying out Shore Patrol duty. In the past, Chinese soldiers had been attached to Marine MPs and Navy SPs to do the rounds with them. They were supposedly interpreters, but there wasn't much they could interpret. They didn't speak English. This would be my job, the colonel said, but first I had to help out with brig duty, the nastiest duty a Marine could get. With more old hands being transferred back to the States, the brig watch found themselves short handed, and I was to help out until replacements arrived from the States. The brig warden, a disgruntled old sergeant major, demanded that I move into the guards' quarters in the brig. I had Chandler take over Little Lew once again until my brig duty was over.

The Marine brig was located within the university compound. It had a very tough reputation with Marines stationed in Tsingtao and sailors of the Seventh Fleet. Manned by the biggest, meanest Marines in China, it deserved the reputation it had. Sailors and Marines of the Tsingtao area who had violated the Rocks and Shoals were confined here. Being a redline brig, prisoners received harsh treatment. Redline brigs are ones in which every two feet a red line was painted on the deck, especially at every hatch. A prisoner would have to halt at all red lines and request permission from a turnkey before he could advance to the next red line. what it meant was if a prisoner had to go to the head he had to cross two or three red lines and request permission to proceed. This could consume several minutes, depending on the mood of the turnkey. Talk was that the Tsingtao brig had very few repeat offenders.

At this time Rocks and Shoals were naval laws used to control and maintain discipline in the Navy and Marine Corps. These laws dated far back before World War II. Under them it was very easy to violate an order and be confined to the brig. The law on silent contempt is a good example. Silent contempt charges were filed if a Marine or sailor even looked at an officer or NCO in a contemptuous manner. It was a violation of an article under Rocks and Shoals. Under this military system a Marine could receive punishment of anywhere from five to thirty days on "Piss and Punk," navy slang for bread and water that meant a prisoner received nothing but bread and water twice a day and on the third day received a full meal. The prisoner then served two more days on Piss and Punk. Bread and water prisoners did not have to do manual labor. During the day the prisoners cleaned their small cell, did a few minutes of exercise, and spent the remainder of the day in solitary confinement. Not even reading material was permitted. It may sound like a good way to lose pounds but some Marines actually come out heavier than when they went in.

Prisoners sentenced to hard labor spent their days in a rock quarry just outside of town. Everyday, except Sunday, prisoners marched from the brig to the rock quarry. Each prisoner carried an eight-pound sledgehammer at right shoulder arms and a sack lunch consisting of bologna horse cock and peanut butter sandwiches. Here at the quarry they made big rocks into little rocks by swinging the eight-pound sledge all day. Prisoners received a five-minute break every hour and had thirty minutes for lunch.

The first prisoner I had to deal with was Pvt. Gamble. He was Chandler's buddy. Lt. Brandmire sent him up for five days on Piss and Punk. Chandler saw red when this happened. Lt. Brandmire still hadn't lightened up, and he became even more chicken shit by making the troops learn their General Orders forwards and backwards, and that included even naming the commas and periods. He was getting worse every day. He got to walking the entire guard posts at the docks when he was Officer of the Day, and he demanded strict attention to duty. Chandler and Gamble were on guard duty at the docks when Lt. Brandmire was the Officer of the Day. Their posts were about a hundred yards apart, guarding two warehouses. It was that miserable night watch, the four to eight in the morning, and both men were bored and tired. It was getting light, and Gamble started sending Chandler arm signals in semaphore code, and just then Lt. Brandmire walked around the corner. Gamble reported his post and nothing was said.

When they returned to their quarters at the university, Gamble's sack was empty and his seabag gone. Lt. Brandmire gave him five days Piss and Punk for not walking his post in a military manner—keeping always on the alert and observing everything that takes place within sight and hearing.

Gamble was in the brig office the first day I was on the job. He was an old hand from the 55th Draft days, and I knew him, but the others in the office were new to me. One was a great big brute of a Marine from Texas, and the other man was a Seabee in leg irons. There were more prisoners lined up in the hallway outside the office. I was well aware that first impressions are important, and all these prisoners were, of course, wondering who this new guy on the block was. I had to show them I meant business, but I didn't know quite how I would do this. Beneath a rough exterior that I had to display, there was a meek side of me I always tried to camouflage. I was one of those kids who had been constantly beat up in high school. I was a farm boy and when it came time to putting on boxing gloves in gym class, I would rather get beat up than punch back. Then I joined the Marines. I carried the same philosophy with me into bootcamp, but it didn't last long. One of the methods our Drill Instructor, those feared DIs, used to toughen new recruits up was to take broomsticks and fasten boxing gloves on each end. He then had two recruits stand face to face with one another and slug it out. My opponent kept slamming away at me and all I did was to try to ward off the blows. The DI saw what was happening, grabbed the broomstick away from my opponent and kept poking at me, shouting all the time, "Come on, come on, do something." I kept falling back but he kept after me, jabbing away. The other recruits stopped their sparring and gathered around to watch us. The DI became more violent. "Come on, what's the matter with you boy, you chicken?" Still I did nothing except to try to defend myself, but now I began sobbing, with tears running down my face. My nose too began running. I fell back, tripped and was sitting on the ground, thinking that now he would let up, but he didn't stop. He kept hammering away at me, his voice growing more shrill and louder and louder. "You're a shit bird and that's all you'll ever be—a chicken shit shit bird." Something snapped. I saw fury, blind fury, and got back on my feet. I didn't care if that son-of-a-bitch was my DI or the Commandant of the Marine Corps himself. I took hold of my broomstick and instead of holding it in the middle, I grabbed one end and began swinging it savagely at the DI. He now was the one who fell back. He tripped and fell to the ground, and I stood over top him and kept swinging, wanting to kill him now. I had become insane with rage, and felt no pity as the sergeant on the ground held his arms over his head to ward off the blows. It took a whole squad of recruits and another DI standing nearby to pull me away.

I was sure I'd be put on report, maybe kicked out of the Marine Corps, and I didn't care. I'd do it again. The DI got to his feet, dusted himself off, and said, "Good work, Marine." He called me Marine. We were in bootcamp, and he called me Marine. I was the proudest guy in the platoon, and no one messed with me after that.

Now I was confronted with somewhat of the same problem as I stood in the brig office that morning. All eyes were on me, studying my every move. Would I be a pushover? They waited.

A few minutes before, a chaser had been in the office before me, and as was the procedure, he checked in his .45 and placed it on the desk with the clip of ammo next to it. I saw the .45, went over and picked it up, and turned around and faced everyone. In a voice loud and clear, I said, "I'm a fair guy but I won't take any crap from anyone." The words alone weren't that powerful, and, in fact, I thought they were rather weak, something you'd expect a second lieutenant to say, but what I did next startled everyone in the room, in the office, and out in the courtyard where the prisoners were lined up to go to chow. I suddenly became the most feared assistant brig warden in Tsingtao.

What I didn't know was that the chaser had checked out from the turnkey the .45 and not one clip of ammo but two clips. When I saw the pistol I thought it was unloaded. But in the Marines we have a policy, and that is that every weapon is loaded unless proven otherwise. I did what we are trained to do. I pointed the .45 upwards, pulled back the slide, and by doing so, I put a cartridge into the chamber. When I pulled the trigger the weapon went off. The action so astounded me, instead of admitting someone had goofed, I said, "Now let that be a warning!"

"Hey, you got to take it easy," the Brig Warden said to me later that day. Even the Exec had something to say when I saw him the next time. Like in bootcamp, no one fooled around with me after that.

The prisoner from Texas had a name that was hard for a Marine to live down—Herbert Jones. I believe he became a roustabout merely for defending himself when someone called him by his name. He was a fighter, and tough as they came. They used to joke that he made Charles Atlas look like the skinny kid on the beach. The irony was that he was mild mannered and soft spoken. It was only after he got liquored up on Hubba Hubba that he got wild. He got drunk one night and cleaned up a whole bar filled with Marines and Swabbies. When they called for the MPs, they asked for reinforcements, but when two 4x4 weapons carriers loaded with MPs and SPs arrived, Herbert was sitting quietly at a table by himself. He went without a struggle, and got 30 days in the brig on a Summary. I liked the guy from the start.

Another prisoner I quickly got to know was Ralph Cuzzo. He was a Seabee, a very likeable guy, but being likeable didn't help him much. He was deeply involved in the black market. He didn't sell cigarettes and toothpaste like most of us did from our PX rations. He sold stockpiles, like sacks of sugar, by the truckloads. He not only sold the sugar but he sold the trucks that delivered the sugar as well. The rumor was that he had a fortune hidden away somewhere in Tsingtao. The other thing they said was that he was in cahoots with Tony Stompano.

Tony was one of those guys that no one liked but whom we all envied. He liked to make us think that he was one of the West Coast Mafia, with connections, but a couple guys figured he was no more than a Detroit Zoot Suiter. Even without duck-tails and sideburns Stompano was still a greaser. What annoyed us most about him was the silk Chinese robe he wore to the shower room, a true Hollywood dandy. When you saw him in bars and dancehalls around town, you could be sure he'd have his necktie off and his shirt unbuttoned and wide open down the front, exposing a hairy chest and a heavy gold cross on a gold chain. He also wore a gold Rolex. He was quick to cover up when the SP appeared. Everyone figured Cuzzo was his fall guy. But I didn't think Cuzzo would stoop that low.

Tony Stompano was basically a coward. He'd back off from a fight, but the guys never challenged him. They feared him, not for his strength, but for the fact that he might pull a knife and stick them. They felt he might even do it at night when they were sleeping. He fed on this type of glory and it made him even more obstinate. He got along great with the White Russians in town. They say he was a gigolo for a couple of White Russian women at Rusty Mary's.

We were warned Cuzzo was going to attempt a breakout. He wore leg irons at all times, and it was kind of pathetic to watch him hobble along every day with a Marine chaser with a carbine at port arms following him. I never really thought that he would attempt it, for where could he go, but that was my mistake. He broke out one night on my watch.

Cuzzo had been tried by court-martial and found guilty. He was sentenced to 20 years hard labor and was waiting transfer to Leavenworth. His Chinese girl friend Ping Ping came to visit him during visiting hours on Sunday, and that may have been when they planned his escape. She was a pretty thing, a bit voluptuous and very sexy. Any guy would chance going over the hill for one night with her. You could tell when you saw them together that Cuzzo was very much in love with her. That same night when I was on watch, after taps and bed check, Cuzzo slipped up a back set of stairs to the attic, worked his way through a roof hatch, dropped twenty feet to the pavement below and cut through the mesh fence. Being a clever Seabee, he had fashioned a key and was able to remove his leg irons. It was probably Ping Ping who had sneaked him a metal cutter to cut through the fence.

The authorities assumed Cuzzo would make contact with Ping Ping; they were aware of her connections on the waterfront. She and her two hood brothers had rented a room there. Chinese police began staking out the place the very first day Cuzzo was arrested. The moment we reported Cuzzo's escape, the CO dispatched a patrol to search the place, and I was assigned to go with them. Our orders were to apprehend Cuzzo, and if he refused to surrender and resisted, we were to shoot, and shoot to kill. This wasn't like fighting the Japs; he was one of us. I put a clip in my .45 but debated about putting a round in the chamber.

It was dark, near midnight, when we struck. An entire company of MPs cordoned off the street along the waterfront. The place where Ping Ping was reported to be holed up was in a row of low clapboard buildings that extended over the water on pilings. A squad of five Marines, with a lieutenant in charge, two Chinese police and me were to approach from the sea. We climbed aboard a sampan sculled by a Chinese boat boy.

We kept our heads low and worked our way slowly between the pilings. It was black with only glints of light that reflected on the rippled water. Sewers from the houses above emptied into the water and the stench was terrible. It was eerie; each dark shadow was a menace and a threat. I noticed the lieutenant kept his hand on his .45. We pulled ourselves along, from one piling to the next without the boy needing to scull. The pilings were crusted with barnacles and covered with slime. The boy knew where to go. He guided us through the maze with certainty. Overhead beneath some of the buildings were trapdoors, and a few had ladders that dropped down to water level. The ladders too were covered with barnacles and slime. We worked our way around one set of pilings, ever so cautiously, when suddenly, only a few yards ahead, we heard muffled voices and the sound of wood banging against the pilings. Someone was getting into a boat. We no longer hesitated but quickly pushed ahead, and at the same time the lieutenant shouted for whomever it was to halt. The voices in the dark turned into shouts, and then an engine coughed, once, twice, and finally sparked to life. In the next instant we could hear the roar as the boat shot off into the darkness, pounding and banging recklessly into the pilings as it went. Once out into the clearing and away from the buildings the sound grew faint and was soon gone.

We worked our way to the ladder where the suspects had made their hasty exit. The trapdoor was open. The lieutenant gave the signal and stepped back as we scurried up the ladder, our weapons drawn.

The room was dimly lit and in disarray. Drawers had been emptied, clothes were scattered everywhere and the door to the walkway that led to the street was still locked. It was then that we saw Cuzzo. He was lying in a heap under a pile of rice sacks. My heart went out for poor Cuzzo. We thought he was dead and expected to find him in a pool of blood, but he was alive. The lieutenant shook him, and then slapped his face a couple of times. He moaned and opened his eyes, but they were unseeing eyes. He had been drugged.

MPs from the outside, hearing the commotion, pounded on the door and we let them in. An officer from G-2 appeared and said we were to touch nothing, and then he gave orders to his men to begin a search. We stood Cuzzo up on his feet, and with a man on each side of him we led him out the door and down the walkway to an awaiting Shore Patrol paddy wagon. He was taken to SP headquarters for custody. Two days passed before I saw him again, and that was when he returned to the brig. Ping Ping had engineered his escape, and after she directed him to the waterfront and got from him what she wanted, she and her brothers drugged him and made good their escape. By now they were probably swallowed up in Shanghai's underworld, three very rich people, and Cuzzo faced a sentence of 20 years. It was about a month later when I was on MP duty that I learned he had been transferred back to the States.

Mail from back home was always welcome, even when it brought bad news. "What do you expect?" Cpl. Marsden said when one of the guys got a letter about all the strikes going on in America. "The war's over. Don't expect any parades when you get back, for there ain't gonna be any."

I wondered about this. I remember precisely when we left San Diego with the 55th draft. There was a band playing John Philip Sousa's marches like you have never heard them before, and hundreds of people were gathered there on the docks, waving and shouting, some crying, all wishing us well. I recall in particular a very attractive young lady in tight black slacks, high heels, and a low cut black blouse. I remembered every thing about her. She was beaming and throwing kisses to those of us who were lining the railing, and she called out that she would be there waiting for every single one of us to return. I never forgot that lady, and even though I knew her vow could not be kept, I still half expected that she might be there.

Cpl. Marsden was not as optimistic. I remember when we were bogged down on the southern end of Okinawa, and said something that got us all thinking. He said if they could have put a grandstand around Iwo Jima, where people could watch wholesale slaughter taking place, they could have made a for-tune selling tickets to the public for a thousand dollars apiece, providing people had the assurance they wouldn't get hurt.

"Like in the movies," someone said.

"No, stupid, you're not listening, not like the movies," he replied. "They want to see it alive, when it's happening, just like in the Roman coliseum. Human nature hasn't changed."

Sometimes my mother's letters weren't much better. She became active in some sort of women's league and kept me informed on current events. The war had made women free from the bondage of men, she said. They had discovered they didn't need men. She wrote to tell me that Mrs. D. Leigh Colvin, President of the Women's Christian Temperance Union, was outraged when she heard that Shirley Temple would be taking a drink in her next picture. The guys went into a rage when I told them about the Little Princess. Shirley Temple was the sweetheart of every Marine in the Pacific Theater. And now she was grown up. Why in the hell couldn't she drink? We also started thinking, when we got back to American, many of us would be under age and not be allowed to drink in bars. The age limit in most states was 21. We had fought in the war, some guys like Whittington and Marsden from the first campaign, and we had all served a couple of years in China, but we were too young to drink. We'd have to sit on a park bench with Shirley Temple.

We all got a kick out of hearing that Margaret Truman, the President's daughter, spent her summer taking voice lessons in Missouri. Although she had been offered radio and concert work, she had her sights aimed at a career in opera. Upon hearing this, Terry and Chandler went around singing a duet from Don Giovanni. They weren't bad.

My father wasn't much of a writer but he did his very best to keep me well informed. His news about Ben Hogan got every Marine wild with envy. The world famous golfer was the sport's top money winner for the year. No one could imagine making the amount of money that he did. Everyone got to joking about taking up golf when they got out.

The bad news was that 4-1/2 million workers went on strike, crippling the coal, auto, electric and steel industries. After 113 days, the strike at General Motors was resolved when workers settled for an 18-1/2¢ hourly wage hike. Not bad. Which one of us China Marines wanted to start making cars?

China duty was getting to be pretty good duty, especially

in Tsingtao. We had the latest movies, some even before they were shown in America. My sister wrote and said the public was anxiously waiting for the opening of "The Best Years of Our Lives," and I wrote back that we had already seen it. The new rage was detective Philip Marlowe, played by Humphrey Bogart. He gets involved with a wealthy woman, Lauren Bacall, and her headstrong younger sister in "The Big Sleep." Although the film was made in 1944, it was held back for general release until after the war ended.

My father claimed the biggest thing on radio was Parks Johnson, host of the popular program Vox Pop. But my father was even more enthusiastic about a new medium they called television. "Television is the thing of the future," he wrote.

The dancehalls around town picked up on the latest hit tunes. Marines and sailors swooned with their taxi dancer girl friends to the words and tunes of "Give Me Five Minutes More" and "The Girl That I Marry." When they wanted to get sentimental the bands played "How Are Things in Glocca, Morra" and for happy tunes it was "They Say It's Wonderful" and "Zip-a-Dee-Doo-Dah." It was amazing how the girls could mimic the words. When the bands struck the first note of any popular song, they could all sing out in unison the words to the song. It was a fun time. But ask them what the words meant and they didn't have the slightest clue.

A letter from my mother had the news that her sister, my Aunt Liz, had a good friend whose son was on his way to Tsingtao, and she asked that I give him a "helping hand" when he arrived. "You know, kind of show him around. It's his first time away from home," my mother wrote. His name was Scott McCaffery, but I could call him Scotty. His family had something or other to do with the Universal-Cyclops Steel Company. She didn't say it, but hinted that with that backing he would be a good contact later when I came home. The last place on earth I ever wanted to work was the Universal-Cyclops Steel Company. Just thinking of the place made me ill. I could just picture the place as I read the letter: two big chimneys pumping out clouds of greenish evil smoke, and workers wearing overhauls with suspenders, carrying lunch buckets, crossing the railroad tracks every morning at 0600, just as the second whistle was blowing. I'd rather sell radio tubes in my father's shop. I don't remember if I ever wrote back to my mother about Scotty McCaffery, but I do know I soon forgot about him, until I was in Fox Company office picking up my liberty pass one afternoon. Stevenson announced that someone from back home wanted to see me and would be at the office the next morning.

"Who's that?" I asked.

"A Lt. McCaffery. He wants to see you tomorrow morning at 0800," he said. "Who you brown nosing with now?"

"I don't know any Lt. McCaffery," I said. "And who the hell is a brown noser, sitting behind your desk. All you need is a dress. You already don't have any balls."

"You wana feel them you're welcome," he answered, and then added: "He said he's from your home town."

He didn't have to say more. I remembered the name, but I had no idea the guy was a lieutenant. That didn't sound very good. I pictured him now as the son of one of the company bosses at Universal-Cyclops Steel Company. "He'll be at the Adjutant's office," Stevenson added.

I was at the Adjutant's office a little before eight the next morning, and Lt. Scott McCaffery was already there, waiting.

He was a disappointment. He didn't look much like a Marine Corps officer. He was slight of build and so mild mannered it was disgusting. Shaking hands with him was like shaking hands with a Girl Scout.

"You can call me Scott, or Scotty if you wish," he said. I could hardly do that, but I didn't want to tell him to his face. He was an officer in the United States Marine Corps. I could see he wanted to be friendly, but that didn't matter. He was an officer. I don't even think he noticed my discomfort. "I would like to take you out to dinner tonight," he said.

"I don't know," I said.

"Sure, why not," he countered.

There were regulations about officers and enlisted men socializing. I remember the nurses in the Navy Hospital on Okinawa. They were all officers, and when they had parties on Saturday night, enlisted men couldn't attend. But Lt. McCaffery had already considered that. "I talked to the Adjutant, said you were family, and he said no problem."

"Where we going?" I hemmed and hawed around.

"I know a great place. They told me at BOQ in San Diego that I should look it up. It's the Sofuku Geisha House."

Without thinking I blurted it out—"That's for officers only."

"No it's not," he protested. "Mostly officers go there I have been told, but it's for anyone."

I heard about the Sofuku Geisha House. It was a club for Japanese officers during the occupation, but that had changed and the place now catered to snob-appeal diners. Chandler was the only Marine I knew who had gone to the place to eat, and he came away pretty sore. He had a pair of black dress shoes, and, as requested, he left them outside when he went in, as was the custom. He told us how miserable it was sitting on the floor at low tables, with the waitresses sitting at your side cooking your meal in front of you over a brazier, and then stuffing the food down your throat whether you wanted it nor not. His biggest complaint was the waitresses; they wore robes with all kinds of do-dads attached; they had their hair piled up on tops of their heads; and their faces were so pasted white with powder they didn't look well. "They looked as if they smiled their faces would crack," he said, "and they watched you with little beady eyes from beneath their powder masks." We all laughed at his description of Japanese geishas, but I was sure it wasn't all as bad. Chandler had his reason for presenting the picture as he did. It seems when he entered the Sofuku he was instructed to leave his shoes on a rack in the foyer, however, finding the rack full, he put his shoes outside the door. When he was leaving, his shoes were gone. Someone had stolen his fine black dress shoes, his pride and joy. He did the only thing he could do, and that was take someone else's shoes. He ended up with a badly worn pair of boondockers, the only shoes that fit, and from that day forth he cursed the Sofuku Geisha House.

Everything Chandler had to say about the place was right, but I found it quite amusing. It was totally un-Chinese. Chinese restaurants and tea shops are loud and noisy; this place was quiet and subdued. Even the music, harps of some kind played by two musicians hidden in a corner, was so soft you wondered if it was real. True, it was very uncomfortable sitting on the floor, but the geishas did everything possible to make us as comfortable as possible with a ready supply of pillows and cushions. There was something bewitching about their manner, their delicate smiles and their painted lips. Their lips seemed to tell a story, and you felt you wanted to gently press your lips to theirs, maybe to see if they would respond. They were more like caricatures in pictures than real people, maybe more doll-like than human. For sure, they were not like Chinese taxi dancers. I immediately tried to wipe away the image I had of them, naked and dead in the caves on Okinawa. No, these women were lovely. How could Chandler be so wrong, but then I didn't lose my shoes. He was right, geishas do put food in your month, but they do it with sweet care and grace.

On our way to the Sofuku Geisha House I made no pretenses to Lt. McCaffery—I wasn't about to call him Scotty—that I liked the Japanese. The Marines taught me to hate them. Now as we were dining, and I appeared to enjoy my sukiyaki, he asked, "Why don't you like the Japanese?"

"The Japs!" I blurted out, disregarding all protocol. "Hell, what do you expect?" I suddenly felt I was being cornered and didn't like it. I wished I hadn't come. When we first stepped into the restaurant I felt I was betraying the Marine Corps by my being there, dining with the enemy, but for the sake of respect I kept putting my feelings aside. But now I felt that this officer who I hardly knew, and who had not fought in the war, was leading me into some kind of trap.

"Maybe you can tell me your experiences," Lt. McCaffery said. Now what was he up to? Was I about to be lectured that the war is over—so let's forget? I found it hard to trust him so instead of talking I kept silent. He began talking about Shinto, the national religion of Japan, and he explained how Emperor Meiji issued an Imperial edict in 1882 to soldiers and sailors that became holy writ and the basis for meditation for the armed forces. The lieutenant was a true Jap lover.

I didn't want to hear any more. Emperor Meiji and an Imperial edict, it was all hogwash, and had Lt. McCaffery been on Okinawa with the 29th he would not be talking this way. I was glad when the evening was over and I didn't have to listen to him anymore. I didn't think I would ever see Lt. McCaffery again, and if I did, I would avoid him. Less than a month later I was seeking him out. Could he possibly have the answers to the questions that troubled many of us?

We were taught to hate the Japanese. We were like those watch dogs they train to attack their victims, to tear at them viciously, not to stop until they kill their opponents or until they are pulled away. Now something very strange was happening. The Marines who were guards on the LSTs that carried the first Japanese repatriates back to Japan returned to Tsingtao with reports about how devastated the country was, and those who had been to Tokyo talked about how the city had been laid flat. The next group returned from Japan, only a few weeks later, with a different report. They had noticed progress. The rubble was being swept away and new buildings were appearing. After six months the Marines had completely different tales to tell. They were beginning to like Japan and the Japanese. Some Marines even praised them, and were prepared to defend their feelings with their fists. I didn't have to go to Japan to see for myself that something was wrong. It started when I decided to take a couple of the guys on my own to the Sofuku.

When I came from the restaurant that night after being with Lt. McCaffery, the guys wanted to hear all about it. I told them that I thought the lieutenant was full of crap, and a Jap lover, but as for the Sofuku Geisha House, that was something else. It wasn't an officers' hangout as everyone thought, and it was well worth visiting to see how the Japanese entertained customers. Chandler didn't agree but Terry and Hecklinger wanted to give the place a try, and I said I would take them. We agreed to go the following Friday night.

I should have known something was wrong when our rickshaw boys stopped a block before the restaurant and insisted we get out. Still not sure, I led the way up the street, and then hesitated. The street in front of the Sofuku was crowded with Chinese mulling about. They appeared to be waiting for something to happen, or for someone to appear. It wasn't this way when I went there with Lt. McCaffery. This was different. There were no women in the crowd, only men. I was about to ask two Chinese who stood nearby what was going on, when a hush rose from the crowd and all heads turned toward the Sofuku. We too looked in that direction. Coming down the three steps that led to the street was a Japanese officer. He was the one the mob was waiting for.

He had no bars on his shoulders, no insignias, and no marks to show that he was an officer, but you knew instantly that he was. You could see where the insignias and rank had been removed from his uniform. His jacket was high-neck with a cloth belt. He wore breeches and high leather boots. He was uncovered, that is, he wasn't wearing a hat. He hesitated, looking out over the mob, and then boldly walked down the steps to the street. The Chinese nearest him fell back.

He walked only a dozen yards when the Chinese began to close around him, first from the rear, and then in front. He stopped, and in a loud commanding voice he shouted for them to step back and clear the way. He spoke in proper Mandarin Chinese and at once you knew he was no newcomer to China. You knew immediately he had been around Chinese for a long time. The mob fell back, bumping into one another, scrambling to get out of the way of one another. After a short distance they stopped. The officer began to walk ahead again. No one moved. I was sure the man would walk away without further interruption, but then I saw the Chinese in the back ranks picking up stones. It was not over.

From over the heads of the mob, a single stone flew through the air and struck the ground a dozen yards in front of the officer. It was a signal, the needed encouragement for the mob to close in again. The officer stopped short, and shouted again to the crowd, and for the second time they fell back, but not as far this time. I thought he would begin walking again, but he only stood there, waiting. He seemed to know. Now a rain of stones came flying from every direction, striking the ground in front of him like hail. Then one of the more daring men in the mob, a man far in the rear, threw a stone, and it struck the officer on the side of the head. He stood firm. Blood trickled down his forehead. It was the impetus the mob needed. The stones that rained down now were direct. They struck the officer from head to foot. Still he did not move, nor did he cower or plead for mercy. He just stood there, defiantly, bleeding profusely from the head. His jacket turned crimson red. The first thing to give way were his knees; his legs became rubber and began to falter. He collapsed in one heap, like a wet cloth, and now the mob descended upon him in mass, throwing stones, shouting jubilantly, kicking furiously at the inert body on the ground.

Their deed done, the mob turned to us. "Come on you bastards," Terry shouted. "Who's gonna throw the first rock?" We quickly realized they were looking at us for praise, not in anger. They were proud, but they were also disappointed. We didn't join in their fun.

I had no plan to see Lt. McCaffery again, but after the incident at Sofuku Geisha House I went to see him. I was looking for an answer but I didn't even know the question. All I knew was that he was sympathetic with the Japanese and maybe he could explain, but his response was nothing that I expected. He only confused the matter more. "You hold the

Japanese in contempt for their atrocities, and rightfully so," he said, "but let me tell you another story. On August 19, 1945, four days after the Japanese surrendered, a civilian group of Chinese managed to capture 26 Japanese soldiers and executed them near the town of Hankow in northeast China. Four of them were beheaded, four were tied to posts and shot through the back of the head, another four had their arms and legs broken and then crudely amputated, four more were found minus hands and feet and had their genitals stuffed into their mouths. The remaining ten had their eyes gouged out and then they were bayoneted to death. In this act of reprisal, the past methods of killing by the 'Sons of Heaven' had been copied to the letter."

I was sorry that I had gone to see him. What good did his college education and all his books do him when he couldn't give me an answer.

There was no rest for us in the MP Battalion and I had little time to visit with Little Lew or look up Roger. I had been back more than a week and I had neglected visiting my old teacher Mrs. Djung. I was looking forward to meeting with her and her daughters, and maybe even Dr. Fenn. Mrs. Djung would be proud of my Chinese. Secretly I was hoping to get transferred to another outfit but for the time being there was no chance of that. A considerable number of dependents had been permitted to come out from the States in keeping with a new postwar policy of reuniting service families wherever possible. Duty at Tsingtao had become much like that at any overseas station, but dependents also meant more troubles for the Provost Marshall. Clashes came between officers' wives and enlisted men's wives. Kids also spelled trouble. Marines had not seen white women, except for nurses, in months, even years, and suddenly frustrated wives and teenage girls with agendas were fluttering around the bases and on the streets of Tsingtao. Some women were certain to cause destruction. Buxom Bonnie, a navy Chief's daughter was one. She was sexy and knew it, and wanted everyone else to know it too. Bringing her to Tsingtao was a mistake. She should have attended high school dances back home rather than tempt combat-hardened Marines to engage with her in sack time. She was successful, and that's where the problem began. But like the stories you hear back home, about the girl who screws the whole football team, Bonnie was taking on the whole Baker Company. Her father the chief was a drunken sod and his wife was no better. She was always causing a stir in the NCO Club. Instead of the Chief accepting conditions as they were, he was putting blame on the Marines, those "lecherous bastards."

Tsingtao was like Stateside duty but with one critical difference. The fighting between the Nationalists and communists grew steadily more violent and bitter and the possibility of Marine involvement was always present.

There was no question about it, Marines in the north were assuming more and more responsibility for guarding rail lines and all rail bridges between Tangku and Chinwangtao. Extensive security commitments were made on the 7th Marines. IIIAC recognized the need for additional troops and they would be sent in from the States. The Marines were plagued by incidents involving blown tracks, train derailments, and ambushes. While the casualties were not great, these China dangers were particularly distasteful because the war was supposed to be over, and any casualty list in the eyes of Americans back home did not look good. Nevertheless, China duty had much of that same appeal as it did in the prewar Marine Corps. And in Tsingtao it was much different than in the north. Tsingtao was considered an R&R Center. It did have some fine beaches and good recreational areas in its favor. Indeed, China duty was good duty in our eyes, and we felt we were in the best city in China.

Most of the time Tsingtao was peaceful, until the Seventh Fleet sailed into port. When the British Navy arrived at the same time, there was always hell to pay. There was an arrogant first sergeant with the British Royal Marines whom we all detested, He never failed to give us a hard time. He was filled with self-inflated egotism and somehow he always managed to get the upper hand over us China Marines. "Not this time," Terry said. He outlined his plan. It was outrageous, but only if it would work.

Chapter 14

DELAYED ACTION

MP duty in Tsingtao was tough. It wasn't the long hours that was so bad, it was when we had to turn in our buddies who were breaking the rules, when we had to put them under arrest. Many of the old establishments had been put out-of-bounds and this made it tough on the old hands. Some places were home to them. Even married Marines used to go to Ping-Pong Willies to sit and drink tea with the girls. They didn't indulge and often they gave money to the girls out of sympathy. Nevertheless, we had to patrol these places and those Marines and sailors we found in them we had to arrest. It wasn't always fair, like putting the bathhouses out-of-bounds. The guys really enjoyed a hot bath and a rubdown but the Provost Marshall put bathhouse off limits. The Provost said it was due to leprosy. But that was hard to believe. Lepers didn't go into a bathhouse for recreation.

In time I got to know every bar and dancehall, every cabaret, every joint and every bordello in Tsingtao. I dreaded when the Seventh Fleet sailed into port. If the British Navy arrived at the same time, pandemonium was certain.

When fights in bars and dancehalls broke out, we accepted it. We knew by the time we arrived, the places would be squared away, and all we would find would be Marines and sailors with black eyes and missing teeth, sitting quietly at their tables. With the bordellos it was much more difficult. The larger, better known ones, had four floors built around courtyards. It never failed, when we walked into a courtyard, there would usually be a couple of Marines and sailors who were scrambling to make their escape. The Chinese had clever ways of assisting them. They blocked the passageways so that we couldn't get through. Masses of people, women, kids, old men, all would appear on the stairways; pushcarts and bicycles suddenly jammed the doorways; and more often than not, mamasans decided to empty their chamber pots into the courtyards just as we were arriving. I don't know how many times we got doused until we learned how to take cover, while the "good guys" made their escape.

Sometimes these guys didn't quite make it and we caught them with their skivvies down. This was the case with a tall slender master sergeant from Texas. One night he stopped by Ping-Pong Willies to get some poontang, to sample the wares, so to speak. He didn't give much thought that Ping-Pong Willies at the time was out-of-bounds. We knew someone was upstairs, but this was one of the rare instances when the Chinese couldn't block our passage in time. We were in a dilemma. We really didn't want to arrest him. The sergeant knew if caught, he would probably lose his stripes, but after a few drinks, and the strong urge for a woman, he decided to gamble and chance it. After making his selection, he entered a room on the third deck. Stripping for action, leaving only his field scarf (necktie) on, he began to enjoy himself. Suddenly, the mamasan burst into the room screaming, "MPs, MPs."

The sergeant didn't want to get busted so he opened the window, climbed out and hung on to the windowsill by his fingertips while we searched the room. We knew he was there, for his clothes were on the chair, so we just took our time. The poor sergeant. It was winter and in North China winters there are very cold, and there he was, hanging buck-ass naked from a window ledge in a whorehouse in Tsingtao. After a few more minutes we gathered up his clothes and left. We figured the sergeant must have sobered up by the time we cleared out, but none of us could imagine what he would do without his clothing.

The only article of clothing he had was his field scarf which he hadn't bothered to remove at the start of the evening. Spying a filthy blanket in one corner of the room, he wrapped it around his body, and caught a rickshaw back to the Marine compound. Arriving at the back gate and bumming a quarter from the sentry, he paid his rickshaw boy and sneaked into the barracks. The next day we gave him back his clothes. We also saved him his stripes.

Walking through the black streets of Tsingtao at night was eerie, and yet we had to make checks on the out-of-bounds dives. We weren't welcomed, naturally, but we did get to know the keepers. Sitting at the tables in these places were an odd mixture of humanity. Derelicts and war profiteers from the world over. Dope peddlers and smugglers. Black marketers. Russians, Frenchmen, Germans, Arabs, occasionally renegade Americans who challenged us to check their passports. Here you could buy anything you wanted, or sell anything you had to sell. We stumbled into one bar, by accident, and found it was holding an auction, much like cattle auctions you see in western cattle towns in America. The auctioneer was standing on a three-legged stool, and in one hand he had a fist full of US dollars that he waved above his head. He was Chinese, with a little round skullcap on the back of his head and a long robe that extended down to his cotton shoes. He had a couple of hairs growing out of a mole on his chin. He was shouting in Chinese and taking bids. However, he wasn't selling cattle. He was selling young girls. He had half a dozen girls on display. They were young maidens, maybe twelve, no more than fourteen, and I gathered they had just been brought in from the country. The auctioneer made them stand on the bar, and then prodded them to parade up and down the counter. Brothel keepers and mamasans were bidding for them. Three white men, unshaven and scruffy, who were quite drunk, were hollering and hooting to the annoyance of everyone there, but they couldn't have cared less what others thought of them. One of the men, who spoke with a Dutch accent and wanted to get attention, went up to the bar and insisted a young girl pull up her long *cheongsan* so that, as he put it, he could check out the merchandise. The girl refused so he jumped up on the counter and forcefully pulled down her *cheongsan*. The crowd broke into laughter, for in her very innocence, the girl made a fool out of the white man. Beneath her cheongsam she wore long breeches that reached down to her knees. In a fit of rage, the man yanked down her breeches, exposing her naked body. She began sobbing, and now instead of giving her sympathy, the crowd roared with laughter. This was really hilarious, a sideshow they didn't expect. But the show wasn't over. Another white man sitting with his cronies at a table in the back of the bar shouted to the auctioneer.

"I give twenty dollah short time," he called. His accent was German. He was a huge man, with jowls that hung down over his frayed shirt collar. When he spoke he coughed. A Chinese man next to the auctioneer translated the message. Pleased, the auctioneer acknowledged the bid.

"Twenty dollars," he said in Chinese.

The Dutchman standing on the counter with the half naked girl wasn't happy. He wasn't about to surrender the girl for twenty dollars, even if it was only for half an hour in a room upstairs. Without hesitation he yelled for all to hear, "Thirty dollah."

"Fifty," shouted the German without hesitation.

I stood with the other MPs at the entrance to the rear of the bar. The place turned into frenzy. Even those who had been sitting drinking and showed no interest in the auctioning now suddenly perked up. Everyone left their tables and pushed closer to the auctioneer. He was pleased, and like a referee at a world-boxing match, he waved his hands above his head in anticipation of who would be the victor. The room grew silent and all eyes centered on the Dutchman standing on the counter.

He liked the attention he was finally getting. He reach out, grabbed the girl by her naked buttocks, and gleefully shouted "One hundred dollah!"

All heads now turned to the German. It was obvious he wasn't pleased with the Dutchman's outrageous bid. All during the bidding he had remained seated at his table, but now he got up and stood on a chair. He began coughing. His whole body shook like a bowl of Jell-O. "You, you—" he began, coughing and wiping his face with a towel he wore as a scarf around his neck—"you are a fool! A fool! Take her, and may she give you the bloody pox."

A cheer rose from everyone in the room, and while they watched, the Dutchman jumped down from the counter, reached into his pocket and withdrew a hundred-dollar bill. He handed it to the auctioneer, and then reaching up he grabbed the girl, pulled her down over this shoulder, and with her bare bottom still exposed, he marched with her up the stairs to the rooms above.

My impulse was to tear into everyone in the bar with my billy club swinging, but the sergeant in charge pulled me back. "There's nothing you can do," he said. "Nobody is breaking the law."

Breaking the law! What idle words. Whose law? I guess this spectacle was no different than the public executions they had in Tsingtao. If you were looking for something to amuse yourself, and it was Saturday afternoon, you could go to the central prison, and there in the courtyard you could watch public executions as they lobbed off the heads of the accused. No one was breaking the law there either.

We could deal with these shady characters, for in the end we knew they would come running to us for help. But what we couldn't deal with were the British Royal Marines. They bred Royal Marines in England for their toughness. You knew if you picked a fight with a British Marine it was to the end. There was no giving up. One British Marine, a Sergeant Major, had a reputation that defied all others. He was a legend in his time, and feared by everyone. He was tough, and he always wore his blue uniform with all the medals and stripes and hashmarks covering his sleeves from shoulder to cuff. He didn't smoke cigars; he chewed them. He could out drink any man, and out fight them if they were fool enough to try. It wasn't just hearsay, not just scuttlebutt; he proved himself many times.

The sergeant was a heated topic of discussion back at the barracks. Long after the British Navy pulled out, the sergeant was all we talked about. He was an arrogant sot if there ever was one, and there didn't seem to be any way of defeating him. I guess we wouldn't have minded so much, but every chance he had he put down the US Marine Corps. "You are all a bunch of pussies," he said the last time he was in port. "Bloody hell, I must say you yanks go a bit bonkers over dentistry and shampoo rather than good whiskey and a good fight."

We agreed, the next time the British Navy came to town we wouldn't put up with him. Terry had a plan. It was a wild idea but we all agreed. A month passed and finally the British navy steamed back to port. We went to the EM Club and sure enough there was the British Royal Marine Sergeant Major with a couple of his hooligan mates. We put Terry's plan into action.

We marched up to his table and asked if we could buy them all drinks. "Bloody 'ell," he shouted, "you 'aven't got 'er knickers down so I guess you cum to the right place. Let's see the color ah your money."

"You ain't gonna drink wid these bloody yank blokes, er you?" his sidekick corporal demanded to know. He was just as arrogant as the sergeant was.

"Shut your bloody gob, ye wee bastard," shouted the sergeant to the corporal, "before I smash me pint glass into your flamin' face." He then pushed the corporal away from the table. "I'll take this piss for beer you yanks peddle." We pulled up our chairs, Terry, Chandler, Hecklinger and me.

Sitting with the sergeant and his men was like sitting on a keg of dynamite; any spark would set it off. "We always wanted to get to know you," Terry said, "but we didn't know how you would react." He was lying through his teeth, and he had to kick me under the table to let me know he was in agony to say what he did.

For the first time the sergeant smiled. He had a heavy moustache that cascaded down over his upper lip, and when he smiled he revealed teeth crooked and bent and stained brown from years of smoking and neglect. When he swilled down a can of beer he didn't stop until the can was empty, and then he'd wipe the suds from his mouth on the sleeve of his dress blues. His breath stank of stale beer. It was disgusting sitting at the same table with him but we had already started the ball rolling. So far our plan seemed to be working.

"You bloody blokes ain't so bad after all," he mumbled and picked up another beer from the table. The beer was in cans but he called them pints. "Another pint in 'er eye, you bloody loafin' yank bastards."

He was unreal; he was a human sieve. As fast as he could pop open a can of beer with his church key he kept on a chain attached to his belt, he swilled them down. His mates couldn't keep up with him, try as they did, and one by one they deserted him until only the corporal was left. But even he, after a while, wouldn't be any trouble for us; he passed out in the head. We told the sarge he had left. "Wee bastard," he said.

It was near closing time, and somehow the sergeant still managed to hold on. He just wouldn't go down. Hecklinger came up with an idea, got up from the table and went to the bar. He came back with a fifth of White Horse Scotch. "Y'all never ask a barber if you need a haircut," he said, "so why y'all ask a sailor if he needs a drink."

"They're closing," Terry said, "let's drink outside."

"You sons ah bitches," the sergeant bellowed out. "At's want yar doin'." He turned up a beer can but it was empty. "

Yar gettin' me shit face, and at's da only way you can take me.
I can whip all yar asses."

"Hey, sarge, stay here if you wanna," Terry butted in. "We
can drink by ourselves." We got up to leave, with Hecklinger
waving the whiskey bottle much like a farmer throws corn
out to the chickens to draw them into the coop.

"Nar you don't," the sergeant said and staggered to his
feet. He stumbled and nearly fell down the steps while
following us out to the street where our rickshaw boys were
waiting. The boys smiled and Terry nodded. It was working.

"Here's to yah," Hecklinger said, and pulled the cork out
of the bottle with his teeth and then took a long swig. He held
the bottle up to the sergeant. "Careful," he said, "careful, this
ain't that watered down piss you've been drinking. I reckon
this is powerful stuff."

"Powerful shit, we were weaned on this stuff," the sergeant
replied and snatched the bottle away from Hecklinger. He put
it to his lips, threw his head back and didn't stop until the
bottle was half-empty. He stood straight and tall for a full
minute, and then his eyes rolled back. That was his end. He
would have fallen on his face had Hecklinger not caught him
and propped him up.

"When you're throwin' your weight around," Hecklinger
said, "be ready to have it thrown around by somebody else."
He then leaned the sergeant towards the rickshaw and let him
go. He fell into the seat with a thud. "Whow," Hecklinger
said, "he's got the breath that'd make a sow turn and run."

"So far so good," Chandler said with delight. "Now let's
get this over with." Five rickshaws, with the sergeant passed
out in one, bolted down the street to the waterfront. We didn't
have to tell the drivers where to go. They already knew.

The street was dark but there was a light coming from the
second story window where we stopped. We grabbed the
sergeant, one of us under each arm, and dragged him up a
flight of steps to the second deck. The door opened and a man
in a black greasy apron stood there. He pointed to a barber-

like chair and there we laid the sergeant down, face up. The man with the apron unbuttoned the sergeant's blue jacket and opened his shirt. Satisfied, he turned to us, and then picking up a piece of paper from a table, he held it up. "*Zeige*," he said in Chinese.

"*Zeige*, yes, that one," I replied, and the man took out his tools. He said he would need at least a half-hour, and we said not to hurry. We wanted a good job. After all, it wasn't every British Royal Marine who had an American flag tattooed on his chest.

We sent the Sergeant Major back to his ship in a rickshaw, wondering what he would think when he stood in front of the mirror the next morning to shave. We never did find out. The British Navy sailed two days later. There were some high ranking British officers poking around headquarters the next day, and they questioned Stevenson, but he said he knew nothing. We had to keep away from the EM Club until the British navy sailed away, and then we had a big blast.

I finally found the time to visit Mrs. Djung. I bought some of the goodies she liked from the PX, but when I arrived at her house, Bee Ling, the amah, opened the door partway and said the madam wasn't in. I asked when she would be back but I could not get a proper answer. I wanted to leave the things I bought for her but Bee Ling refused to accept them. What was going on here?

Next came the task of finding Roger. In spite of having been kept constantly busy since I arrived from Peking, I still had time to think about Ming-Lee. I missed her terribly. I saw her face before me at every turn. I didn't want to go to the Prime Club any more, so I had Stevenson and Chandler ask around about her when they went to the club, but the answers were always the same. No one knew where Ming-Lee was, except to say she was in Shanghai. Roger would know.

I located Roger's letter in my seabag, next to some hand-knitted doilies Mrs. Djung had given me for my mother. I never sent them. I had found some silver Chinese waterpipes

I was sure my mother would like more and sent those home instead. It was disappointing; my mother wrote back and said she would rather have had the doilies. I decided to save them and give them to her on my return home, whenever that would be. I was hoping she didn't throw out the waterpipes.

There was an address on the envelope but it was an old letter and I doubted that Roger lived there at the same place anymore, but I had to take the chance. I had no other lead. The address was that of a small hotel right in the center of town.

The hotel wasn't hard to find. It was a dreadful rundown place, the kind you only see in Chinatown, and after seeing it there was no wonder Roger never wanted me to meet him there. He was probably too embarrassed. I really didn't care. What were friends for if you had to worry where they lived?

There was no room number on the envelope but it didn't matter. When I showed the envelope to the desk clerk, he told me without hesitation Roger's room number—349 on the third floor. There was no lift. I walked up to the third floor, found room 349 and knocked. I can't remember when I had been so excited.

I could hear voices inside, and there followed a long moment of silence. Presently the door opened, just a crack, and I could see a woman's face peering out. That old renegade, I thought. He has a girl in his room. It was a moment of enlightenment. All the time I had known Roger, he had been a woman chaser but he never seemed to end up with one. There was always the question in the back of my mind, could he be gay? Some Marines thought that he was. They were wrong. He had a woman in his room. Hallelujah. She wasn't bad looking either, from what I could see of her. "You there, Roger," I called. "Is my friend Roger in there?"

The woman turned to talk to someone, and now being impatient and excited, I pushed the door partly open and yelled, "Hey, Roger, it's me! Your old buddy, remember?"

There was no immediate response, bur I could hear shuffling going on inside. I didn't give it much thought. They were probably tidying up the room. The door then opened and there stood Roger. I was prepared to throw my arms around him in a big hug, but he merely held out his hand for me to shake. "You are back in Tsingtao," he said, without his usual enthusiasm. This was not the same Roger I knew.

"You gonna ask me in?" I asked, not knowing what else to say.

"Yes, come in," he replied.

It was a small room, rather dimly lighted. There was a large unmade bed, and tables on both sides. The only other furniture was a clothes closet that occupied a large portion of the room. There was a long awkward moment of silence as we stood looking at one another; the woman stood behind Roger slightly to one side. She was painfully shy and obviously wondered who was this American in uniform. He saw me looking at her. "This is my wife, Li-Yuan," he said.

"Your wife," I said with excitement. "You got married."

"Actually, we've been married."

"Been married," I repeated.

I suddenly felt like a stranger. This wasn't the same fun-loving man I knew before. I was at a complete loss for words. I mumbled something. "I'm trying to find Ming-Lee," I said.

Roger was uncomfortable, and a bit edgy. Something was wrong and he kept moving back, bumping into Li-Yuan. He turned his head slightly, and then I saw it. In a pile on the floor was a uniform. It was still on a hanger and had fallen from the door where it obviously had been hanging. Roger saw me looking at it, and at first tried to kick it back out of sight, and then as though giving up a fight, he picked it up and held it there for me to see. It was a white navy uniform, a Chinese officer's uniform. I was not familiar with the epaulets, what rank it was, but I did know the red star. It was a Chinese Communist uniform. My heart sank.

"You, you're in the navy," I said. He nodded. "You're in the Red Navy." He didn't answer. He just nodded again. "What are you, a spy?"

"A spy! What do you mean?" he snapped.

"Just what I said, a spy!" I replied. "You've been spying on us. All this time you've been spying on us."

"Spying on you. You have to be kidding! What military secrets do you have? What do you know that we don't?" His tone of voice was completely different than what I knew. He was now speaking in a very proper English and not in slang. He continued, "I was interested in you Marines, yes, interested in you as Americans."

"Why didn't you say so?"

"What, and then what would you have done? Me, an officer. I could never have gotten to know you men."

"You are a traitor," I said. "You are an enemy."

"A traitor, an enemy? You can't be serious, or else you're very naive. Your country didn't even know which side it wanted to support. Think about it. The Balu were your friends just as much as the Kuomintang was. Communists risked their lives time and again to rescue American flyers from the Japanese; crews of B-29's bailing out on their return from bombing Japan had been smuggled to safety by villagers who are now held to be enemies."

"But that's different now."

"Different, what makes it so different? You Americans couldn't make up your minds who you would support. Even your ambassador, Mr. Hurey, he resigned his post after issuing a statement to the President and the Department of State that America was no longer the judge in the dispute; we are in a civil war. You are Marines supporting Chiang K'ai-shek, at a great price."

My head was spinning. Maybe he was right, but I was wrong listening to him. I walked out of classrooms at the university when there was talk like this. I started to leave but Roger pointed to the edge of the bed and asked me to sit and stay awhile.

"I came here to ask about Ming-Lee," I said and sat down. "I didn't come prying in your business."

"I know you're not. But don't think I am not in hell. I am thinking not of myself but of China. We have suffered. We have suffered from the opium wars when European powers stuffed opium down our throats and took over and divided China into their own spheres of influence. We suffered from the Japanese. The soldiers of Nippon during their occupation of Manchuria inflicted every criminal act known to man on Chinese civilians. Indiscriminate killings, beheadings, bayoneting of live victims and the vicious raping of tens of thousands of women and young girls, were the order of the day. Living with this constant terror and barbarity the civilian population could offer but little opposition. We are in a civil war and again we fear, we fear China will be split. Nothing can be worse, to split a country. It's best to have total victory of the Kuomintang with Chiang K'ai-shek as supreme master, even with American surplus war equipment and aid."

"But you are against the Kuomintang or you won't have that uniform in your closet."

"There are many such uniforms in closets in Tsingtao. No, my friend, this is not what China wants but what your army generals would want. You see all around you China as it is today—people, old people, kids, freezing to death in the streets, armies bought by foreign aid, young girls sold into sex slavery, justice where a man's hands are cut off for stealing rice, or his head cut off because he preaches against the system. Unless there is change, these evils will not only continue but will grow worse. The cleansing of China must be complete; we must get right down to the roots."

Every last Marine in Tsingtao agreed to this, that something had to be done, but not one of us had a solution. It's so easy to criticize. "And what do you offer?" I asked.

"It's not what I offer. Your country preaches democracy as the solution, but your western form of democracy in Asia cannot work. Warlords rule China. What do you think Chiang K'ai-shek is? He's a warlord masquerading as a leader of democracy. But believe me, the beliefs and hopes of all Asians

253

are changing. New ideas are creeping into the peasant's village, and there are those who are telling him there is another system, a system by which not only the white masters but all the masters will be wiped out and the land will be divided, a system in which village elders no longer rule, of which their religion is no longer valid, but they are told the peasants can decide their own fate. They will tell them their religion is wrong and they no longer have to support archaic monastic systems. The peasant will believe that this new system is best and offers the most liberty which gives him the quickest solution to the troubles of his daily life. He will vote for it, and he will be willing to fight for it, and to die for it. This is what you are up against. Nothing can turn the tide."

"I have to go," I said and stood up.

"Please, be my friend," Roger said. I started for the door without giving him an answer. He put a hand on my shoulder. "I will tell Ming-Lee you asked about her."

I wheeled around to face him. "You know where she is then?" I exclaimed.

"Yes, I know," he replied. "I have friends in Shanghai and they know where she is staying." He could see the expression on my face change. "No, she is not involved in this struggle. She is there because Tsingtao has too many bad memories for her. She feels she was deceived by you."

"No, no, you don't understand either," I said and sat down again on the bed. I explained to Roger exactly what had transpired in Peking. I asked that he understand and I confessed to him that I was in love with Ming-Lee and would do everything to get her back.

"Call me in a couple days," he said. "I will have some word from Shanghai." I promised that I would call.

Roger's message kept pounding through my head on my way back to my quarters. My rickshaw driver was waiting but I dismissed him and walked. It was a long distance but it gave me time to think. Was I dealing with a force that was beyond my comprehension, a force beyond my grasp? There was this business about Chiang K'ai-shek being a warlord, and all the West being deceived by him. No one liked to think of him as a warlord. Warlord was a dirty name; the warlord era began after the Revolution of 1912 when China was up for grabs.

Warlords maintained they must unify the country, and each one uttered he was the one to do it. I remember Su Fung and Mae Chu at the university saying that with the rise of warlords no longer did common people feel that men of humble origin and little education could not rise on the basis of daring, ability and force of personality. "Military rank depended on the successful raising, training and leading of troops, rather than on high birth or classical education," they said. The business of warlords was our constant subject of discussion at the university. The prototype of the "bad" warlord, they insisted, was General Chang Tsung-ch'ang, military governor of Shantung from 1925 to 1928. Chang's father was a barber, his mother an exorcist. He was said to have "the physique of an elephant, the brain of a pig, and the temperament of a tiger." He may have been a villain but I did have an admiration for him. He was known as the "dog-meat general" because of his culinary preferences, and he was also famous for his "virtual zoological garden" of wives of all nationalities. My favorite writer Lin Yutang described him as a lover of women. He would see foreign consuls with a Russian girl sitting on his knee. If he held orgies, he didn't try to conceal them from his friends and foes. He was called a *san pu-chih* warlord, the "three don't knows." He didn't know how much money he had, how many troops he had, or how many women he had in his harem."

In contrast to Chang, there were warlords of polish and morality, and the students were certain to remind me about them. They told how General Yin Ch'ang-heng of Szechwan surprised the American ambassador in 1914 by his knowledge of the arts and the masters of the Renaissance. The warlord of Nanking, Li Shun, earned great prestige by his selfless labor as a mediator between rival Peking and Canton governments from 1917 to 1920.

Whether or not they were bad or good warlords, they were powerful enough in their own spheres to ignore social conventions and indulge personal whims. Chang Tsolin, the ruler of Manchuria, raised his fifth concubine to the status of first wife, and Chang K'ai-shek was not much different. He elevated his wife to such a lofty position that she was able to go to the American Congress and woo both houses to give more money to China, a China ruled by her husband's regime.

I thought about warlords, about Roger and his wife, and about all Chiang's problems. I thought about them all on my way back to the university, but most of all I thought about Ming-Lee. I really missed her. When would I ever see her again?

Chapter 15

THE EIGHTH ROUTE ARMY IS COMING

The Marines in Tsingtao hated to see the summer season come to an end. The beaches during these summer months were as crowded as Coney Island, and there was just not one beach to choose from but dozens. The waterfront began at the harbor downtown and continued for twenty miles or more up the coast to the north. The entire coastline was indented with neat little coves, and each cove had fine bathing beaches. The one nearest town was the restricted officers' beach, and one about seven or eight miles farther north was Long Beach. It was the biggest, and often referred to as "the enlisted men's beach." The beach was sealed off to the Chinese, but Marines could bring their dates there. Marine lifeguards patrolled the beach from atop tall stands set back from tide level; the Seabees had constructed Quonset huts to be used for storage. Staff Marine and Navy NCOs who were married and had dependents could use the officers' beach. Their dependents were instructed to stay away from Long Beach, but that was where all the excitement and most fun was.

At Long Beach over weekends and holidays, two Ducks were stationed and positioned next to the lifeguard stands. Various Marine and Navy outfits had beach parties on weekends, with barbecues and tubs filled with cold beer. Aside from swimming, the guys played badminton and volleyball, and when they consumed enough beer, they usually turned to gridiron football, without the padding. The games could get pretty rough. They played wild and furiously while their Chinese dates looked on. Chinese girls seldom went into the water, unless the men dragged them down to the water and threw them into the surf. Then, there would follow a lot of shouting and cursing, and threats by the women that they were going home. Some of the taxi dancers and bar girls could curse like a Marine, and this was one reason dependents were advised to stay away. If a Marine did have a Chinese girl who liked to swim, then, he had a sweetheart. Sometimes White Russian women came to the beach, and they would not go into the water. They were mostly heavy set and bulky, and they looked more like Mae West than Lana Turner in their ill-fitting bathing suits. There were some very fine-looking Russian women, but these women you'd see at the officers' beach.

During the week when the beach was practically empty, Chinese fishermen worked the waters off shore. Their method of netting fish was as ancient as China itself and interesting to watch. On one of those lazy afternoons when I didn't have the duty, I checked out a Jeep from Motor Pool and took Stevenson and Little Lew out to Long Beach to watch the fishermen at their trade. We arrived just in time to catch the fishermen as they began laying out the net, but what we didn't expect was to find a party of sailors from one of the US ships in port, whooping it up down the beach. They came in three Jeeps, about a dozen enlisted men and one chief, and had cases of beer stacked up about a yard high. They seemed to be more interested in their own activities and took little notice of the fishermen, which was well and good. Chinese fishermen didn't like it when drunken Marines and sailors attempted to help them pull in their nets.

I parked on high ground and the three of us went down to watch the fishermen. The net they used was hundreds of yards long, and no more than six feet high. On the topside of the net were floats to keep the top at water level, and along the bottom were weights to hold the bottom down. The sampan set out from the beach with the net neatly stowed aboard, and with one end of the net attached to a line held by half a dozen fishermen standing on the shore. We watched as one man sculled the sampan and two others laid out the net over the side. They made a large semicircle and came ashore about a few hundred yards down the beach, with another line attached to the net on that end. At a signal, two lines of fishermen began pulling in the net, while the younger boys coiled the line as it came in. Tending the lines, with slings over their shoulders, was backbreaking labor. The line was as thick as a man wrist.

It would take the fishermen hours to pull in the net, and wanting to see their catch, we decided to stroll down the beach to some high rocks on the far end and return in about an hour or so. We had no idea when we were climbing among the rocks that a crisis had arisen with the fishermen and the sailors. It wasn't until we were returning, walking partly in the water, letting the incoming tide lap at our feet, when we became aware of a commotion ahead. I couldn't believe it, but one of the Navy Jeeps was in the sea, almost completely submerged. Sailors were running up and down the beach while the fishermen were having their own problem. It appeared that one of the lines had broken, and the fishermen were struggling to pull the two ends ashore. The net was in a tangled mess.

The fishermen were too busy to explain what had happened. I went up to the Navy chief who was standing in the surf with water up to his knees, shouting orders that no one was listening to. The sailors were in a frenzy, screaming and cursing the Chinese, apparently for not giving them a helping hand. I finally got the chief to explain what had happened.

It seems one of the sailors became curious and went down to the seaside to see what the fishermen were doing. After seeing them laboring at pulling in the net, he ran back to his mates with an idea. Why not help the fishermen pull in the net? "With none of this backbreaking crap," he said. No, they would pull in the net with one of the Jeeps.

The sailor jumped behind the driver's wheel and three or four others piled into the back seat and off they went to help the fishermen. The driver turned the Jeep around and backed up to the line of fishermen pulling in the net. The Chinese were at first too bewildered to know what the sailors intended to do, but when they saw them making fast a cable to the fishing net line, they began protesting. But the sailors wouldn't listen to them. If I am correct, it even got a bit violent with some shoving and pushing. But the US Navy out-muscled the Chinese, finished attaching their cable, threw the Jeep into four-wheel low gear and began to pull. What they didn't realize was that, when fishermen pull in on the lines, they can feel the rhythm of the sea, when it's time to apply effort and when it's time to slack off. Before the Jeep could move five feet, the net snapped in two, about a hundred yards from shore. As the chief was relating the story, he chuckled from time to time. "It was the funniest thing you ever saw," he said. "The chinks did everything but cry."

The sailors returned to drinking their beer while the Chinese labored to salvage their net. But what the sailors forgot was that the tide was coming in. They had left the Jeep where it was, down by the water, and when they did take notice of it, the tide was almost up to the wheel. The driver, loosing no time, ran down to the Jeep, jumped in behind the wheel, started the engine and slowly began to pull away. He didn't get far. The rear wheels sank into the sand. The sand was rapidly becoming water logged. He revved up the engine and let out the clutch, and the wheels only sank deeper and deeper.

Panicked now, he called his mates, and half a dozen Swabbies came running, stumbling and falling in their half-drunken stupor. They began pushing the Jeep while the driver spun the wheels, but the vehicle only sank deeper into the sand. The water was now up to the axle. "It was too late to get the other Jeeps to pull it out," the chief said, "but then we didn't have any rope anyway." After that, he threw up his hands in disgust. "Those bloody chink bastards could have helped us. There were enough of them. But they just stood there with stupid looks on their friggin' faces." He went on to tell that a couple of sailors grabbed a few Chinese and began punching them, but still they wouldn't help. In the end they sat on the beach and watched as the sea swallowed up the Navy Jeep.

As Stevenson, Little Lew and I drove back to the university, we wondered what the Navy men would put into their report. "Jeep lost at sea," Little Lew said and we all laughed.

Being attached to the MPs, I could check out a Jeep from Motor Pool and drive around town at my own leisure. Sometimes, I went a step further and would drive out into the countryside. Little Lew didn't like these long drives but if Stevenson could get away, he'd go with me. Most often I'd go alone. Out in the country it was fun to put the vehicle into four-wheel drive and cruise along the watersheds of farmers' fields. After a few trips into the same areas I came to know some of the farmers, and I would park and talk to them. Often they invited me to sit and have tea with them in front of their mud houses and I would break open a pack of Chesterfields or Lucky Strikes and lay out the cigarettes. This was a real treat. The tea, served in bowls, wasn't very good, but I enjoyed their company. I listened to the tales they had to tell, and they would ask me questions I could not answer. They wanted to know about the communists, but they didn't call them communists. They called them *balu*, Chinese for "the Eighth Road." The new army was coming via the Eighth Road. Soon all you ever heard talked about was the *balu*. The *balu* are coming! I picked up a little about the country's politics while I was at the University of Peking, but it didn't take a geo-politician to know there were great forces at play in China.

Winter came quickly that fall, like all winters in north China, without warning, and overnight we switched from khaki to greens. The smelly, round kerosene stoves came out from hiding and windowsills became our refrigerators. Terry brought cheer to the troops when he provided a ready supply of whiskey to everyone in his squad bay. Every time he returned from guard duty at the dock, he had two canteens filled with whiskey. He willingly shared his booty with the squad, but he would never tell how he got the whiskey, that is, until he had too much to drink one night, and the guys cajoled him into talking. In one warehouse guarded by the 22nd Marines, he claimed, there was whiskey for the officers' mess stacked in wooden crates half way up to the ceiling. Terry knew if he busted into a crate there would be an investigation, and the Marines guarding the warehouse would be put on report. But, he concluded, he didn't have to bust into a crate to get the booze out. At the maintenance shop in our compound, he rummaged around until he found just what he needed—a spike about six inches long. The next time he had guard duty at the docks, he sneaked from the warehouse he was guarding over to the one with the whiskey that the 22rd Marines were guarding. While the sentry did his rounds and walked around to the back of the building, Terry picked the lock and entered. He took one of the crates, tilted it to one side, and with a heavy blow from the butt of his M1 he drove the spike into the crate, breaking a bottle inside. The whiskey ran to one corner, and there Terry held his canteen cup, filling it up and pouring the contents into his two canteens. This went on for about two weeks, until the quartermaster came with trucks and transported the crates, some with broken bottles inside, to the storeroom at the officers' mess. Terry's heart broke when this happened, and so did the troops', but he knew not to attempt to break into the officers' mess. "That would be thievery," he said.

Months were flying by and still no word, not one single letter, came from Ming-Lee. I was contemplating trying to get TDY and go down to Shanghai to find her, until I went to see Roger one evening. "I told you," he said, "she's in school."

"Why can't she come to Tsingtao?" I demanded. "There are schools here."

"You have to understand that she doesn't want to go back to taxi dancing," Roger said. "She's been studying in Shanghai and she wants to continue. She has support from her friends."

Then he said something that made me shutter. "The civil war is going to come to an end, and the new government will bring about changes," he said. He didn't call Mao's army communists, nor did he call them *balu* as the people did; he called them "the new government." He continued: "One of the changes will be to close down all the brothels and dance halls. Prostitution will be outlawed. Service girls, prostitutes, taxi dancers, they will all be sent to camps, to be re-educated. You wouldn't want that to happen to Ming-lee would you?"

"Ming-Lee is not a prostitute," I protested.

"And who's going to believe that?"

"I don't care who believes it or who doesn't. I do and that's all that counts."

Li-Yian had gone to visit her mother. Roger suggested that we go to a teahouse where we could talk. "You will be leaving one day, and what about Ming -Lee?" he asked when the tea came.

"I'll be back," I replied.

"Perhaps, but not as a China Marine. You are the last of the China Marines. You will be no more than a memory in the minds of the Chinese people."

"So you are against Marines in China," I said.

"No, you are missing the point. It's not Marines," he replied, "it's all foreigners, all those who want to take over and dominate China."

As Roger sat there talking, I couldn't help wondering if he believed in what he was telling me, that he was an idealist? I knew his heart was with the Chinese people, but was this the Machiavellian case of the ends justifying the means?

"Tell me, you do believe you are our liberators," he began. "You believe you freed China of the imperialist Japanese, right?"

"Right," I replied, careful not to fall into a trap.

"For what purpose?" he asked

"To help the Chinese," I answered

"Do you remember me taking Ming-Lee to meet with you at Long Beach?"

"Yes, you were a great help, and I appreciate it. I couldn't have gone out with Ming-Lee without your help," I replied. No sooner had I said it, than I knew I had taken the bait. I had fallen into his trap.

"That's correct, but think of this," he said. "I'm Chinese, and this is my country. I take Ming-Lee, a Chinese woman, out to a beach in China, and there are US military guards there at the entrance, and a sign that reads No Unescorted Visitors Allowed. What it really means is—No Chinese Allowed. It's no different than a sign on the Bund in Shanghai that says—No Dog and Chinese Allowed."

"You sound like my professor in Peking," I said, hoping to change the subject and avoid an argument. "You talk just like him. What happened to that phony accent you had when we first met?"

"If I had talked like a professor, you Marines would have avoided me," he said. "But don't change the subject. It's not only Long Beach where you guys hang out, but most of the beaches are closed to Chinese. We Chinese can't go on our own beaches."

"We needed some privacy, that's all," I explained.

"Privacy, at what cost?" he fired back. "At the cost of the Chinese. You preach righteousness but you are no different than all the other imperial foreign powers that preyed on China.

"You come not to liberate but for your own interests. I hate to keep mentioning the Opium Wars, but think about them, think what the British did. What an easy way to conquer a country. Feed them drugs. No guns. No armies. No fighting. Only drugs, that's what happened, and then it was so simple. All the European powers march in and chop up China into what they call Treaty Ports. The British, the French, the Germans."

"Come on, Roger. That's history."

"In your mind it's only history. What would you think if

drugs were introduced into your country the same way? How simple it would be for a foreign power to conquer mighty America!"

"Let's be reasonable," I said.

"Okay, I'll be reasonable. You think it's nothing for the US to march into Tsingtao and commandeer every important building in town. You don't pitch tents or move into the warehouses on the docks. You take over every major building, places like the university. You throw out of the windows desks and lab equipment, and all the thousands of books written in Chinese because no one can read them. But worst of all, you throw out the students. You take away their place to study. You make their schools your quarters, not for a few months, but for years now."

"Roger, you speak with such know-it-all authority," I said, "well tell me, what if you are wrong?"

"Wrong about what?" he asked.

"Wrong about this new government you are talking about?" I asked.

"Maybe it won't be the best," he admitted, "but it will be better than what we have now."

After an hour or two with Roger I felt I had been run over by that two-ton Japanese tank Stevenson and I had found in the hills on Guam, and almost gotten blown up in. I went back to the quarters to talk to Stevenson but he was out with Judy. I wanted to talk to someone, and I then thought about Mrs. Djung. I hadn't seen her in a long time and I wanted to tell her I knew who Kierkegaard and Jean-Paul Sartre were now. I wanted her daughters to be there, and maybe Dr. Fenn too. I would tell them that I not only knew about Kierkegaard, but about Hegel and Kant as well. We could discus Descartes and his *cognito, ergo, sum* theory. We could talk about Chinese history, and I would ask them if they thought James Hilton got his theme for *Lost Horizon* from T'ao Yuan-ming's *Peach Blossom Spring*. "You know, I might go and look for Peach Blossom Spring," I would say. "It's possible that it does exist, you know. Professor Heng at the University of Peking thinks it does. We talked about it. You know him, don't you?" And then I would tell them about Dr. Franz Weidenreich and ask if they knew about his research on the Peking Man. I might even tell them I thought they were wrong about Lin Yutang. I read nearly everything he wrote, and I might even quote a passage of his from the *Wisdom of Laotse*. I was trying to recall the lines when I went to the office the next morning to get a pass to Sick Bay. But I did not go to the Sick Bay. Instead I had Sammy drive me out to Mrs. Djung's place. I could have driven myself but I thought it might be nice to talk to Sammy about all the pressing things on my mind, but it was a bad choice. He had met a bargirl from Ciro's and had fallen in love with her. Instead I had to hear all about her, and what a great girl she was.

I was shocked when I reached Mrs. Djung's house. The lovely garden that she had been so proud of, had gone to weed. The house and grounds that once looked so neat and trim had peeling paint and were unkept. No one had even bothered to sweep up the leaves. This was not at all like Mrs. Djung. I knocked on the door once, then twice, and must have waited a full five minutes before deciding to leave. I turned to go when the door partly opened. It was the amah Bee Ling. She said her madam was not at home and then pleaded that I leave. She did not explain.

I waited several days and decided I would try again to see Mrs. Djung. I was curious. Stevenson went with me this time. It took a lot of courage to walk up the steps to her house, not knowing what to expect, with each of us pushing the other ahead. When we did reach the top of the steps, we were too late, far too late. The doors and windows were boarded up. Mrs. Djung and her two daughters no longer lived at the grand house on Lai Yang Road.

Christmas was coming and everyone was looking forward to the holidays. I was hoping that Ming-Lee might come up from Shanghai but according to Roger there wasn't much of a chance. She was deeply involved in her studies.

We were lacking a Christmas tree, and the only place to find a proper tree was in the Low Shan Mountains to the north of the city. At better times we had made hikes into the mountains. There was still a Christian monastery for orphan kids further back in the hills, but since then the communists had taken over much of the territory. Nevertheless, we needed a tree. Terry took it upon himself to organize a party to find the biggest and best Christmas tree in north China. I don't know how he finagled it, but he did. I had the duty and couldn't join them, but he and the others set out early one freezing winter morning just as dawn was breaking over the city. Anyone seeing them might have thought they were going to war. They weren't taking any chances. Armed with M1s and carbines, they boarded two ten-wheelers and took with them for support a 75mm-pack howitzer and a couple of 50 cal. machine guns. They also had standing by, and on call, a Sherman tank. "In case the friggin' commies attack us," Terry said. For the sake of a Christmas tree, we could have started a major war with the communists and changed the course of history, but fortunately they didn't, as fate would have it. But they did come back with a grand Christmas tree. It made a splendid show in our compound at the Shantung University.

We had a new commanding officer fresh from Nav Pers at the Pentagon, and he decided, after seeing all the street urchins around town, that the Marines should have a Christmas party for the "lost children of Tsingtao." The old man had Motor Pool send out trucks on Christmas morning and round up all the kids they could find on the streets of Tsingtao. He called in the press and had news photographers on hand.

The kids would have a grand feast in the mess hall, everything that American kids got at Christmas—roasted turkey, chestnut stuffing, mashed potatoes, green peas, pumpkin pie and ice cream. He had presents flown out from the States. Jigsaw puzzles with beautiful paintings of mountains and lakes and farm yards with fat milk cows grazing. There were coloring books and crayons, pencil boxes with half a dozen pencils in each box and all kinds of weird looking paper hats, and whistles that when you blew them, long streamers of colored paper appeared. Since I spoke Chinese, I was called upon to act as master of ceremonies. Chinese children in better, more affluent families, do have a Santa Claus, of sorts, which they call *Lao Kungkung*. But I doubted that the kids that Motor Pool rounded up in the streets of Tsingtao ever had heard of *Lao Kungkung*. To complicate matters, the CO wanted me to give a little pep talk to the kids. "Tell them about Santa Claus," he said. "You know, that he rides on a sleigh in heaven, drawn by reindeers, and that he comes down through the chimney, and gives presents to all the good boys and girls. Ask them if they have been good little kids."

I needed Little Lew to help me, but as soon as he heard what we had planned, he hid out somewhere and we couldn't find him. I thought it was rather odd behavior. I imagined that he would have felt pretty proud about the party, a hero to all the kids, but he reacted very strangely when I first mentioned it to him. Like most kids his age, maybe he was getting a bit spoiled.

The chief cook was to be Santa Claus. He was a huge grumpy first sergeant who must have weighed 330 pounds. He had a permanent scowl on his face and they say he had never smiled a day, not even once, in his entire life. Even staff officers were afraid to cross him. And now the new CO told him he would make a good Santa Claus. Strangely enough, he accepted.

The mess hall was decorated with all kinds of Christmas cheer, even stuff left over from Halloween. Actually, anyone who didn't know Christmas and Halloween, might have found it a bit spooky, and that's exactly how the orphans felt when they arrived. Motor Pool had rounded up more than a hundred orphans, or what they thought to be orphans, cleaned them up the best they could in the parking lot, and marched them into the mess hall. They entered, to the loud cheer of "Merry Christmas" by a dozen Marines dressed like Santa's helpers They were terrified.

I don't know what went through their little heads. Maybe they thought they were going to be beaten, or sold, or that some other horrible nightmare would befall them. I tried to calm them down and give them my little speech, but I could see I would make it much worse to tell them about a bearded old man named Santa Claus. Besides there was too much chaos and pandemonium for anyone to do any talking. And the cook didn't help matters when he charged into the mess hall shouting, "Ho! Ho! Ho!" He would have frightened anyone. He wore his long-john underwear, which he had died red, and had on his feet a heavy, size fourteen, pair of Army boots that telephone repairmen use. For a beard, he had wrapped the kitchen mop around his face. The kids screamed with terror when they saw him, and knocked things off the tables as they scrambled to hide underneath. It took a great deal of cajoling and coaxing to get them to be seated again, but only after the mess sergeant got out of the mess hall. It was probably the happiest, and what he considered the most successful, day in all his life.

There were no chopsticks, and Chinese kids don't know how to use knives and forks. Then there was no rice. What is a meal in China without rice? As for the mashed potatoes, who could explain they were to be eaten, not to be thrown at the kid next to you. The hot cocoa was too hot and the ice cream too cold, so they mixed them together, and made a mess. They jumped when the kid next to them blew on a whistle and a piece of paper flew out at them. Jigsaw puzzles were a complete mystery. They had pencils, but no paper to write on, so they wrote on the tables and each other. When the meal was over and the presents opened, drivers from Motor Pool ushered them back outside into the cold and deposited them once again on the streets where they found them. The photographers got some very fine pictures that appeared in *Stars & Stripes*, photos showing happy kids with turkey and mashed potatoes.

There was a dance that night at the gym, and all the Marines took their dates. I went back to my room and read Toynbee's *Study of History,* but I didn't get much from my reading. I kept wondering what Ming-Lee was doing in Shanghai. I also wondered if Roger was right. Was the Eighth Route Army really coming?

Chapter 16

FULL CIRCLE

With each passing day, refuges by the thousands flooded into Tsingtao. They came by land, by rail and lorry truck; by sea, by junks, scow and coastal steamer. They came seeking security under the American flag, and they brought with them all the belongings that they could carry. Some even brought their furniture. They were the wealthy, the Chinese and the White Russians. The poor came in carts and riding bicycles, and some pushed wheelbarrows. And there were those who had nothing to ride or push. They walked with rags wrapped around their feet for shoes, carrying all they had left in the world on their backs.

The *balu* were not far behind them.

Marine headquarters felt we should make our presence known, and once again long hikes into the hills around Tsingtao were initiated, but now we would go armed and with full marching packs. "We are not to look for trouble," our CO said, "but to ward off trouble if it comes."

Sometimes we took along scouts to guide our patrols through unfamiliar terrain. They were Chinese ex-soldiers, hardened to warfare and who had spent years fighting the Japanese. They had horror stories to tell, and during our breaks I translated them. They told about the Japanese invasion, how the peasants had fled before the soldiers came with their guns and swords, slicing to pieces anyone who got in their way. The fleeing Chinese took with them everything from seed grain to furniture. They herded their pigs and cattle off into the hills, hid their clothes and valuables in the ground, and fled to the mountains, and when the Japanese came they entered a barren wasteland, and became even more enraged.

The Japanese, in turn, fled when the Marines came, but they left behind a blazed blackened earth and devastation that stretched across the countryside. We could still see burned villages that were simply huddles of ruins. In some places the roads were so torn that even walking was difficult. The land was bare, and not a tree or even a shrub stood. They had long been stripped away, the wood to be sold for firewood, and, as the guides said, the bark to be eaten.

Our eyes, however, were not on the ground where we walked, but to the hills that lie beyond. We could hear heavy gunfire and sometimes feel the very earth beneath our feet shake. The Nationalist Army was defending China from the advancing Red Army, but the soldiers we met along the road were not advancing. They were in retreat.

When the road was clear on a far ridge, we could see clouds of dust puffing into the air from the movement of troops. Then as the hours passed, we could see the troops, endless columns of haggard and wounded soldiers coming down the dusty road from out of the hills. There were convoys of military vehicles that rumbled along at reckless speeds. The vehicles were empty, with guards to keep soldiers from climbing aboard. They didn't even stop for the wounded. The guides explained it took more fuel for vehicles that were loaded. By the thousands the soldiers were giving up, abandoning vehicles wherever they stopped, throwing away their weapons, discarding their uniforms. Their will to continue was gone.

How strange it all was. With the sound of artillery echoing in the distant hills, life in the city continued on as always. The bars were open, taxi dancers waited for customers, restaurant owners stood in front of their establishments beckoning customers to come in, pimps on street corners offered their clean virgin sisters waiting at home, money changers had special last-chance deals, and everywhere there were crowds.

Many believed that the Marines would stay, and that certainly the all-powerful Nationalist Chinese Army would defend their city.

The burden to keep the city alive was placed on the Americans. Food, medical supplies, oil, and all necessities had to be imported by sea, and everything depended upon the US Navy to keep the sea-lanes open. For the Marine garrison, some 8,000 men now, morale began to wane. The problem was, the men of the old China hands were leaving. Stevenson cried in his beer the loudest. He really loved China. "Remember Mr. Wong?" he lamented. "I will always feel bad that we didn't help him." I remembered Mr. Wong. It would be hard to forget him. We ran into him in the street near the docks one afternoon. He introduced himself and said his wife was very ill. He had a little vial of penicillin he had bought on the black market. Penicillin was new then. We could see the vial had already been pierced with a hypodermic needle. He had tears in his eyes and pleaded when he asked if we could take it to a sick bay somewhere to find out if the penicillin was still okay. We told him there was nothing we could do to help. We left him crying on the sidewalk. The poor man was worried about his wife. "I often think of that," Stevenson continued. "There was a hospital ship nearby and it would have been so easy just to walk up the gangway to the quarterdeck and ask the OD if he could help us out. Maybe he would have turned us away, but it wouldn't have hurt to try."

Maybe our wounds were deeper than we realized. None of us were truly free from the war. We had our fears, some deeply submerged in our subconscious. These were dreadful scars to burden tortured minds of youths. They could erupt at any time. We could control such emotions, as long as we had "our buddies" with us. Maybe this is why we didn't want to go home; we would no longer have buddies to rely upon.

Back home, we had heard, there were many people—psychologists, sociologists and just plain mothers and wives—who were determined to believe we had a readjustment problem. They were all worried that they didn't know how they could solve it. Hell! We were condemned and labeled even before we got home. Articles ran in women's magazines with titles like "What You Can Do to Help the Returning Veteran" and "Will He Be Changed?" *Good Housekeeping* wrote: "After two or three weeks he should be finished with talking, with oppressive remembering. If he still goes over the same stories, reveals the same emotions, you had best consult a psychiatrist. This condition is neurotic." *House Beautiful* suggested that "Home must be the greatest rehabilitation center of them all." The magazine then showed photographs of a living room designed for a returning general or admiral. All we wanted was our same old room back.

On Okinawa and later in China we came to understand man's unbelievable inhumanity to fellow man. We survived the battle but we could not forget the Marines who had been mutilated hideously by the enemy. Who could forget the Marine who had been decapitated? When we found him, his head lay on his chest; his hands had been severed from his wrists and also lay on his chest. The Japanese had cut off another dead Marine's penis and stuffed it in his mouth.

Each Marine had his own fears he had to battle. Terry could not get over the terror of being under artillery or mortar fire. Hecklinger would wake up at night screaming. He was knocking out the gold teeth from a Japanese corpse when the man came alive. Chandler thought he had killed a Marine. It had its roots when our replacement draft landed on Okinawa and we were assigned to our outfits. We ended up in the machine gun platoon. Our first night we were bivouacked on a ridge and had to stand guard duty. Chandler was on watch when on the road below, he heard footsteps. He called out to give the password, something like "lucky legs," but the intruder did not respond. "Shoot, shoot," we all shouted to Chandler. Finally, pressured, he pulled the trigger on his M1. The shot rang out in the dark. He fired again, and again. A flare went up, and in the road below was a body. Someone thought it might be a Marine. Chandler was in hell all night long. He was sure he had killed a Marine. In the morning, with first light, we could all be seen peering over the edge of the cliff; the body was that of a Japanese soldier. When we scampered down the hill and investigated, we found that the soldier was about to pull the pin on a potato masher. It exploded in his hands before he could toss it up the hill at us. Had he succeeded, a half dozen Marines may have been killed. Still, Chandler was haunted by the thought that it could have been a Marine that he killed.

Smitty was obsessed with the smells. Everywhere on Okinawa was the putrid odor of rotting flesh. The island was all rock, and digging holes to bury the dead, or to dig saddle trenches, was near impossible. Dead rotting bodies and human excrement was everywhere. Blowflies had a field day and enjoyed the banquet that had been made for them. That horrid smell would be with Smitty wherever he went. "That stinks just like the time—" he would remind us when we were on liberty or on patrol with him.

"Shut up, Smitty," we'd say. He ruined many meals for us.

Stevenson had a problem of a different sort. He didn't think he could ever marry. He confided in me that afternoon after we had left Mrs. Djung's abandoned house. It was afternoon and we had stopped in Rusty's Russian Cafe for a couple of Tsingtao beers. "I'm afraid if I got married," he began, "and I had kids, and one was a girl, I'd see in her that little girl on Okinawa." He poured the last of the beer into our glasses and ordered two more Tsingtao. A Russian hostess, built like that two-ton Japanese tank we found on Guam, with died blond hair and black roots, came to sit with us. Stevenson barked at her to get lost. He had something to say and didn't want to be interrupted. He lit two Chesterfields, handed one to me, and he began telling about the little girl and the time he was on patrol on Okinawa during the mopping operation. "We were told there was activity in an abandoned village to the south of Naha," he said, "and we had to check it out. A couple of guys from Able Company had gotten there just before us, and we watched two Marines approach a young girl about four years old. All she had on was a straw G-string. She was the cutest thing you could imagine, but with a real look of fear in her eyes. One of the Marines, feeling pity for her, stooped down to pick her up, and just as he did, the kid pulled a sash cord and set off a charge. I swear at that moment she looked up at me standing there. It killed both of them." Stevenson thought for a while, until I touched a hand on his shoulder. Words were not necessary. He continued: "When I see my daughter, I will see that little girl. I will forever see that face."

We called it "shell-shocked," when a Marine suffered trauma from the fighting and killing. I always prided myself that I wasn't bothered with such memories. I was spared that fate and felt lucky about it, or so I thought. That changed for me one afternoon when I went to the head to shave and clean up for liberty. The guys were outside clamoring for me to hurry. I did the best I could. I lifted my shaving brush to my face, tilted back my head, and looked into the mirror. I froze, and immediately began to quiver. My hand shook so violently that I dropped the brush. I fell back in terror. I trembled so much I had to toss my razor aside. I could have cut my wrists wide open with the blade.

What I had seen in the mirror was not my own face but one of a dead man. I had seen it before. We were on patrol on Oruku Peninsula, skirting the hills searching for hidden caves. We climbed up one steep ravine by grabbing on to roots and tree stumps to pull ourselves up. I had reached the crest, and just as I pulled myself up, I came face to face with a Japanese head stuck on a spike. It was but inches from my face. I was so close, in fact, my eyes gave a distorted view and had to get back to see if what I was looking at was real. It was, indeed, real. The poor devil's mouth was open wide, his skin drawn tight around the lips. There were only holes in the sockets where eyes had once been. There were bits of whiskers on his chin; the hair on his head was matted and caked in dried blood.

A patrol had passed before us, maybe the day before, and a Marine had obviously cut off the Jap's head and stuck it on a spike and placed it is such a way that anyone coming up the ridge would come to it face to face. The skull had been separated from the torso to which it was attached and lay in a ravine near by.

It took my buddies an hour or more to calm me down, and a bottle or two of Hubba Hubba to make me forget altogether.

Whether it was the memories of Okinawa or the thought of getting involved in another war, we were becoming unnerved. We began drinking more, and if we weren't on guard duty or on patrol, we'd get drunk, almost every night. And we began fighting more. I even had a knockdown fight with Terry, or I mean he knocked me down. Terry and I had shipped out together from the States. I had gone through the entire Okinawa campaign with him and survived. We had spent days and nights in the same foxholes, and we held off banzai charges, and then one day in Tsingtao when I neglected to wait for him at liberty call, he caught up with me in town, and knocked out my front teeth in a brawl. He felt so badly about it, he bought a bottle of Hubba Hubba and we got drunk, and the next morning he never remembered a thing. "Hey, who hit you in the mouth?" he asked when he saw me. I was about to slug him but I thought it was best to wait until we were away from quarters, so as not to go on report, but I never got the chance. Terry's orders for his transfer back to the States came before he had another liberty.

Orders began arriving right and left for our transfers back to the States. You would imagine we would be anxious to leave, but for many it was not that way at all. "What am I gonna do back home?" Terry asked. "Pick up coal along the railroad tracks and sell it. Who has any use for a China Marine?"

Hecklinger didn't fancy going back to working in a funeral parlor in Oklahoma City. "You have to accept it," he said, "that sometimes you are the pigeon and sometimes the statue. I don't wanna be a statue again."

Ruker admitted that even if he had a laundry room back home in West Virginia it would not be the same. "Unless," he said, "I could take back a couple of Chinese dollies, and I'd have all the coalminers in the state coming to my laundry room." He thought for a minute and then said, "Can you imagine coalminers in starched khaki!" Ruker dreaded leaving all the girls behind. He did have a way with women, and it wasn't until he was shipping out that we learned he even had a way with enemy women. That's right, with enemy women. He had a hard time living down an experience he had on Okinawa. No one could understand how he did it. It was one of those black edgy nights when the earth and sky don't seem to meet. The Japs had captured our Fox Company runner and Ruker and the others on the gun could hear them torturing him all through the night. His screams kept up until the Marines couldn't bear it any longer. The squad sneaked off into the night to see what they could do—which was what the Japs wanted, to find where we were holed out—and they left Ruker alone on the gun. The next thing he knew was stars. He was knocked out. Cold! Someone had sneaked up from behind, hit him on the head and knocked him out. When he awoke he saw two Jap nurses were standing over him with a couple of rocks in their hands.

"Then what happened?" we asked him.

He couldn't give us an answer. He just didn't know. For some reason, that he will never understand, they didn't kill him. We joked that he was such a lady-killer, the ladies couldn't kill him.

Chandler and Smitty, they both felt much the same about going home. It wasn't that the guys didn't want to go home, they did, one day, but not right now. Marsden had already left, a couple of months before and we heard he had re-enlisted. All he had talked about was going back to his wife and then he re-enlisted.

We thought we might be redeemed when we read a news story in *Stars & Stripes*.

NAVY CANCELS CHINA TRIP
FOR 500 MARINES

Pearl Harbor, May 7 (AP) The Navy disclosed today that it has held back 500 of the 650 men of 7th Marine Battalion bound for China and that they are here awaiting transportation back to the United States mainland. The 7th Battalion had been scheduled to relieve the 3rd Battalion, now in China waters. "The men were found to be in excess of present requirements in the Western Pacific," the Navy announced in explaining that orders were changed just before sailing time Monday.

We reasoned if our replacements didn't arrive, then we could stay on for a while longer. It made no difference. Transfer orders kept coming. Samuel Carver Washington from Motor Pool got his orders and he was on his way the same day. They hardly gave him time to pack. A priest in Tsingtao reported to headquarters that he applied to marry a local girl. None of us saw him go but we could only imagine he didn't leave without a fuss.

One Marine who didn't have to worry about transfer orders was Melanowski. His got his discharge in Tsingtao. He began immediately as a driver for UNRA. We heard that he and Monique took an apartment out along the coast road near to Mrs. Djung's old house.

In the past it was possible for a Marine to extend his stay in China a year at a time. No more. Marines whose time was up had to go back. Stevenson broke the news to me when his orders came. "This times it's me who is going," he said sadly.

When a buddy is leaving, and you realize you may never see him again, you say all the things you really don't mean. "It's about time," I said. "Maybe we'll get a good office clerk this time." But when the ledger is closed and he has departed you miss him terribly. You remember all the little things, like the time when you thought you couldn't make it on a hike due to a hangover from a heavy bout of drinking the night before, and to save you from going on report, he carried your gear and helped you stumble along so that you wouldn't have to fall out. There was real meaning when he gave you his Sam Brown belt, and said to you, "Here, I am not gonna be around to protect you in a fight anymore." And even more important, when he handed you his prized barracks hat, and you replied, "Hell, it's pretty much worn out now anyway." Marines know no other way to express their gratitude to a fellow buddy except by sarcasm. You wonder, if you ever meet again, will it be the same?

We had two weeks before they left, and one big last shindig was planned. It was the finals for the China-South Pacific Area Boxing Matches held in Tsingtao.

Marines like to fight. They teach Marines in bootcamp to fight, and they become good at it, but when a war is over, how do they expect Marines to stop fighting? China Marines were no exception. They lived to fight. When the navy was in port, they fought the navy. When there was no navy to fight, Marines from one battalion fought Marines from another battalion, like the 29th verses the 22nd and so it went, battalion against battalion, company against company, platoon against platoon. When there was no one else to fight, squad member battled squad member.

Some fights became legendary. Whittington will always remember the one he got into with Vic Christopher. That was the time when they cleaned up the Camay Club. The bar was Stevenson's favorite hangout, other than the Prime Club. He took pride in giving the place the name Camay. The first time he went into the bar, when we first arrived in Tsingtao, the place had another name. Stevenson had some PX supplies he was trying to sell on the black market and offered some pogey bait and bars of soap to the owner. One of the bars was Camay Soap. The owner liked the soap, and renamed the bar after it.

Stevenson wasn't too happy when Whittington and Christopher wrecked the place.

Christopher who hailed from New Orleans was a street fighter, and he thrived on fighting. He didn't care who it was, he'd fight him. He never lost a fight. For some reason Whittington liked to pal around with him. "But he was really a dangerous mother to go on liberty with," Whittington admitted after their big fight. Christopher hated the US Navy, and he loved Tsingtao beer. The two didn't mix. When he drank he became belligerent and terribly antagonistic. He'd then look for the biggest sailor in the room and begin to crowd him a little. As soon as the sailor became aware of Christopher's presence and looked him in the eye, Christopher would always shout, "What the hell are you looking at, shithead?" After that, it was every man for himself.

That was the night they destroyed the Camay Club.

But there was one fight in Tsingtao that no one can ever forget. It will go down in history books, and it wasn't even the main event at the championship China-South Pacific Area Boxing Match. It was another match.

The championship fight went on as planned. The US Navy from the Pacific Fleet pitted their top boxers against the top boxers in the China Marines, and winners in each category would go to Guam for the South Pacific championship fights. Most of these top contenders had already made names for themselves. The scuttlebutt was that there were scouts from the World Boxing Commission who were ready to sign up the winners when they got out, and both press reporters and radio announcers were on hand to record the moments. Roy Heinecke from *Stars & Stripes* came all the way from Japan to cover the event.

But there was one match that our guys and the sailors from the Seventh Fleet wanted to see more than all others. The match we had in mind was between two men listed at the bottom of the program. But for us, it was the main event.

The man the Marines wanted to see win, and betted on,

was Herbert Jones. The Seventh Fleet put up a seaman named Frenchy. Herbert had faithfully served his time in the Tsingtao brig, where I first met him, and ever since he got out he had followed a straight and narrow, and above all, a clean path. He gave up his boozing and trained at the gym hours every day. We used to go watch him train. No one wanted to spar with him, and more often than once he knocked the heavy punching bag right of it's chain and swivel with a couple solid blows. We were all betting on him. We were convinced he could beat any Swabbie in the Navy.

But Seaman Frenchy was no pushover. There was no doubt about it, he was a mean bastard. He beat every sailor on every ship in the Seventh Fleet, and they said he could have beat everyone in the entire US Navy and some thought the British navy as well. He really was a brute, and when you saw him you did a double take. He looked very much like the black-bearded sailor in the Popeye comic strip. We saw him around town a couple of times when the fleet was in, and he was always surrounded by a dozen of his henchmen, like one of those movie stars you saw on a Movie Tone newsreel.

The first time the name Herbert Jones was mentioned to Frenchy, that a Marine by that name wanted to fight him, he laughed until his sides hurt. "Bring him on," he shouted. It wasn't an easy thing to do, to put the two unknown men on the program, but by pulling a few strings, we finally succeeded. The matches were set, the programs were printed up and distributed, and then the match was cancelled. Lt. Brandmire announced that the match was illegal.

He read in the books that any Marine or sailor who served brig time for a Summary offense could not participate in any boxing match for a period of one year after completion of the sentence. Herbert had only been discharged from the brig nine months before.

No amount of pleading could make Lt. Brandmire change his mind, and probably it wouldn't have done any good if he had. It had been entered in the book and even the CO could not change the ruling. The Rocks and Shoals are black and white and there are no grays between. Herbert Jones and Seaman French could not fight.

But it was not over.

The championship matches lasted three days, and on the night of the final day, we arranged for the Jones-Frenchy fight. But it was not staged in any auditorium, and there were no timekeepers, seats or bright lights. Standing room only. The fight was in the wide-open street in front of the Prime Club.

There was no law saying the men couldn't fight, and there was little the MPs and SPs could do to stop it anyway. The rules were simple: no gloves and a knockdown was the end of a round. When a fighter could no longer get to his feet, the other fighter was the winner. A large circle was formed and the crowd was soon boisterous, shouting for the fight to begin. They wanted blood. Bets were being made and fists full of money passed hands back and forth. I sat, along with my buddies, on the railing at the Prime Club. We had the best view anyone could have had.

We could see from our vantage point both men sweating profusely. They had stripped down to their waists and circled one another clenching their fists. The crowd cheered, and soon the cheers became chants—"Fight! Fight! Fight." They were gladiators in the ring, and when they looked up at the mob of blood crazed spectators, you wondered if the spectators would give thumbs down like the Romans did in their time. No one really cared who won, just so there was violence and blood. The two men raised their hands, and the crowd went wild. The chanting became louder.

Then the strangest thing happened. The two men approached each other, bent over in kind of a huddle, and with lowered headed began conferring with each other. Were they setting their own rules?

Presently they stood up, and Herbert motioned for silence. The crowd became deathly still. "You will have your fight," he shouted for all to hear. "You will have your fight but you will have to wait for the results." At that he and Frenchy pushed through the crowd and headed towards a darkened alley next to the Prime Club. A couple of spectators, sailors and Chinese, attempted to follow them, but the two men turned on them and they quickly withdrew. Herbert Jones and Seaman Frenchy disappeared into the darkness.

Five minutes, ten minutes, fifteen minutes, still not one nor the other man appeared. Which one would it be? We kept peering into the darkness down the alleyway, wondering. We even had thoughts that they might have killed each other. Perhaps one of us should go and investigate.

There was no need. In the deep abyss of the alley we could see a shadow emerge, ever so faint at first. Then it became clearer, and clearer. It was not one shadow, but two. The two men came walking out of the darkness, side by side. They were scuffed up, their faces marked and bruised. Their hands were bloodied and their trousers covered with dust. The crowd grew silent. With all eyes upon them, Herbert slowly raised his right hand; his fist was closed. The victory was his, and we were all about to shout when Frenchy raised his right hand. His fist too was closed. They both held their hands high, both with closed fists in victory, and like two longtime buddies, shoulder to shoulder, they marched into the Prime Club and up to the bar, and when the crowed followed them, they made their announcement. "None of you will never know," Frenchy said, and Herbert Jones vouched for him. No, we never did know who won that fight, but those who were there will never forget it either.

Lt. Brandmire had his day. Ours was coming. We combat Marines had learned the hard way that in battle, officers must not wear sidearms nor carry binoculars, both of which would identify their command function and make them prime targets for the enemy. The Marines under Lt. Brandmire's command presented him with two gifts of appreciation: a brand new pair of binoculars they bought at the PX and a very fine, handmade leather holster for his .45. "So you look sharp when you lead a patrol," they said, and they thanked him. He was pleased and proud that his men appreciated him.

The guys were fortunate they didn't have to take a slow troopship back to the States. Times were changing. They shipped out aboard C-47s to Cherry Point Air Station in California. Hecklinger ended up in sickbay and missed the flights. As for me, they figured with my speaking Chinese I might be of some use and held back on my orders. Hecklinger and I decided to celebrate. I knew he would be heading out to see his girl but we could have a few beers first at the slopchute at the EM Club. When we went into the office to get our liberty passes, the duty clerk announced that I had a visitor at the main gate waiting to see me. He didn't know who it was, except to say it was a woman, and the guards would not let her come in. Hecklinger told me to go ahead. A dozen thoughts ran through my mind as I rushed to the main gate. It had to be Ming-Lee. Who else would come to the compound to see me? I didn't walk the last hundred yards; I floated.

Sentries stood at the gate checking passes and saluting officers in their vehicles as they passed. Whoever it was had to be inside the guard shack waiting. I opened the door, and I had the shock of my life. My eyes were deceiving me. Sitting on a wooden bench was Katarina. She saw me and jumped to her feet. Her eyes filled with tears. Before I could say a word she said, "I came to say good bye."

"You already said good bye, once," I replied.

"Come, where can we go?" she said. "I have to tell you the good news."

We went to a small White Russian café down from the university and took seats at a small table. Katarina did look wonderful, and it took all my effort to not be taken in by her again. She reached out and placed her hand on my arm. She explained she was on her way to Shanghai and had a steamer to catch that night. She admitted she felt bad about Peking.

"You are returning to your family then," I said.

"Not exactly," she said. "I'm going back to Russia."

"Back to Russia!" I exclaimed. "You can do that?"

"Yes, it's okay now," she replied. "The Russians are allowing White Russians. It's part of the Yalta Agreement made between your President Roosevelt and Stalin. It has just been made public. American ships are providing transportation for us from Shanghai to Vladivostok."

Katarina was very happy. At last she had a homeland to return to. She asked about Ming-Lee and I explained I had not seen her since Peking, and that Ming-Lee was in the lobby when she, Katarina, was in my room. "Oh, I'm so sorry," she said. "You do love her, don't you?" I didn't reply. What was the use?

We finished our drinks and I wished her luck and saw her to a rickshaw out in the street. I didn't think I would ever see her again.

Chapter 17

SAVING CHARLEY COMPANY

The Poet William Cowper once wrote: "Pernicious weed, whose scent the fair annoys." That pernicious weed was China, and the "fair" in this case, if I may be so bold, was the China Marines. I don't think there was a China Marine who didn't have a legitimate complaint about the smell of China. It was not like the smells back home. The scent at home which played the best upon my mind was that of morning air on the farm, the sweet scent of grass and bloom, the damp earth from a field just plowed, or the freshness of a hayfield newly mown. Maybe those who came from the big cities had their own memory of smells, but mine were about the farm. Even the barnyard had a pleasing smell. China was so much different. When we arrived in China, we got our first whiff of the land miles off shore, and those smells never left us. In Tsingtao we got used to them, more or less, but when we went on hikes into the countryside the odors there manifested themselves. It was most unpleasant. Farmers used human excrement to fertilize their fields, and the odor seemed to be permeated into the very soul of the land.

But the rankest and most villainous smell that ever offended nostrils, was what we experienced on Okinawa. I think the memory of those smells on Okinawa made China tolerable. Replacements arriving in China from the States would complain, and then you would hear one of the old combat men say, "If you think this is bad, you should have been with us on—" No, nothing could compare to Okinawa. Nearly a quarter million corpses lay all over the place, busting open from the hot sun, stinking even through their shallow graves. There was neither time, nor did we have the energy, to bury all the dead. Marines who were killed in action, came back from the front lines stacked like unwanted logs one on top another in ten-wheel trucks.

By the fall of 1947, the number of old China hands in Tsingtao was dwindling very rapidly. Smitty was scheduled to return with the rest of the troops, but he was on a run with a load of Japanese prisoners en route to Japan when the transfer orders came through. When he returned to Tsingtao, the others were gone, with the exceptions of Hecklinger and me. It took Headquarters a while to sort out the records, and Smitty was quite happy about it. He had a job he liked—security guard on LST's escorting POW's back to Japan. He was no sooner back in Tsingtao than he quickly offered to make another run and was accepted.

One wondered if the repatriation of Japanese from China would ever end. The problem continued because Japanese soldiers had been hiding out in the mountains ever since the war's end, refusing to surrender, fearful that they may end up in Soviet hands as several hundred thousand of their comrades had. But then as the *balu* swept across north China, they flushed out scores of enemy soldiers, and rather than suffer an unknown fate, they began surrendering. When they did surrender they had to be repatriated. That task was left to the Marines. LSTs were converted to troopships and as many as 500 Japanese— civilians and whole families as well as POWs—were herded aboard and transported to Japan. The accommodations given them weren't luxury liner, and according to Smitty, more like 15th century African slave ships, except that voyages lasted only a week compared to months at sea that it took for a slave ship to reach the New World. Nor were the Japanese placed in chains, and they were going home, a big difference. Some, who had been born in China, had never seen their homeland.

After I finished my brig duty, I went back with the MPs, and found myself constantly on call as an interpreter for any number of assignments. Most of these were routine and boring, but a few were packed with real excitement. One that I liked was classified. I was to assist with the search for "Tojo's Treasure." That was the code name. Whether it was fact or fiction I never knew, but the quest was real enough. The month before the Sixth Marine Division landed in Tsingtao, a few of the Japanese high command did a bunk and fled China by sea, and with them they took a vast treasure from north China. Intelligence estimated that the Japanese had melted down tons of gold, gold stolen from the Chinese, and it included everything from jewelry to gold teeth. At $36 an ounce, it mounted to millions of dollars. The big question was, what ever happened to this gold bullion and other treasures? Anybody who knew anything about the gold had also fled before the Marines arrived. The authorities doubted the loot ever reached Japan. Any booty or spoils of war brought from abroad was certain to be confiscated. The only solution was to bury the treasure before they left, and return for it later. The question was, where did they bury it?

The search for Tojo's Treasure began immediately upon our arrival in China. G2 had their hands full. Records were scrutinized and thousands of Japanese, both military and civilians, were interrogated. Every lead was investigated and always stopped at a dead end. The breakthrough, however, came when a white-hulled yacht flying an American flag appeared off the coast of the Shantung Peninsula. The yacht was the *Scandia* out of Honolulu.

Scandia was a beautiful gaff-rigged sailing schooner, a hundred or more feet long with a 20-foot beam. It was odd to see an American sailing vessel in Chinese waters and the Navy ran a check on the vessel only to discover it had been stolen twelve months before from its mooring at Ala Wai Yacht Club in Honolulu.

The Navy immediately dispatched a patrol boat and boarded the vessel. Instead of finding Americans aboard, the captain and crew they found were Japanese. A further check revealed the captain had been an officer in the Japanese garrison in Tsingtao. They had aboard salvage equipment that included an air compressor and deep-sea diving gear.

At a Naval Board of Inquiry, the Japanese officer claimed he had purchased the vessel in the Philippines, and he produced documents as proof. The documents, as expected, were forged, but the investigation was unable to prove whether or not the captain had faked the papers himself or if he had purchased the vessel believing it was legal. The vessel was confiscated and the Japanese were dismissed with all charges pending. What no one could answer was why was the captain attempting to return to Tsingtao waters? A vessel flying an American flag certainly had a better chance, of course. But was he after a sunken treasure? The hunt for Tojo's Gold was renewed with more zest than before.

The Navy began systematically searching the waters around Tsingtao, under pretenses other than treasure hunting, of course. I would have known little about the mystery had I not been taken out to a navy barge one morning to do some interpreting. It seems Chinese fishermen claimed their fishing lines were constantly being snagged by unknown objects on the ocean floor a mile or two off the coast. When G2 received the report, they thought it might be sunken vessels but after checking found there were no reported ships that had gone down in the area. Could it be a vessel or barge that was deliberately sunk?

The fishermen were already aboard the barge when I arrived. They pointed out the location and the Navy diver was preparing to be lowered over the side.

I couldn't help envying the diver when I saw him sitting on a capstan on the fore deck. He was the very soul of adventure and romance, fitted out in his rubber deep-sea diving suit. While the Chief Petty Officer gave orders, his dive team huddled around him, each sailor with a task to do: one checked the air gauges, another coiled air hoses, a third man tested the pump handles on the air compressor. Two men made ready to place the three-windowed hardhat over his head and shoulders while still another man stood by with a wrench ready to bolt the hardhat in place.

The barge was anchored about a mile off shore from the rocky peninsula near Long Beach. I knew the place well for it was here that I had taken Stevenson and Little Lew several times.

The diver and his crew bantered back and forth, and I listened to the chief telling them that the deep-sea diving equipment they were using would be outmoded and obsolete in a couple years. A new type of diving apparatus called a "diver's lung" had been developed by a Frenchmen and the US Navy was testing it. "You just strap this thing on your back and away you go," the chief said.

What the chief had to say was perhaps true, but what romance was there in a backpack replacing the deep-sea diver's hardhat? My attention focused on the diver. The two assistants were about to lift the hardhat and fit it into place, but it wasn't the Navy diver I was now seeing. It was John Wayne. We were on Guam, seated in the outdoor movie theater. Our seats were coconut logs, and our ceiling was a star-filled sky. All around us were palm trees, silhouetted against the night's sky. We had been anxiously awaiting the movie for weeks. It first had to do the round of navy ships, and finally it came to us in Tent City. It was "Reap the Wild Wind" with John Wayne, Raymond Massey, Ray Milland, Paulette Goddard and Susan Hayward. I remembered the names, even John Wayne's name in the movie—Capt. Jack Stuart.

On a silver screen—that fluttered when there was even the slightest wisp of a breeze—we watched John Wayne in full Technicolor standing at the helm as he skippered a salvage boat in the tropics, while fighting off both pirates and the advances of two beautiful women. His competition was Ray

Milland, and the action peaked when the two men donned deep-sea diving gear and descended to the bottom of the ocean in search of a sunken treasure. When Milland was attacked by a giant octopus, it was John Wayne who saved his life, but at the expense of his own, and Milland won the hand of Goddard. Whew, what romance.

Romance in China wasn't gone; it was still with us. The diver wasn't John Wayne, but he did have the reckless appeal of Capt. Jack Stuart in "Reap the Wild Wind." I wished at that moment I could have been with that Navy diver, diving to the bottom of the ocean in a deep-sea suit, and what did it matter if an octopus was there waiting? But the Navy would never have let a Jarhead without training go deep sea diving. It was impossible. The Navy had its regulations. But I could still dream.

When the diver came up empty handed, not once but half a dozen times, everyone lost confidence, but I vowed that one day I would come back to China and look for Tojo's Treasure. Nor had I forgotten Peach Blossom Spring. I'd go searching for that too, one day when the communists backed off.

Looking for lost treasure was fun; saving Charley Company was not. History does repeat itself. We were living in a period reminiscent of the Boxer Rebellion.

Communist guerrillas, who had watched American Marines join forces with Kuomintang troops to bar them from the railway lines for so many months, grew impatient and trigger-happy. A field detachment of guerrillas ambushed a Marine convoy on the highway between Tientsin and Peking, and soon Americans and communists were killing each other.

A more serious incident involved Charley Company, Fifth Marines. I was called to accompany our regiment commander on an investigation of the conditions, but when we arrived it was too late.

For more than a year Charley Company had been defending the ammunition supply point at Hsin Ho, north of Tankgu and south of Tientsin. The Japanese, aware of its vital importance as a port, first invaded Hsin Ho in 1932. Now with General Chiang K'ai-shek's forces withdrawing, it was up to the Marines to defend the depot. They had little supplies and equipment, only their old Mls, some BARs, a few mortars and a machine gun platoon to guard an eight-mile periphery around the ammo dump. There were no tanks, and no planes flying overhead for support. Their defense required them to man eight towers on rotation of four hours on, eight off. At night eight sentries, one on each milepost, stood guard. They manned these positions for ten straight months. They had no time off, and no liberty.

With incidents happening almost every night, Charley Company was literally in the midst of a war, while Americans back home thought the war was over. Mao's forces finally became convinced that the Marines were not about to give up, and on April 5, 1947, they attacked. They attacked with several thousand men. Throughout the night Charley Company fought off the Chinese troops at the odds of 100 to one.

Finally, after a night of fierce fighting, Charley Company drove the enemy back, but at a cost of five Marines killed-in-action and sixteen more wounded.

No Marine unit deserved more credit than Charley Company, Fifth Marines. The company served beyond the line of duty without relief from any other unit, and it fought on with minimum supplies for ten months. The fighting was over when we arrived. The depot at Hsin Ho had been a living hellhole, and the site of the worst U.S. fighting in North China. When I talked to a few of the Marines who had survived, I pictured them, had the circumstances been different, playing a game of football back home at their high school. They were so young, too young to vote, and too young to go into a bar back home to have a beer. But not too young to die. They were Marines.

After month's of fighting, Mao's army was pushed back, thanks to this gallant company of teenage Marines, but disheartening was the knowledge that waiting in reserve were two million or more Chinese troops ready to attack at a minute's notice.

Smitty was setting off on another trip to Japan, and Hecklinger and I went down to the docks to see him off. He was happy as a recruit getting his emblem after graduating from bootcamp. He rolled back the sleeve on his field jacket, ran his hand over his Hawaiian dancer tattoo, and said, "Baby, we are off again."

Smitty always came back to Tsingtao with the latest news from MacArthur headquarters. What would he have to tell this time? He had a couple of buddies who were assigned as guards to the Tokyo Trials and from them he gathered the latest skinny. In the beginning we liked the way the trials were going. The International Military Tribunal for the Far East began its trial of Japanese war criminals in Tokyo on May 3, 1946. Every one of us, down to the last Marine, waited to hear that Emperor Hirohito had been sentenced to death. The only thing we couldn't agree upon was whether they should shoot him or hang him. We were certain he would be held responsible for the deaths of three million Japanese, 35 million Chinese, 109,656 Americans, and many millions of Asians. His guilt, they say, was greater than that of Hitler. Undoubtedly, had Hitler lived, he would have been tried at the Nuremberg Trials, condemned and hanged as other Nazi leaders had.

But Emperor Hirohito was not sentenced to death, nor to life in prison. He was not even tried.

The first group of 70 Japanese war criminals—all major leaders in the military, political, and diplomatic sphere—were apprehended and set to stand trial. But only 28 of the war criminals on the list were brought to trial. The others were released and their cases were closed.

Across the China Sea in Tsingtao, we knew that Japan was under U.S. occupation, and we were aware that the Supreme Commander was Douglas MacArthur. Despite Australia and China demanding that Emperor Hirohito be tried as the chief culprit of war crimes against humanity, the US took Hirohito from the list of war criminals.

As Supreme Commander, MacArthur had the authority not only to select judges but also "to reduce, but not to increase the sentences." Chief Prosecutor Keenan, a politician from the State of Ohio, cooperated slavishly with the Supreme Commander; under such circumstances, the Tokyo Trial dragged on for two and a half years and closed on November 4, 1948, with its sentences meted out to the 28 criminals. Only seven received death sentences. MacArthur insisted it was for the sake of expediency for the governing Japan under occupation that the Emperor was not tried.

MacArthur didn't win favors with the Marines who fought on Okinawa and with those who witnessed Japanese atrocities in China. No, not with way he handled the Emperor, nor when he struck a deal with Lt. Gen. Ishii Shiro, former commander of Japanese biological warfare Unit 731, that he and all members of Unit 731 were to be exonerated from war crimes in exchange for data they had acquired through human experimentation of many thousands of Chinese, Korean, Soviet, and even US POWs. Without a shadow of a doubt, Ishii's crimes had far exceeded those committed by the infamous Nazi doctor Josef Mengele for conducting human experiments. Unit 731 had murdered many times more than the number of Jews, Gypsies, Polish, and Russians killed by the Nazi doctors.

And Emperor Hirohito went free, to reign again in the grand Imperial Palace. If General Douglas "Dugout Doug" MacArthur had some other objective in mind, we Marines never knew it.

Mail call brought slews of letters from the guys who had returned home. They all had the same tune to hum. Hometowns had not changed much except the people had gotten older and the girls were more independent. Gasoline prices were up, at 29 cents a gallon, but ration books were no longer needed.

The guys keep in contact with one another. Some of them returned to their old trades and some went to college on the $500 yearly tuition plus living allowance—$90 a month for married men—provided by the GI Bill of Rights. And the letters always had the latest skinny from the home front: "Night Baseball Revived in America," "Jackie Robinson becomes first Black to sign a contract with a major baseball club," "Joe Louis retires from the ring after fighting 25 title bouts since 1937," "Shirley Temple is Engaged," and "Benny Goodman plays at the Dome in Chicago."

And the same old talk was still there—girls.

They were all looking for girls, and wanted them, but they did not want to have to work to get them. China had ruined them. They were finding life at home all too complicated when they had to explain their actions. There was not all this need to talk to Chinese girls. It was so simple. After a while at home they didn't want to talk about China, nor the war, for no one wanted to listen, nor did they believe them anyway. Every letter I received had a message to pass on to a Chinese girl left behind.

Some former Marines, of course, were having harder times than others. Stevenson was able to pick up with his old sweetheart he knew before the war, but he still had his dark confusions of the mind. Ruker and Chandler returned to their hometowns and took up life where they left off. Terry wandered the streets, got arrested for vagrancy, but found an older girl who took him under wing. Whittington started college.

Although it was obvious some Marines would always bear physical and emotional scars from the war, I could read between the lines that they would eventually let the war memories pass and forget about China, at least for the time being. They were quickly getting caught up in the new America they discovered—the latest cars like Studabakers with convertible tops and whitewalls, the gadgets like television, new personalities in politics and entertainment and the new fads.

Not all the mail came from America. A letter came from Shanghai. It was from Ming-Lee. I couldn't believe what I was reading. Katarina had found her and they became friends. Katarina explained to Ming-Lee that our relationship in Peking was not intimate. Upon receiving the letter I immediately went to see Roger, but I was terribly disappointed to learn he had moved out. He and his wife no longer lived in the hotel, and they left no forwarding address. I had the feeling I would never see Roger again. One day might he be at the opposite end of a Marine's gun sight? It might even be mine. Could I pull the trigger?

I answered Ming-Lee's letter, and more letters followed. She liked going to school, and enjoyed the new friends she had made, but she confessed she missed me. In one letter she said she was thinking about taking a respite from school and coming to Tsingtao. Would that be agreeable with me? With great joy I told her to come ahead. She arrived the day before New Years. She was the best present I could ever have had.

For the next two months we were together every minute. I was earning enough money, with the help of a few black market sales, to rent a small room in a hotel in town, and with my MP pass I could come and go as I pleased. We had much to talk about, and so much to learn about each other. We were two cultures trying to be one. However, we knew we had to be rational and we agreed we would use logic. But logic has to do with words and arguments, and the tools of logic are thinking. And a man in love is not a thinking person. A kiss can annihilate all logic.

Nevertheless, we did our utmost to close off the world outside our door. While letters from home talked about peace and prosperity, Asia was in turmoil. Harry Truman was elected president of the Unites States, and he appointed General George Marshall to US Secretary of State. Marshall, who had replaced Patrick Hurley as US Ambassador to China, turned a cold shoulder on the Far East and concentrated on rebuilding Europe by initiating the Marshall Plan. Marshall not only turned a cold shoulder but he also withdrew as mediator in China and let Generalissimo Chiang K'ai-shek and Mao Tse-Tung fight their own battle. The China Marines were in the middle.

The end of the war saw the beginning of the end of colonialism in Southeast Asia but it did not end political strife. It created it. India gained her independence from Britain, and before the ink was dry, the partition of the subcontinent began with Hindu battling Moslem. The Dutch East Indies fought tooth and nail to free themselves from the yoke of the Dutch and did get independence, but at a great cost. Burma was set free but the French were fighting a loosing battle in an attempt to hold on to Indochina. When would it end?

It was no secret that Chiang K'ai-shek was loosing his grip on China. The Marine garrison in Tsingtao was ordered to pull in its perimeter. Patrols went out to warn those in the field that the US could no longer guarantee their protection. Among the relief organizations was UNRA, and everyone was concerned about Melanowski. I had no word from him in months. We used to see Monique once in a while at the PX but no more. Patrols now were a daily occurrence and the circle kept getting smaller and smaller. Even the beaches were closed to military personnel. The Provost Marshall ordered a patrol to proceed to the Loh Shan Mountains north of Tsingtao to assist with the evacuation of a Christian monastery nestled in the mountains. The monastery was run by nuns who maintained an orphanage for abandoned children. I was assigned to go along as interpreter. When Hecklinger heard about the patrol he volunteered as driver. We were notified on a Friday that we had to depart early Monday morning. There would be six of us on the patrol, and we were authorized the use of a Jeep and a 4x4 weapons carrier. We were to be lightly armed. No heavy guns. On standby were another six 4x4s if we needed more space for transporting the nuns and orphans out of the mountains. We had no idea how many people were there, or if they would even come with us.

Ming-Lee became very upset when I told her about the assignment. "Do you have to go?" she pleaded. She had already made up her mind not to return to school in Shanghai but to remain with me in Tsingtao. We wanted no more separations.

I promised I would be back in a few days, and I vowed I would never leave her again. She agreed to move in with Judy at the Prime Club while I was gone.

I spent the night with Ming-Lee, with her curled up at my side, but I knew she wasn't sleeping. With a faint light coming through the window, I studied her gentle face. She looked so beautiful, and we were so helpless, two kids, neither of us 20 yet. We had no control over anything, not even our own fate. We were at the mercy of whatever came our way, and there was no changing our destiny. How hopeless a situation; such agony we had to suffer. Just before dawn her breathing grew steady and I knew she was asleep. I had to leave now, or I might never be able to tear myself apart from her. I wanted to kiss her gently on the cheek but that might awaken her. Instead, I slipped silently out of bed, dressed, and before the light of dawn befell the sleeping city, I made my way back to the university.

I met with the others in the mess hall where they were having an early meal and discussing our plans. I joined them for morning chow. Nothing like hot coffee in a canteen cup that burns your lips and a plate of shit-on-the shingles to start the day off.

When we went to the office to check out, the duty clerk handed me half a dozen letters. "Something for you to read on your trip," he said. He mentioned they were waiting for a news report from the Associated Press, and asked if we wanted to wait round for it, but we didn't have the time. We had to get moving to reach the monastery by nightfall. By 0600 we had cleared the outskirts of Tsingtao and headed north. Hecklinger was at the wheel of the Jeep, with Staff Sergeant Benny Gray in charge sitting in front beside him. I sat quite contentedly in the rear with another Marine. I had my mail to read and for the first time I didn't stop to enjoy the scenery.

But we did make a mistake; we did not wait for the news report from Associated Press. It would be some time before I did read it.

Shanghai, May 8 (AP)—The Chinese Communists tonight announce capture of a town 33 miles north of Tsingtao in a drive aimed at the anchorage of the U.S. Western Pacific Fleet.

The two warships off Tsingtao were listed as the light cruisers *Pasadena* and *Springfield* and 10 destroyers.

Chapter 18

THE NUNS AT LOH SHAN

Our Little Lew was still asleep when I returned to my quarters after spending the night with Ming-Lee. A few weeks before a third bunk had been moved into the room and one of the new replacements had taken it over. We called him Sam but that wasn't his name at all. It was Shirley Jackson, a tough name for a *gung ho* Marine to live down. We wondered about him when he first arrived, with a name like that, but on his first liberty he went to Ping Pong Willies and got laid. After that we knew he was all right, so we started calling him Sam. Unfortunately, he was a dreadful bore. He was a California beach-boy jockstrap, a sun worshiper, who loved surfing. No one objected to that, except that all he talked about was the California surf. After an hour in his company you wanted to tell him to shut up. It did little good. He still raved about surfing and told how the waves were better at Rodonda Beach than they were at Peblo Beach, and that he would rather be stationed in Hawaii than in China. He was disappointed that Tsingtao beaches didn't have surf. Sam, however, did impress Little Lew with all his tales about challenging monstrous waves and things like "wipe outs" and "pipelines." Little Lew was a willing listener, and for me, that was fine. It was much easier on me, especially when I was spending so much time with Ming-Lee. I did take Little Lew on my outings with Ming-Lee as much as I could, and it was fortunate that he and Ming-Lee got along fine. In fact, Ming-

Lee became his *jiejie,* his big sister.

Both Little Lew and Sam were asleep when I came into the room. In the dim light from the glow of the kerosene stove, I noticed someone had placed a few letters from the last mail call on my bunk. I carried them over to the window where the light was better so I could read who had sent them. They were from the guys back home, Terry, Stevenson and Whittington, all civilians now. I couldn't wait to open them. Maybe the guys had joined up again and were coming back to China. That would be great, just like old times. I had an hour before we had to muster for the patrol to Loh Shan, enough time to read the letters before I packed my gear. Rather than sit in the head to read my mail, I hurried down to the mess hall. It was always open and well lit. I was surprised to find Smitty sitting at a table by himself, drinking a cup of joe. He had just returned from Japan after escorting a shipload of POWs and their families back home. I waved the letters above my head and saw his face light up. I knew he would be as anxious as I was to hear the news from the home front. He had been very concerned about Terry, who the last we heard, had been locked up for vagrancy. I opened Terry's letter first. By nervous habit Smitty began rubbing the Hawaiian dancer tattoo on his forearm, beneath the sleeve of his field jacket.

Although the letter was addressed to me on the envelope, it was addressed to the "whole gang" inside. It was the usual stuff, how was life in Tsingtao? And he admitted he missed China. He was sorry he left, and said life in the US was mighty hard. He tried a couple different jobs but always got fired when he punched out the foreman, and as a result he couldn't get his 52-20 money any more. He was bitter about that. But things were looking up. When I read the next line, Smitty and I couldn't believe it. He had gotten married. Her name was Mary. She was a former WAC and a few years older than he was. They got married after the VA notified him there was a shoe cobbler school in Kansas City, Missouri, that he was eligible to attend. "Well my wife Mary and me packed all we owned which we got in two suitcases and off to K.C., Mo. we went," he wrote. It was almost as if he was sitting in the mess hall talking with us. I could hear his voice as I read. "Well I wasn't there in school two days when an instructor said to me that I shouldn't be doing what I was doing, that I hadn't reached that point of progress yet, and I didn't like his attitude. Even Lt. Brandmire wouldn't have done that. So I decked him and he was a head taller than me and I was kicked out of school. So the VA sent me out to Thompson School of Watch Making on main street, and here I am. Ernie runs the school. He's a navy vet who went through the thick of it with us, so we get along. I hope you guys are not still running from those gook cops, but if you are, stay off the firing line."

Terry's letter ended with a sentimental note. Neither Smitty nor I, nor any of the guys, had been aware of some of the anguish Terry had suffered. One was a simple thing like getting mail. At mail call we always crowded around the company clerk as he called out names, sometimes smelling the letter and then holding it up, saying, "Get a whiff of this!" and then he'd put the letter at the bottom of the pile and make the Marine whose letter it was wait till the last. I read on with Terry's letter: "I know how much mail means to you guys, you fighting boys overseas, so I'm writing these letters. I'm going to tell you something I never told anyone before. When I got a letter from home, which wasn't often, I would not open it right away. I was like a little kid with a piece of candy who wanted to make it last as long as I could. I'd keep it in my dungaree pocket and make believe I had just gotten it. Of course I wouldn't let any of you Jarheads know what I was doing and you were all so busy with your own mail you never knew anyway. I would do this, even though I wanted to read my letter very badly, and after a few days I would open it and read it slowly, and I'd even make up things to tell you guys. Be good and if you can't be good, be careful. Semper Fi, Terry."

It wasn't only Terry who lamented. Everyone made up tales and exaggerated about mail from home. Every time a Marine got a love letter, we all had to hear about it. They made glowing announcements like how their girls back home bought "these new see-through nighties" for when they get back home. There were other letters, of course, maybe a Dear John from the girl back home who ran off with Billy Smith next door, the 4F guy who never went to war but who made manager at Sears & Roebuck and bought a new Packard with white walls, just like Tokyo Rose predicted. You never heard about these letters. You only knew something was wrong when the Marine went out and got drunk and swore he would re-enlist.

And so it was this way with Terry. We both agreed that maybe Mary was good for him. We all deserve a chance, and I had my chance waiting in a hotel room in downtown Tsingtao. I would have to write to Terry and congratulate him.

I opened Whittington's letter, and as I read the neatly typewritten pages we felt that he too, like Terry, was sitting next to us in the mess hall. He wasn't having the same hard time with the 52-20 payments that Terry was having. He was still the company runner with all the gold bricking skills in tact and applying them to civilian life. He wrote: "I took advantage of the 52-20 Club for almost a year. All I had to do was show up at the Veteran's Office once a week and sign for my 20 bucks. There was the mandatory 'interview,' and I made friends with the girl who conducted them. In the winter I told her I was looking for work as a lifeguard, and in the summer I told her I was an unemployed snow plow driver."

He bought a car right after he got home, a 1933 Plymouth Coupe for $75.00 that had been up on blocks during the war. He said he had his eyes "on a beautiful 1937 Buick Convertible but that will have to wait for now." He took aptitude tests at the VA and planned to enter college in the fall. "I'm thinking of journalism," he wrote. "If you don't know what that is, it means to be a writer. If I go full time, nights and summers, I'll get my 120 hours in, in three years, and earn my 'badge of social acceptability.' Look out Walter Winchell."

He went on to tell us that he thinks of us guys often. He

learned that a couple of former Marine buddies, boyhood pals, were killed; one on Iwo Jima and one on Saipan. "I guess we in Fox who survived were just plain lucky. It would be great if 50 years from now we could all get together, but that's too far away to even think about. I guess that's hoping for too much." He then gave me some tips. "Pick up some of that good jade and ivory stuff around that can be had for a pack of Luckies. You can bring them in with no trouble. But not everything. Remember that Thompson Sub Machine gun I stole from that Army mess tent? I field-stripped it and buried it in my seabag. I got it all the way back to San Diego, and then I got this lecture the sergeant gave us about stolen Government property and a place called Leavenworth. He scared the crap out of me and I left that beautiful piece under my sack in a Quonset Hut. It turned out that no one ever touched my seabag." Then even Rick Whittington got sentimental. "In many ways I'd like to be with you guys. Every once in a while I think of re-enlisting, but I go out and have a few cold ones and the feeling goes away. Take it easy. The news coming from China isn't good. Keep in touch and stay off the sky line. Semper Fi, Rick."

Stevenson wrote to say he missed China too. He wanted to know about Mrs. Djung and Roger. I hadn't told him in my letters about Roger being a naval officer on the other side. But I did tell him about Ming-Lee, and that Judy always asked about him.

In the last paragraph he said he was back in college, and that he had enlisted in the Marine Corps Reserve. He was almost apologetic when he said that after graduating he'd be given a commission in the US Marine Corps.

"I'll be gawd damned," Smitty said. "You mean he might come back to China and this time we will all have to salute him?"

I couldn't wait until I told Judy the news, but that would have to wait until I returned from patrol in a few days. I rushed back to my room, put away the letters in my seabag and quickly packed. I strapped two blankets to my field pack, grabbed my helmet and trusty carbine and met the others at company headquarters. The Jeep and 4x4 weapons carrier were parked outside.

Staff Sergeant Benjamin (don't call me Benny) Granger was in charge and sat up front in the Jeep beside the driver. I sat in the rear with another Marine, one of the replacements. Hecklinger was behind the driver's wheel of the 4x4 weapons carrier. The Jeep took the lead with the weapons carrier a good hundred yards behind, far enough to avoid most of the dust we coughed up. In spite of the cold, everyone seemed to be in good spirits, but my mind was elsewhere. My thoughts were on Ming-Lee. She would be moving in with Judy at the Prime Club while I was gone, and I wondered if that was a good idea, just to save a few bucks. I didn't like the idea of her hanging around the club at night.

The drive north from Tsingtao led through flat open farm land of brown rice paddies laid out in neat but odd shaped patches that looked like the quilts grandma made. There was frost on all the water sheds that divided the land, and a mist hovered over the land. From mud-brick farm houses thin columns of smoke rose skyward and lingered motionless in a colorless sky. The wind was bitter and in an open Jeep rumbling along on an unpaved, pot-holed road did not make for easy traveling. We pulled our parkas tightly around us and for extra warmth we unstrapped our blankets from our field packs and draped them around us making us look more like Franciscan monks than Marines on patrol.

After three or four hours of bouncing up and down, and with our knuckles white from holding on, the road turned into a track and we had to reduce our speed to a crawl. We came to road signs but we were unable to read the faded Chinese characters. It wouldn't have done much good if they had been readable. Chinese place names don't translate well. The students in Peking were forever quizzing me on place names, and then made fun of me whenever I attempted to translate them—Fortune Showing Village, Terrace of Tower Watching

Place, Town of Temple of Fragrance Gathering. I was sure these faded signs were no better. We attempted to ask peasants we met along the way for directions, but when they saw we were "foreign devils," they turned their backs on us. Some even took off running across the open fields. I had not witnessed such behavior before when I drove my Jeep into the countryside on weekend outings. I could feel that something was dreadfully wrong, especially when we reached the next walled village. Villages always had a warm welcome.

The village was no different than others I had seen scattered around China—clusters of buildings surrounded by walls. Roads run right through these villages, and at each end of the towns there are huge gates. At one time the gates may have had a purpose, but now were merely vestiges of an unsettled past. All the buildings, whether homes or shops, were constructed from sun-dried mud bricks of uneven shapes and sizes, the same stuff as the surrounding walls. The color of the buildings, the town, the walls, they were all brown. It must have been that when God made the Chinese countryside he was running low on colors in his palette, and the only one he had left was brown. Even the clothing the Chinese wore was brown, and so was the color of their skin—brown. The food they ate was brown, and they ate it from brown bowls. And there was a brown dust that settled over the entire area.

It was a brown village that we entered.

In villages in China, and even in the big cities, when a motorist drives through the streets he toots his horn to get people to move out of the way, and they always responded. Not in this village. The people refused to give way, and the louder our drivers tooted their horns, the more defiant they became. These were not the same Chinese we knew when we arrived. We had grown accustom to people smiling and waving, and kids running along side attempting to keep up with us. We soon worried that their defiance might turn into open hostility. We were relieved when we finally reached the other end of town and exited through the gate. This behavior we witnessed was strange and I didn't like it. For my first time in China I had an uncomfortable feeling. I was considering suggesting to the sergeant that we turn around and return to Tsingtao but I knew we were under orders. "Gut feelings" don't justify one to disregard orders. So a few natives were unfriendly—that would be the reaction back at headquarters. We pushed on.

Once we were beyond the village, the track began a steady climb to the hills above, and beyond these low hills were the mountains of Loh Shan. Their summits blended into the sky and it was impossible to discern where one began and the other left off. It was no small wonder our two F7F Tiger Cats and the SB2C Hell Diver crashed in the mountain when they became disorientated when trying to fly across the Loh Shan Mountains. That seemed like ages ago. Before long the track narrowed. Steep precipices dropped down from one side and deep canyons formed below. At times so narrow were the gaps we could reach out and touch the rock walls as we drove by, and several times the driver of the weapons carried had to back up and start over again to ease through a narrow pass. Whenever we reached an opening the view was always spectacular. I had heard the Mongols cut the first road through the mountains centuries before, and we did come upon strange markings carved in the stonewalls that could have been left by them. Every now and then we came upon a temple ruins. We seemed to be driving not only forward over an ancient road but backwards into time. We came around one bend and standing there on a rocky overhang was a rather large temple which, after a closer examination, appeared to be a watchtower of sorts. It had crenulated walls and open embrasures facing the road from which we had just come. It was a striking structure, partly in ruin, with a crumbled roof and sagging lintels over the doorways. It had been long abandoned.

The road above and beyond the tower appeared to be even more hazardous than the one we had just driven. We estimated we had no more than a dozen miles to travel to reach the monastery, but we had only a few hours of daylight left. Traveling would be slow with the two vehicles. We reasoned if the sergeant, driver and me went ahead in the Jeep we could reach the monastery by nightfall and spend the night there. Those left behind in the weapons carrier could set up camp and await our radio report. If we needed them, they could follow the next morning. Everyone agreed and Sgt. Granger put Hecklinger in charge. We hated leaving him and the others behind but he assured us he would be fine.

The monastery turned out to be less than a two-hour drive. We arrived at a heavy wooden gate flanked by mud brick pillars. The gate was open and we entered. The monastery, a lonesome, forlorn building, was set back a hundred yards from the gate on a high rise of ground. It had the appearance of one of those imperial palaces you see in Peking, with red tile roofs and supporting pillars, painted red, and walls of stuccoed brick between the pillars. There was a long open corridor in the front of the building with flagstone walkways. But unlike the imperial palaces in Peking, this one was in need of repair. The pillars only had a semblance of having once been painted, and the bricks between the pillars were crumbling. But the place was clean and the yard in front was swept. You could see broom marks in the earth floor. A nun, in fact, was sweeping the yard when we drove through the gate. When she saw us, she dropped the broom and took off running for the monastery, as if she had seen monsters from a Lon Chaney horror movie. She was yelling something but we could not hear what it was.

We parked in front of the building and waited. We knew someone would appear shortly, and we were right. An elderly nun in a black habit came marching out the door and without hesitating came straight at us. We could see anger in her face. We were thrown completely off guard. We thought she would be pleased to see us but that was not so. Before we could extend our greetings she demanded to know why we there.

"We are under orders to come and give you assistance," Sgt. Granger said.

"We don't want any military here," the nun announced emphatically.

"Then who's in charge here?" Sgt. Granger asked.

"I am," she replied. "I am Mother Superior, Sister Bernice." She was a cagey, hatchet faced European woman, and we gathered that she demanded respect. Sgt. Granger was taken back by her tenacity, but only momentarily. Two other nuns in black habit appeared, and in the back ground we could hear the murmur of children's voices. Mother Superior immediately admonished the nuns and instructed them to get back and keep the children away.

Sgt. Granger stepped down from the Jeep and I followed. We stood facing Mother Superior. "I am sorry if we surprised you," Sgt. Granger said politely and in carefully chosen words explained our mission, that the communists were closing in and we were the forward echelon, prepared to evacuate them.

"This is not our war," snapped Mother Superior.

"I understand that, ma'am, but you may not know the communists," he replied, but his words were received without conviction.

"We know God, and that is all that is important."

"Mother Superior," he replied, angered now, "we are tired. We came a long way. Don't give us that crap about knowing God. So does Satan know God."

"Young man, how dare you! I won't let you mock the Bible."

"Ma'am, I am not mocking anything. We are Marines and not altar boys. We are not here to be lectured. We are here for your sakes, and the kids, not ours."

I couldn't believe what I was hearing. The sergeant was a holy roller.

We were interrupted when we heard voices coming from the monastery. It was children's voices. The children had seen us and suddenly came storming out of the monastery, full of happy innocence. At that moment, Mother Superior turned to face them and raised her hands. The children stopped in their tracks. "Go back, go back," she shouted in Chinese. They stood there, confused, until two more nuns appeared, ushering them like sheep back into the building. There must have been at least 30 children, boys and girls, perhaps three to ten years old. With Chinese children it's difficult to judge age. They were dressed in blue uniforms; the girls in skirts and the boys in shorts. They kept stumbling, one falling over the other as they retreated, attempting to keep their eyes on us. Soon they were gone and Mother Superior turned to face us again.

"God will take care of us," she repeated.

"Well perhaps it is God's will we came to evacuate you," Sgt. Granger said, "to take care of you!"

"I told you, God is not to be mocked. God's power is everywhere and it reaches to the ends of the earth. We do not need to be evacuated. God will protect us, no matter where we are."

"Ma'am, I told you, we are tired and hungry and it's getting dark and we don't have time and energy to play chess with the scriptures, alright? I may not be a priest or a holy man but I know my Bible too." The Mother Superior stood back in awe. Sgt. Granger continued. "God was on the Israelites' side, yet why did he command Moses to evacuate them from Egypt? Why didn't God protect his people in Egypt if he was all powerful and everywhere? And why did God's angel tell Joseph to take Mary and Jesus and flee from Bethlehem when Herod was out to kill the infant Jesus?"

Was I hearing right? Who would ever have believed Sgt. Granger could quote scriptures from the Bible. He didn't stop here. He continued. "You may know God, ma'am, but you don't know what the communists are capable of. If you want to risk your lives, that's fine but why are you risking the children's." He hesitated, staring at Mother Superior. "We do have our orders."

Mother Superior looked at the children, and a subtle change came over her. She was now unsure of what to do. When we first arrived, she wanted us to leave immediately. Now, when

Sgt. Granger pointed out that the road was dangerous at night, she mentioned another road that led down to the coast on the north side of the peninsula, and that was the route they used. Sgt. Granger explained it would be impossible for us to return to Tsingtao that way, for the weapons carrier was waiting for us at the watch tower below, and most likely the entire north of the Shantung Peninsula was in communist hands. Finally Mother Superior relented.

"There's an empty room at the far end of the hall," she said quietly. "You can stay there for the night."

We moved into our new quarters for the night. It was a simple room with four beds, whitewashed walls and a cross on one of the walls. There was one window and it appeared never to have been opened. There were extra blankets on chests at the foot of each bed. Servant boys brought a charcoal brazier to keep us warm and a pot of hot tea to drink. We had our C-rations for dinner.

When things settled down, I asked Sgt. Granger about his religious beliefs. He was reluctant at first but eventually after some prodding gave his thoughts. "My parents are Jehovah's Witnesses," he explained. "They were very upset about my enlisting. Witnesses are opposed to war and killing, and I joined the Marines. Hypocritical, ain't it? But now when I see all this that is going on in China I am beginning to wonder. Maybe they are right. Where does it stop? Nothing makes sense anymore."

"C'mon, Sarge! Someone's got to do the killing. We can't just stand back and watch misfits like Hitler and the Japs murder people by the millions. Wouldn't that be a sin to let them go? To watch someone get bullied and not do anything about it, that would be worse! I know little about the Bible but I know about David and Goliath and Samson and Delilah and Moses and the Egyptian army; I've seen the movies. God said it was okay to kill, you know, the bad guys."

"I agree, and that's the dilemma that I'm in. It's got to stop somewhere," he said, kicking off his boondockers and stretching out on the bed.

"Exactly, it's gotta stop, and that's why we are stopping it. Right?" I replied.

"Yea, by being bigger, with bigger guns," he said. He slipped under his blankets. The driver was already in his bed for the night.

"Tell me, Sarge, how else can we do it? If we aren't bigger, and don't have bigger guns, we can't stop it. We'd be just in the middle, and maybe get killed at it. If your folks are true Christians, Jehovah's Witnesses you say, don't they still have to fight wars and save those who are being bullied?" He didn't answer, and I continued. "You parents must be proud of you, Sarge. You know who the bad guys are."

"That's exactly it!" he said and sat up. "That's precisely it! Who are the bad guys? Just because they are fighting for their principles, what they believe in, are they bad guys? Wars are simply matters of opinion. People kill one another over an opinion, when the other guy's opinions doesn't agree with theirs. Then others step in and they get involved, and the killing gets bigger."

The driver became bored with our conversation and put a pillow over his head. This was the same talk I had at the university with the Chinese students in Peking. Who was right and who was wrong? I was tired of these games of political volleyball. "I thought you might have a Bible solution," I said to change the subject. There was a long silence and he didn't answer. "Okay then, Sarge, aside from your parents and their religious beliefs, do you regret being Marine?"

"You're back to the matter of opinions. You're asking me to pick one side, the one you stand for, and it becomes my opinion. He thought for a while and continued. "Is it wrong to be a Marine? You're asking me a question that requires an opinion. It doesn't matter what my opinion is for no matter what I say, it will only be my opinion."

"There has to be one opinion that is right," I said.

"There is, the Bible," he replied. I knew it. I knew it all the while. Sgt. Benjamin Granger was a holy roller. He then cut me short. "If you are looking for the truth, then get a Bible. That's your highest authority, and that's all I have to say."

"Look, Sarge, one last thing I don't understand," I said. "Your parents and their kind would rather be killed than defend themselves."

"Look at it this way," he replied. "Is there a guarantee we won't get killed in war? Not at all. The Bible says if we must suffer, we might as well suffer doing what is right rather than doing what is wrong. You figure it out and go to sleep."

The discussion was over.

The beds were quite soft, and most comfortable, but too many conflicting things were running through my head to sleep. Sgt. Granger's words kept echoing though my head, and I thought about Hecklinger and the others bivouacking in the open. Hecklinger had hopes about sleeping in the watchtower when he first saw the place, but then he discovered the concrete floors inside the building were covered with human excrement and the place stunk horribly. "Why do these gook bastards have to crap inside a building when they have the whole countryside?" he ranted. I could still hear him as we drove off.

There was little sleep and at the first light of dawn we were up. Already the children were playing in the open compound. We dressed and went out to greet them. They came running and were soon climbing all over us. Each one vied desperately to get our attention. Unlike most orphans we saw, generally shy and withdrawn, these kids were friendly and filled with cheer. We had to give the nuns credit. They did a fine job in raising them. I had wondered before we came, why did the nuns choose these kids above all the other orphans in the country. Why them? What criteria were they using to judge? When I saw the kids that morning I immediately knew. A young lad about three approached me, eager to hold my hand. He had blue eyes. At his side was a young girl, about the same age, and she had light brown hair. The children were of mixed blood—Russian, American, English, Japanese. My heart went out for them, and I wished we could carry all of them back with us to Tsingtao. Maybe we could. We would need to go back to get more vehicles. We had to hurry.

While the driver and I were cavorting with the kids, Sgt. Granger wandered off to make one last plea with Mother Superior and the nuns to evacuate the monastery. Before he left, he instructed us to make radio contact with Hecklinger. He returned half an hour later, and he was steaming mad. "Let's go and get the hell out of here," he said and made no further comment. I wanted to say that this was not the way for a Jehovah Witness to act but thought it best to let it go. I knew that sooner or later he would tell me what had happened with Mother Superior and why she had refused our offer.

We were unable to reach the others by radio. We assumed bad radio transmission in the mountain area was the cause. We made several more attempts while en route but still we had no luck.

I am one who doesn't believe in premonitions, but I have to admit there was an eerie and uncertain feeling during our drive back from the monastery. I was very uncomfortable, and I could feel that Sgt. Granger and the driver felt much the same way. Maybe it was the gloom of having to leave the nuns and orphans to an uncertain fate, or it could have been the feeling that we were pushing our luck too far. I don't know what it was but when we rounded the bend in the road before reaching the watch tower, expecting to find the weapons carrier waiting for us, and it wasn't there, we knew immediately that something was wrong. We leaped out of the Jeep and began looking around. Sgt. Granger suddenly froze in his tracks; the expression on his face changed to one of horror. He pointed towards the tower. There in the semidarkness of the interior were two shadows, two bodies, hanging in mid air. My pulse quickened. We advanced ever so cautiously, peering hard into the interior. Sgt. Granger withdrew his .45 from his holster and slid a round into the chamber. At the door we stopped, not wanting to believe what we saw. Two bodies hung by their feet from the ceiling, their heads inches from the floor. I felt my knees grow limp. The sight was dreadful! Their arms, their hands and the floor were covered with dried blood. Their eyes were open, their arms reaching out. The men were dead. Hecklinger was one of them. Their tongues had been cut out and they were left to bleed to death.

My first impulse was to get back to the Jeep and get my carbine, but it was too late. It wouldn't have done me any good anyway. We were completely surrounded. Guerrilla fighters had suddenly appeared from everywhere. A dozen weapons were pointed directly at us.

Chapter 19

CAPTURED

The men who ambushed our patrol in the Loh Shan Mountains were guerrillas, not Mao Tse-tung's regulars. They called themselves freedom fighters, but in reality they didn't quite know who they wanted to be free from, the Kuomintang or the Nationalists. We thought of them as nothing more than bandits, the worst kind, lawless to themselves, a ragged, malicious band of renegades on the loose, charging across the face of China ahead of the Red Army. Their dress was a hodgepodge of mufti—bits and pieces of uniforms from a half dozen armies. Some wore Marine Corps field jackets and a few had helmet liners; two men had regulation boondockers. One man had a Japanese peaked cap that he wore rakishly to one side. But mostly they had Nationalist uniforms, quilted coats and canvas shoes. Their weapons were as diverse as their clothing, from old Springfields to Japanese 7-mm bolt-action rifles. The leader wore a Mongolian piss cutter and a long sleeveless goatskin coat, and in spite of his arms being bare he didn't seem to mind the cold. He barked orders in Mandarin Chinese, but it was a plains dialect spoken in the remote northern regions of the Gobi. I had heard it before by students in the language school. His men, more than a dozen, began prodding us with their rifles, pushing the barrels into our sides, their fingers on the triggers. They lined us up, made us kneel down until our foreheads touched the ground. I was the third in line.

One single thought ran through my mind—I was going to die. We wonder about death, how we will face it when the time comes. We all feel it won't happen to us, only to the next guy. Then when we know it's coming, and we are rendered helpless to do anything about it, we become overtaken with anger. It's not as Hollywood portrays death on the silver screen. I had witnessed death at its worst on Okinawa. Dying men didn't utter final words to their buddies, asking them to tell their wives and sweethearts back home that they loved them. They cursed the Japs, calling them every four-letter word they could use. They cursed their enemy to their last breaths. But in death even the most gallant, even the bravest man, is betrayed by the look in his eyes. This is when you want to reach out to him, when all you can do is touch him. It was seeing the look in Hecklinger's eyes, an empty, glassy gaze and yet so full of meaning, that now haunted me. Did he know at the time that death was overtaking him? Did he believe it was happening to him? Did he ever think about his own death when he worked in the funeral parlor in Oklahoma City, when he was surrounded by death? Did he ever think about it when he lay in the arms of that Chinese whore in that dark alley in Tsingtao? Maybe it happened suddenly, and he didn't have time to think about it. It was different with the three of us. Except for these renegades who were about to kill us, who would know what happened? We would simply disappear, vanish, never to return home; they would put on our gravestones—MISSING. Nothing else.

The leader was standing in front of Sgt. Granger. My thoughts now became bizarre. There I was, about to be shot, and running through my mind was the old Marine Corps saying: "Ten thousand gobs lay down their swabs to fight one sick marine. Ten thousand more stood up and swore, twas the damnedest fight they'd ever seen."

They lay down their swabs; I would rather have faced ten thousand gobs than a dozen ruthless bandits. Lord help me! What a way to die. Events that now happened came in a blur.

The man in charge stood in front of Sgt. Granger. I could not see him, with my head in the dust, but I knew his voice. He began shouting in Mandarin. "How many soldiers are you? How many more?" Sgt. Granger didn't answer. How could he? He had no idea what the man wanted to know, and I was in no position to answer for him. I was sure if any one of us made a sudden move we would be shot on the spot. Did it matter if we were going to die anyway? But there was always that one chance that we wouldn't die. Was it chance, or was it hope? In a rage the man gave the command to take the sergeant and shoot him. "Ten thousand gobs lay down their swabs." I could hear them dragging Sgt. Granger away. What had we talked about only a few hours ago, that there is no guarantee we won't get killed in war. Did he really mean what he said, that's it's better to die doing what is right than doing what is wrong? Why does he have to die at all? Their leader now stood in front of the driver, and shouted the same questions at him. When he got no reply, he repeated the same order—shoot him. Moments later two shots rang out.

Their leader now stood in front of me. He put his pistol under my chin and raised my head up to where I was looking directly into his face. Good gawd, he was only a kid, not much older than me. "How many soldiers are you?" he screamed. He never expected me to answer in Chinese.

"Only three of us," I replied. "We came for the children."

"Children! Children!" he stammered. He was taken back for a moment. "You speak Chinese," he continued. "Why do you speak Chinese?" He lowered his pistol.

"I was a student in the Northern Capital," I replied.

He then asked my name. I gave him my Chinese name. "*Wo de be mingzi shi Hsi Huan Loh,*" I said—"My humble name is *Hsi Huan Loh.*" He pondered over this and again asked about the children. I explained about the nuns and the orphans.

A calm seemed to settle over him. The scale was tipping in my favor. It was clear that he didn't quite know what to do with me, and yet he must have thought with my speaking

Chinese I might be helpful to him later on. I was his trophy. He began mulling over the situation with his men. They began arguing, all trying to speak at once. I tried but I couldn't make out what they were saying. I could see in my mind Hecklinger again. I saw his body before me, those eyes, his arms reaching out. The blood everywhere, blood turned black. I imagined him dying the agonizing death that he did, and would this be my fate too? "Twas the damnedest fight they'd ever seen." I could grab a weapon from one of my captors. They would probably kill me anyway. I was no hero. This would just make the end quick. No suffering. Suddenly the leader turned and walked up to me, and stopped less than a yard away. He withdrew his pistol. It was too late. Why did I wait? He pulled back the hammer, and said, "You will come with us." He pointed the weapon skyward and pulled the trigger. The shot rang out and reverberated through the canyon walls. It was a signal. While we waited, the leader ordered his men to get a length of rope, and then he did the most surprising thing. He offered me a cigarette, one from the pack he had taken from Hecklinger. I refused, said I didn't smoke, but never did I want a cigarette more than at that moment. The men came with the rope and tied my hands behind my back. At this point the weapons carrier came rumbling up the road. They pushed me into the back seat and men took positions on either side of me. The leader walked slowly around the vehicle, admiring his prize. The trace of a smile crossed his face but he quickly wiped it away; he then pushed the man behind the driver's wheel out of the way. He took over.

At his command, his men rushed to climb aboard the weapons carrier and the Jeep parked nearby. They suddenly became kids, scrambling to find room, shoving, laughing, shouting, pulling at one another. We soon looked like two overloaded Chinese buses, with men hanging from the sides of the vehicles, sitting on the hoods and standing on the front and rear bumpers. The leader sat behind the wheel, grinding the gears trying to find first, which made me doubt that he had ever driven before. He finally found the gear, let out the clutch and with a jerk we took off like a shot down the mountain road. Bumps, holes, rocks in the road, landslides, nothing mattered. I was sure at every bump, at every turn, we would loose a couple of men but they miraculously—like flies on flypaper—hung on. We were so crowded I was unable to see any of the road ahead.

I had no idea what my captors intended to do with me, nor, did they I suspected. After several hours of breakneck speed thundering down the road we came to the village that had given our patrol a hard time two days before. Without slowing our speed, we shot straight through the gate, but suddenly, in our own cloud of dust, we skidded to a stop after turning sideways and nearly rolling over. I had trouble extracting myself from bodies jammed all around me, and I could not see what caused the abrupt stop. The men began to disembark, and there, blocking the street was an armored car. Standing directly in front of the vehicle, legs apart, his hands on his hips, was an officer. With my hands still tied, I had to raise my knee to wipe the dust from my eyes on my pants leg to see. I thought at first the soldier was an officer of Chiang K'ai-shek's Nationalist Army. I then saw the red stars on his collar and another on the brim of his hat. Judging by the braid on his shoulder epaulettes he was a ranking officer. On both sides of the vehicle were other soldiers, with red stars on their uniforms. They were communist troops of Mao Tse-tung's Eighth Route Army.

Our freedom fighter leader, with his men following close behind, approached the officer. He saluted and then with a wide sweep of his arm, he pointed to the two vehicles he and his men had captured. He called his men to bring me from the weapons carrier, and when I stumbled out, he proudly pointed to me. I could hear him telling the officers there were many others, but they were all dead. He and his men had defeated the enemy.

The people of the village began to gather. They were the

same people our patrol had encountered two days before, but their mood was not the same. They were jubilant now, their faces beaming with smiles and happy grins. They carried tiny red flags and waved them above their heads. They had obviously known the Red Army was on the march, and that was the reason they treated us as they did. Now when they saw me, still in uniform, they began sneering and shouting. The officer in charge raised his arms and they fell silent.

He then began interrogating the rebel leader.

For five minutes the rebel leader ranted on. He was humble and bowed every minute or two. He pointed to the hills, to the two vehicles, and then to me. His men nodded in agreement to everything that he said.

The next move was unexpected. It came as a surprise to everyone gathered there, to the villagers, to the rebels, and to me especially. The Red Army officer walked up to the rebel leader, raised his hand and slapped him as hard as he could across his face. The slap was so hard it jolted the man's head to one side. The officer then began shouting, at the top of his voice, and while he did, his men moved in with lowered rifles. They quickly disarmed the rebels and marched them under guard into the city. The officers ordered his men to untie me. This done, he spoke to me in English. "You Melican?" he asked. His English was barely understandable, but he wanted to impress his men so I answered in English.

"Yes, I am American," I said.

"Me reglet you flend become dead," he said. He was shocked to hear there were but a few of us, and not a whole company as he was lead to believe. He said he would send men to retrieve their bodies. He also explained that it was not advisable for me to try to escape. My fear should not be him or his men; I should fear the masses. He said the Chinese people would kill me given the chance. In his broken English and with many arm gestures he made it understood that the Chinese people, to prove their new allegiance to Chairman Mao Tse-tung, would turn on me. He picked up a stone from the ground, waved it above his head, and then brought it down to his forehead, banging it against his temple a couple of times. He followed by slumping down, in pretense that he was mortally wounded. His men laughed and he laughed with them. He threw the stone down. His message was obvious. The Chinese would beat me and stone me to death, like they had done to the Japanese officer at the Sokuku Geisha House. I didn't find it as humorous as he was portraying it, but I grimaced and smiled, and the men broke into laughter again.

They locked me up for the night in a mud building with but one door. In the morning I was awakened by a guard and taken to a Russian truck and herded aboard along with a dozen Chinese men. I looked for the officer who spoke some English but he was nowhere around. The other prisoners in the truck were not peasants; I assumed them to be political prisoners. The rebels were nowhere in sight.

By evening we had reached our destination, a work camp in a village that faced an island a few hundred yards off shore. I remember seeing the island before on one of my weekend drives. It was a coal storage island. The guards shoved us into a compound with other prisoners, more than a hundred, all were Chinese; I was the only white man. They spoke Cantonese and I was unable to communicate with them. By their dark suntanned skin I took them to be junk boat men, probably captured around the Formosa Strait. The communists were attempting to block off the strait to keep Chiang's forces from crossing and regrouping on the island.

The men who guarded the camp were communist soldiers, mere kids, clothed in heavy quilted uniforms. We were instructed to sit on the ground, and after waiting an hour or more we were told to form a line and strip down to the waist. The line led into a shabby waterfront building. Once inside the door I saw what was taking place. A man in a soiled white apron held in his hand an instrument with tiny needles protruding from one end. The instrument was attached to an electrical cord. A man next to him sat at a table with a ledger before him and was marking names and numbers in the book with a quill pen. The first man in the white apron was tattooing the men in line. He would dip the instrument into a shallow tray filled with black ink, tattoo a number in Chinese characters on each of the prisoner's left forearm and then tell the number to the scribe. He used a much soiled rag to wipe away the blood and excessive ink. He would study the pattern briefly, like an artist looking at his easel, and then call for the next man to step up. The process took less than five minutes per man, and the results were frightful—crude Chinese marks, nothing at all like the hula dancer on Smitty's arm.

The pain was far less than I expected, and I was pleased that my wound had bled a lot, to keep it clean, but still I could only think of some horrid disease that might come from the unsterilized needles. My arm pained during the night but the winter cold, with only a towel for a cover, was far worse. A dozen of us huddled together on a hard wooden pallet two feet above ground. I wondered how many nights I would have to endure this torture.

The next morning, before light, we were ordered outside and each man was fed a bowl of watery rice gruel, my first food since being captured. We were then led to sampans and ferried to the island across the narrow channel. Once we arrived I knew instantly our mission. We had to transport a mountain of coal on the island to flat bottom scows lined up along the shore. It seemed Mao Tse-tung was preparing for a major naval assault against the Nationalists and his ships needed coal to run their steam engines.

The majority of Chinese cargo vessels I had seen in Tsingtao harbor were powered by steam, and coal was needed to turn the turbines in the steam engines. Coal was brought down from the north by trains, guarded at first by Japanese troops and later by the US Marines, to Tientsin and Chinwangtao, and from these ports it was shipped to coaling stations along the coast and to Shanghai to run their industries.

I thought hoeing corn and stacking hay on the farm back

home was tough work but nothing could compare to what now faced me. It was backbreaking labor to carry baskets of coal balanced on poles from the island and unload them on to the scows. The most difficult part was negotiating narrow planks that lead from the island to the scows. At first I could hardly lift the heavy loads; balancing a basket to evenly distribute a load took skill and practice.

Our living conditions were deplorable. Sleeping quarters were mud and plaster barracks, with hard wooden pallets for beds. The rags we used for bed coverings had never been washed. Nor were we given fresh water for baths. In a few days time we were as black as the coal we carried. At night when it was totally black in our quarters, only the whites of our eyes and our teeth showed

Fortunately, after a week the coal supply ran out and I was sent to help fishermen work their nets at fishing grounds up the coast. Conditions improved immediately. I liked anything to do with the sea, just being around water, and I welcomed the change.

Over the years I had gone as often as I could to the beaches north of the city, and there I watched these weather-hardened fishermen at their trade. I was there when US sailors, living-it-up at a beer party lost their Jeep in the incoming tide, and the fishermen refused to help them save their vehicle. The sailors had broken their fishing lines and laughed about it. And now I was going to work with these fishermen. Mao needed food to supply his army, and fishing fleets were called upon to double their catches. Every available hand was put to work.

I had learned to scull a sampan, and so I was assigned to work the nets at sea, while teams of men on shore pulled in the nets. I soon won the favor of the fishermen. It often happened when a sampan laid out a net, it got tangled on its floats, and, of course, it had to be freed. It took time and slowed down the operation. The Chinese preferred to free tangled nets by pulling them back into the sampan and working on them. I made their work easier by going over the side of the sampan and untangling the nets while they were in the water. The water was freezing cold, but if I went in and out as quickly as I could, it wasn't too bad.

The fishermen taught me not only to perfect my sculling techniques but they also taught me the art of catching fish. I learned to lay a net, and to coil a line. Sometimes I gave a hand on shore pulling in a net, but most often I worked from a sampan. Once the nets were in, I learned to sort the catch.

In the evenings we sat around in abandoned huts left by the US military and cooked up baskets of small fish—heads, guts, tails, scales and all—in great circular frying pans called woks. With rice we had more than enough protein. A month, and then two passed. It was coming on April and the weather was getting warmer. I was kept busy during the day, but come nightfall the world closed in around me. Had China fallen? Had the Marines withdrawn? I thought about my friends. What had become of Melanowski? He was a driver for UNRA and maybe UNRA had been disbanded? Did he go back to the US with his wife? I thought about the others, but mostly I thought about Ming-Lee. I thought about her every minute.

One night, as we huddled around a fire, I overheard a Red soldier who had returned from Tsingtao talking to another soldier. He brought news that the Marines were pulling out. Flags were going up all over town to welcome The People's Army. They were being welcomed not as conquerors but as liberators. There was no violence, no executions. It was a peaceful take over. He told how beggars and lepers were rounded up, but he didn't know what was happening to them once they were. He told how the bars, cabarets, bordellos and other establishments that catered to the West were closed and boarded up. He told incidents about how their windows were smashed and tables and chairs tossed out into the streets.

What would become of Ming-Lee? I felt sick at heart. Because of me she was in Tsingtao. She could have been safe in Shanghai. Roger had warned me that this would happen. I wanted to get back to Tsingtao, but I remembered what the Red Army officer had told me, that the masses would turn on me. Still, I had to get back to my outfit. I had to break free. I could make an attempt to reach the south where the People's Army had not reached. I would make my escape, and I devised a plan.

A long peninsula to the north of the cove where we were fishing jutted far out to sea. Junks coming down the coast came around the peninsula but in almost every case they would lose their wind. Their lateen sails went slack. Usually at this point the crew took out long poles which they used as oars, and by walking along the gunwales, they propelled the junk forward, ever so slowly. They continued thus, until they caught the wind again. Our fishermen said many of the junks continued on south as far as Shanghai, and some to Hong Kong. If I could only make it to one of those junks. It would be a gamble. From a sampan it would be a two- to three-mile swim.

I calculated how long it took a junk to round the tip before it lost its wind. If I could tend the net in a sampan at the farthest point out at sea, I could reduce my swim by half a mile, maybe more. I would have to take a chance that the junk people would help a lone swimmer at sea. But first I would need to get rid of my tattoo prison number.

I began to prepare. With rags I collected grease left in the bottom of the woks and placed them under the floorboards in a sampan. I had read somewhere that when preparing to swim the English Channel, swimmers covered their bodies with grease in order to keep warm. I would do the same.

When a morning catch was good, the nets went out in the afternoon again. It was often dark when they were pulled in. The afternoon would be the best time for me to make my attempt. By morning a junk would be far gone, hopefully with me aboard. The fishermen might think l had drowned. I started spending more time in the afternoon sculling a sampan to check the nets. After a while the fishermen didn't take notice of me. I tried to be everywhere at once to confuse them. I tried to spend more time in the water, which was not easy.

Now I had to get rid of the tattoo. I couldn't let anyone see what I was doing. I started staying up at night while the others went to sleep. They got used to me fiddling around with the fire. In one of the wrecked skeletons of a sampan down the beach I found a spike about six inches long. I cleaned it up until it shined. I then took a long piece of board and drove the spike with a rock into the end. I soaked the board in water, making it as fire resistant as possible, and then by sticking the tip of the spike into hot coals I was able to heat it up until it turned red hot. I took a deep breath and slowly burned away the tattoo. I was afraid the stench of burning flesh might awake the others but fortunately they slept through it. I made sure I kept my arm covered from then on.

My chance came one afternoon a few days after I got rid of my tattoo. The catch was good that morning, and we completed laying out a second net in the afternoon. At mid afternoon three seagoing junks, all three masted, appeared coming around the tip of the peninsula. It was now or never. I announced that I would scull out and check the net. No one suspected a thing. I sculled as fast as I could to the far end of the net and tied the sampan by a bowline to a float on the net. I took the rags from under the floorboards and rubbed down my body with grease. I then slipped over the side, and began my two-mile swim to freedom.

In the Nationalist capital of Nanking, Generalissimo Chiang K'ai-shek, who had fought the communists for more than 20 years, announced that he was retiring as president of China, with hope that his departure would bring an end to the hostilities. Li Sung-jen, who was named acting president, announced his caretaker government was ready to negotiate a peace on the basic terms laid down earlier by communist leader Mao Tse-tung. In Tsingtao, the US Marine force of 8,000 were withdrawing. I knew none of this, of course.

Chapter 20

JUNKS ON THE HORIZON

In less than a minute I was numb with cold, so cold I couldn't breathe. My lungs refused to function. I desperately beat on my chest with both my fists, and once I started breathing again, while still gasping for air, I swam as hard and as furiously as I could toward the junks. I had to keep my blood pumping. There was no turning back now. In the water, I could not see the junks and had no way of telling if they lost their wind. What if they had wind? They would be gone by the time I got there. I could only continue, swimming with all I had, hoping for the best. It was all or nothing.

The will to survive is incredible. I had but one thought, and that was that I had to make it. I knew that once I let the thought of failure take over, my body would quit. I thought of myself as the weightlifter, standing before a bar with more weight than I had ever lifted before. I had to psych myself into it. I had to tell myself, over and over, that I could do it. Once I picked up that bar, it was my mind that took command. I had to listen to my mind and not my body.

I could see the high rise of the peninsula in the distance, and I knew I had to swim to the right of that. I kept going, swimming frantically toward an unseen object. I had my dungaree coat and trousers rolled up and strapped across my back, and I was about to discard them when I looked up and only a hundred yards ahead were the three junks, without wind, gliding slowly southward. I could see seamen along the gunwales working long oars. I swam harder. The first junk was beyond my reach. I struck out for the second one in line.

The man at the oar on the second junk saw me, and in seconds, dozens of Chinese appeared at the railing, all shouting and waving. They could see that I wasn't going to make it and pointed to the third and last junk. I was back at the gym, my hands on the bar, and in one mighty grunt I lifted with all my worth, the bar came up, and in my last surge of strength I had to press the weight above my head. I could do it, I told myself. My hands reached out and touched the side of the junk. The hull was all black, coated with tar and pitch, and at the waterline and below was a sheath of barnacles. There was nothing to grab on to. I could hear voices shouting to me from above, but they spoke in a strange Chinese dialect. They dropped a rope over the side, and I reached for it, and missed it. I was near the stern now, and the junk kept slipping by. I made another lunge for the rope but again I couldn't reach it. The junk slipped by and I was now looking up at the high stern silhouetted against the sky. The junk was leaving me! It couldn't stop, nor could it turn around. Like me, it was at the mercy of wind and the sea. I dropped the weight and it came crashing to the floor.

Something hit me square in the back of my head with a thud. It was the bow of a sampan. I hadn't noticed but the junk was towing a sampan on a long tether. The sampan was low to the water and in a half daze I was able to reach up and grab hold of the starboard gunwale, and there I clung. The crew pulled the sampan up along side the junk and two men jumped aboard, and I was aware of hands reaching down and taking hold of me. I could feel them holding my arms above the elbows and pulling me out of the water. A dozen more hands hoisted me from the sampan to the deck of the junk. Everything was hazy before my eyes. Faces in a blur were looking down at me. I could feel that I was being wrapped in blankets, and someone was forcing warm tea into my mouth. I coughed and struggled but they kept pouring.   I felt warmness closing in around me and sleep overtaking me. I didn't have to struggle any more.

I lay there for the longest time, not wanting to move. It was daylight, the next morning. Luck had been with me again. But my rejoicing was only a fleeting moment. Now that I was free, my thoughts centered on how I could get back to my outfit? I surmised that during the night we had passed beyond Tsingtao and were still sailing southward, most likely to Shanghai. I continued to lie there, thinking of my predicament. My eyes took in everything around me.

A junk, what a noble, time-defying vessel! In Tsingtao I climbed aboard a few junks, all moored in the harbor, and I wondered how it would be sailing aboard them. Now I was finding out. Like most other Westerners, I questioned their seaworthiness, especially after seeing all those wrecked junks littering the China Sea on our voyage from Guam to Tsingtao. But maybe I wasn't giving them the credit due, for that was after the typhoon had nearly wrecked the US Navy as well. I also remembered reading Richard Halliburton, the adventurer who went around the world doing crazy things, like swimming the Bosporus and climbing the Matterhorn, and writing about them. They were great, exciting books, especially for a farm kid to read. But it was a junk, Halliburton's last adventure, that finally did him in. In Hong Kong he outfitted a junk and set sail in 1938 across the Pacific bound for the World Exhibition in Seattle, but he never made it. He, his junk and his crew, were lost at sea, never to be seen or heard from again. Junks after that got a bad name.

The junk that was carrying me to freedom was named *Hai Lang*, meaning "Sea Wolf," a fitting name right out of a Jack London novel. I wondered why London never wrote anything about the Far East, and yet in his youth he had served aboard a sealer in the seas around Japan.

Hai Lang must have been around since Kublai Khan's day. It was ancient, and it was a miracle it was still afloat. As I was soon to find out, the crew had to man the bilge pumps hourly to keep the vessel afloat. I didn't know this, of course, as I lay there on deck, amidship, between two stacks of charcoal that were bundled and tied with hemp rope. When I first opened my eyes, I was uncertain where I was. I could see the masts towering above me. The heavy, cumbersome lateen sails strained at their halyards. After my eyes focused in, I became conscious of sounds: the sea lapping against the hull and the creaking of the masts and rigging. No, it was more than creaking; it was groaning. The entire ship was groaning, straining to keep moving and alive. And then came the smells, a hodgepodge of everything: burnt charcoal, fish, hemp rope, tar, the salt air. Mingling with all these smells was the aroma of food being cooked somewhere forward.

Gradually I sat up, and then very unsteadily I rose to my feet. I hadn't noticed but several young children had been watching over me, and now they ran off toward the stern shouting in Chinese. I recognized the dialect. It was Cantonese, much different than Mandarin. Cantonese is guttural, harsh, and unpleasant to foreign ears. Mandarin is soft sounding in comparison. The two are as opposite as French and Italian, although their writing is the same.

Near to where I was bedded down, I noticed a six-foot length of heavy chain. At the time I thought nothing about it, but I later learned it had been dragged there for a purpose. If a communist patrolboat had approached, and I was discovered aboard, it would have been curtains for the junk and all those aboard. The patrol boat would have sunk the vessel on the spot without hesitation. The remedy was to tie me to the chain and push me overboard, a simple solution for the junkmen, but not for me.

The children had hardly gone when a horde of Chinese appeared, and at once I could see they were all from the same family clan. Young children scrambled between the legs of their elders. There were old men, stooped and bent, and old women with tiny feet. They all wore loose fitting clothing, dark blue, with wrap-around belts and sashes. The younger men, obviously the working crew, wore turbans and bandanas wrapped around their heads. Without exception, they were all barefoot, even the old women. When they saw me, and smiled, I had never seen so much gold in any one place except perhaps at a gold shop in Peking. Their gold teeth had to be their biggest investments.

The junks were up from the southern provinces, and were carrying home cargoes of charcoal for cooking and heating fires and dried fish for the market. The cargo of fish was stored below deck. After our initial meeting and introductions, I was at liberty to look about the ship. She was divided into compartments, five or maybe six, each one sealed off from the other. If they touched upon a point or rock and got holed, only one part of the vessel would fill and the others would remain dry. If I ever were to build a boat, I thought, that was the way I'd do it.

A loft poop made for comfortable quarters. The junk was obviously overcrowded, old men, young men, women and children, all jumbled together, eating and drinking, playing, smoking and of course gambling, in its nooks on deck or in its depths far below deck. This is the way they live, for months and years, at sea, in ports, in typhoons, in calms; they live quite happily, knowing no other life.

I soon marveled how at ease everyone aboard was. The youngest toddlers were tethered to the ship, with only enough line to reach the rails. How the lifestyle of these simple sea people differed from those farmer people I had seen living ashore. They are born on junks, grow up, live and die on junks. During this process from birth to death there is nothing they have not learned about the vessel or the sea.

We sailed following off shore winds to the south. I helped at the helm and learned to adjust the rudder, which at sea, is lowered down the trunk and extends well below the keel. Learning to set the sails was quite a chore. I ran around the deck like a Keystone Cop trying to help. With lateen sails, no reefing is needed. When the wind got too brisk, as it did the second night aboard, the crew simply let the halyard go, and the weight of the sails and battens brought the sails down into the topping lifts.

When the wind picked up I became uneasy, but the crew didn't seem worried. My concern was the masts and rigging. The masts were extremely heavy and built up with heavy stiffeners bound around with iron bands. The masts carried no stays whatsoever. They just stuck up in the air on their own. Why they didn't come crashing down is a mystery. The first time we tacked, I fully expected to see the masts lift right out of the boat as the heavy yard swings across with a rattle and crash. It didn't. Jibbing without stays was an easy procedure. The secret I figured was the even distribution of the weight all up and down the mast.

I was shocked out of my wits my first night aboard, when they started to tack to change our course. It had to do with superstition, and no one is more superstitious than Chinese sailors. Everything they do is governed by their wishes to please the gods. It is necessary that much propitiation be made to them. "Chinese paying plenty chin chin joss," one of the crew explained to me in his pidgin English. The date of departure is always governed by *feng-shui*, a curious Chinese custom which is supposed to be the influence of the wind and water spirits for good or ill. We anchored in one cove and I expected to set sail the next morning but our *feng-shui* wasn't right and we had to wait another two days. But the worst time to observe *feng-shui* was at night. Unless you know what to expect, it can be frightening.

It was one of those black evil nights when it was impossible to see hardly more than a fathom beyond the bow. It was like sailing into a void. Chinese junkmen seem to be able to see in the dark. But this night was unusual. The crew were up to something. Suddenly the silence was broken and the skies lighted up. Flares were flying and streams of sparks from their tails fell into the sea, lighting up the surface of the water in brilliant displays of color. At this signal the crew without warning began beating gongs. The noise they made was shattering. While some of the crew beat gongs the rest of the men "came about," tacking and changing our course. I was certain the procedure was to signal the other junks that a maneuver was taking place, but the mate explained in his pidgin that it was to frighten away the devils of the sea. We had to give them warning, he said, and not bump into them, and make them angry. The kids thought this was great fun and ran up and down the deck shouting with joy, waiting for the next time we came about.

In Tsingtao when I visited the docks I saw hundreds of rats running up and down the quay, taking cover in the godowns whenever someone approached. I was sure the junks were alive with rats. Imagine my surprise to find there were none. The reason I learned, after one tasty meal, was that the crew trapped and ate them. I remembered our first winter in Tsingtao. We had restaurants we favored, and one was near the waterfront area. We liked one dish in particular that the management always served us. It was a meat dish, very small pieces, cooked in garlic. It had a name but I forgot what it was. One evening, when it was warmer than usual, Stevenson went to open the window, which, when he did, found it faced a small courtyard. That wasn't the only thing that it faced. On lines that stretched from one wall to the other, much like clothes lines for hanging laundry, were skins strung out on hangers and hung to dry. There were hundreds of them, and they were rat skins. The specialty of the house was rat meat. That was our last time to dine in that restaurant.

Junkmen burned endless packets of joss below deck as well as topside, and at times the smoke got so dense below deck I had to run above deck to get a breath of fresh air. The mate in his pidgin explained that every junk carried its own particular little joss idol on the poop. When the weather grew foul they moved the idols below deck. Much burning of silver joss paper representing sycee took place before them. I soon noticed when we met with bad weather, an extra supply of joss paper was burned, and when we safely anchored in that cove, the crew lit more joss and beat gongs.

After all my time in China, I still found it difficult to squat for any length of time. It was most difficult aboard "Sea Wolf" during meal times. We all squatted around the wok, and waited in turn as our gruel was ladled out into our bowls filled with steaming rice. There were no spoons, only chopsticks, and with these we had to push the food into our mouths. Dried fish was served every second day.

I couldn't complain. They fed me and kept me alive. After a week I was almost one of the family, which got me thinking. If a patrol boat came now, would they still tie me to a chain and toss me over board? The chain was where it always was on deck, and I thought about it every time I passed it. It wasn't a very happy thought. I made up my mind. If it even looked like they might have thoughts about dumping me over board, I would drive over the side and take my chances with the sea.

I spent hours sitting at the bow, aside the anchor. It was a massive single fluke, wooden anchor with shanks twelve or more feet in length, weighted down with stones tied in place. As we plowed through oncoming seas, our painted eyes below on both side of the bow, "seeing the way" for us to go, my thoughts would not rest. What was Stevenson doing now? Studying to be an officer no doubt. Terry, did he and his new wife make it to Kansans City, and was he a watch repair man now? And there were the others. They were pleasant thoughts, reminiscing about them, but not so pleasant were my thoughts of Hecklinger and Sgt. Grander. Melanowski was lucky; he got out. He could have been with us. There were the others too on that patrol, and I couldn't even remember their names. Try as I did, I couldn't even remember their faces. Little Lew was different. His smiling face was constantly before me. What was he doing now?

And Ming-Lee, where was she now? Maybe Roger got her out of Tsingtao. Certainly, with Roger's help the communists wouldn't do harm to her. I pictured Roger in uniform. He didn't have to hide it in his closet any more. Maybe he would be on one of the patrol boats, and they would sail up and I would call out to him. Wishful thinking. He might be another Judas and say he didn't know me.

Sitting on the bow gave me time to reflect, and I imagined—no, dreamed—all sorts of things. Would Shanghai be the last stronghold? Would the Marines fight to defend the city? Our navy must be standing off shore, with her heavy guns pointed to the shore. I pictured those ships, the battle cruisers and destroyers. They called the destroyers "Tin Cans." I even pictured one now, on the high seas, coming straight for us. It's bow rose high out of the water, and then dropped deep into a trough. I saw it rise again, and then I heard the junkmen yelling. Low and behold, this was no illusion, no dream, not a thing imagined. It was a real US Navy Destroyer followed by two destroyer escorts. The junkmen began waving, and I quickly stood up, removed my dungaree jacket and began waving it above my head.

Like us, they were running south toward Shanghai, two hundred yards off our starboard beam. I could see a deck officer on the bridge with binoculars looking at us. One minute the ships were on our beam, and the next they were leaving us behind. I waved even more frantically now. My hopes were dashed. They must not have seen me. Suddenly the destroyer began flashing signals to the other ships. The two escorts stopped. The destroyer did a sweeping turn and came back towards us. It came to within a hundred yards, and I could see sailors lowering a whaleboat from its davits. They were coming for me.

I was jubilant, elated, thrilled, but also saddened to be leaving my new friends. The children lined the deck, and each of the crew in turn shook my hand. I went over the side and stepped into the whaleboat. I waved my last good-bye to *Hai Lang* and her crew. The next morning we arrived in Shanghai.

Chapter 21

LAST STAND IN SHANGHAI

With pomp, pride and a display of showmanship, the helmsman brought our whaleboat—packed with sailors from the destroyer, going ashore on liberty—up the congested Huangpu River, past ships flying the ensigns of a dozen nations—United States, Britain, France, Russia, Australia, New Zealand, Panama, Nationalist China, and many more I couldn't recognize. Pulling at their anchors midstream were war ships and gunboats, river scows, coastal steamers, oil tankers, rusted freighters, smart cruise liners, huge seagoing junks and even an Arabian *dhow*. There were still more, Chinese lighters with painted eyes, white-hulled government launches with shiny brass rails and hundreds of other vessels. And sculling back and forth, from ship to shore, was a sea of tiny sampans and bumboats carrying passengers and cargo. Some bumboats were so heavily-laden with cargo, their freeboard was but inches above waterline and it appeared that the slightest wave might swamp them and send them to the bottom. The entire waterfront was pulsating with vigor. We continued smartly, our own ensign flying from the stern, up the Huangpu headed for the US Navy Fleet Landing a couple of blocks north on Soucho Creek. It was a proud feeling.

All along the waterfront, cargo vessels moored to the docks, loaded and unloaded their wares, while whizzing cranes swung their booms back and forth overhead. Sweating coolies tottered up and down narrow gangplanks with loads heavy enough to break the backs of ordinary men.

Two sailors with SP armbands had been assigned to escort me to Marine Headquarters. We disembarked at dockside, and there, before us, like a dutiful waiting mistress, was the wondrous, exciting world that was Shanghai. How many tales about Old Shanghai I had heard from Marine salts. "Why, kid, let me tell you, it's the best liberty port east of the Golden Gate," they'd say, and then rave on about ladies like Shanghai Sally "who could out-drink any Marine in the Corps," and about a row of bars in a back street called Blood Alley that never closed. "In Shanghai, for five bucks, you can get fed, drunk, and laid, and still have some change left over."

Indeed, and here it was, Shanghai, a city beyond any law; a city that defied human dignity and lived up to the many names people gave it—"Paris of the East," "Whore of Asia," "Capital of the Tycoon," "Paradise for Adventurers," and a score of other such epitaphs. I couldn't wait to find out for myself.

A US Navy Jeep with a Chief Petty Officer aboard was waiting for us at the gate. The sailors turned me over to him and jumped into the whaleboat for the journey back to the destroyer. "First time in Shanghai?" the chief asked when the sailors had gone. I told him it was, and began to explain what brought me to Shanghai, but he said he already knew. "We got the radio message yesterday from the Tin Can you were on," he said, "and they reported you had been picked up at sea. I guess you're just a lucky bastard." I didn't know what he meant by that last remark, but I assumed it was for the better. I sat back and we took off through the streets of Shanghai, with the chief pointing out the sights.

We drove past the Bund, the waterfront promenade where all the foreigners gathered. Here was the pride and joy of the British community, but for the Chinese, the Bund meant humiliation. I wanted to ask the chief about that sign "No dogs or Chinese allowed" but he was too busy talking about other things for me to interrupt him. I only half listened to him anyway. I was too dazzled by our surroundings. I didn't know which way to look, nor where to turn. Everything seemed to be happening at once. Pedicab drivers hustled cargo as well as passengers through the streets, clanging their noisy bells as they pushed through milling crowds. There were more rickshaws than I had seen in any other city in China. Men, women and school kids peddled bicycles in and out of traffic. Coolies pulling heavy overloaded carts with wooden wheels struggled against the traffic. There were street-side hawkers, amahs in their black-and-white habit buying food for their masters' tables, beggar kids who ran up every time the Jeep slowed down, and people, people, people everywhere. Stern-faced Sikh policemen, complete with beards, turbans and truncheons, stood guard at government buildings, not hesitating to use the sticks upon anyone who didn't pay them heed.

And beyond all this, as far as I could see up and down the muddy river, rose a granite wall of magnificent colonial buildings: banking institutions, customs houses, hotels, private clubs, government offices, foreign consulates—buildings with clock towers, columns and domes, powerful and elegant—so un-Chinese.

It was the Opium Wars that changed Shanghai forever. As we drove through the streets, I could hear the voices of Roger and the students in Peking echoing in my ears. The Opium Wars erupted and China lost to the West. In 1842, the British imposed upon China the Treaty of Nanking that paved the way for the opening of Shanghai to the world. A British gunboat was the first ship to sail up the Huangpu; it hoisted the British flag over the city, and declared Shanghai a free port where all foreigners could enjoy "free" access and extraterritorial rights. Chinese justice, however, did not apply. The official languages became English, French, German and Russian, but not Chinese. But for how long? The cannons of Mao Tse-tung were roaring in the hills not too far away.

We followed Nanjing Road with its thronged sidewalks, past European-style shops, cheap Chinese garment shops and clothing stores, magnificent hotels like the Park Hotel, colonial mansions behind high wrought-iron fences, and terraced houses in densely populated side-streets. We finally came to Main Headquarters. The chief saluted the duty officer, handed him a brown envelope containing my orders and left. He wished me luck.

I learned from the duty officer that the Marines had evacuated Tsingtao. With the exception of Charley Company, 3rd Marines, who were living aboard the *USS Chilton,* a transport ship in Shanghai, the others were on their way home, and all our records were sent to San Diego with them. Until my files could be forwarded, or until some staff officer decided what to do with me, I would be attached to Casualty Company. I explained briefly what had happened in Loh Shan, and that I had been with the MPs in Tsingtao. He looked at me with a distant stare in is eyes. As an after thought, I mentioned that I spoke Chinese and had been to the language school in Peking, and that was the reason I was sent to the Loh Shan Mountains.

"Language school in Peking," he said and his expression changed. "A coincidence. There's another Marine in Head-quarters who went to the language school too."

"Who is that?" I asked, trying hard to think who it might be.

"Cpl. Gilbert," he replied.

Cpl. Gilbert—he was the last person I expected to meet in Shanghai. I hadn't seen him since Tsingtao, after we left Peking. He was only in Tsingtao a short while before he was reassigned to Tientsin, after the 29th broke up. I was sure Gilbert would like to know about Melanowski. He and Melanowski had become good friends in Peking, and he was quite concerned about him. He had doubts about Melanowski's relationship with Monique. "If he wants to shack up with her, that's fine," he said back then. "But to marry her, that's something else." Gilbert would be surprised to learn that Melanowsky did marry Monique, and he got his discharge in

China and landed a job with UNRA.

I told the duty officer I'd like to see my old buddy Gilbert, and he offered to get word to him that I was in Shanghai. He then assigned me to my quarters and told me I would have to make a report later. Shanghai was in its own time of troubles and there were many other pressing matters that had to be settled first.

At the paymasters I got an advancement against my pay, and I had just returned from the quartermaster's with new khakis and greens when Gilbert came charging into the room. He was beaming! For a full five minutes we kept firing questions at one another, hardly giving the other a chance to answer. He was, of course, surprised to hear that Melanowski got his discharge and married Monique. "I never thought it would happen," he said. "I guess I was wrong." The question that neither could answer was, what happened to Melanowski and his wife now that the Marines had pulled out of Tsingtao. Maybe he was in Shanghai. I asked Gilbert if he knew anything about Little Lew and Ming-Lee, but he couldn't tell me. "Hell, you forgot, but I've been stationed in Tientsin," he said. A thought came to him and his face then lit up like one of those folly little cherubs you see in those old religious paintings. "There is one place where you can find all the answers. They can tell you anything you want to know about what's happening in China, and about anyone you want to know."

"Where's that?" I asked. I thought he was going to say he knew someone in headquarters. He completely threw me off.

"At Blood Alley," he said.

"Blood Alley! You gotta be kidding!" I replied.

"Not at all," he said. "Everything happens at Blood Alley, and there's always some drunk or bargirl around who has the latest scuttlebutt, the straight scoop."

"What the hell are we waiting for?" I said.

Outside in the street we caught two pedicabs. We didn't have to tell the drivers twice where to go. They knew, like the old mare on the farm back home that knows well where the stable is. The moment we turned up Avenue Edward VII on to Avenue Rue Chu Pao-san, the official name for Blood Alley, the scene changed. It wasn't a gradual change; it was like an explosion. Even though I had an idea what was coming, it was still a jolt. Those thousands of Marines who came before me hadn't lied. Blood Alley was in a class all its own. We had hardly turned down the block when we were met—no, besieged—by gangs of pimps, panhandlers, conmen offering to serve as guides and who knows what else, all wanting to sell us something, or else wanting to buy what we had to sell. And there they were, the fun houses—dives, brothels, cabarets, cafes, side by side with fancy eateries and the lowest of low bars, all with swinging doors—a thoroughfare entirely dedicated to wine, women, song and all-night lechery.

Swinging doors were left open. From the cabarets music blared out into the street, a cacophony of off-key saxophones and strident trumpets thumping out the hits of the day. We paid off our pedicab drivers, who demanded more money than agreed to, and ducked into the first bar we came to— Monk's Brass Rail. Inside, standing shoulder to shoulder, were US Marines with leather belts slung over their shoulders ready for action, gaunt US Navy men from the Seventh Fleet, Seaforth Highlanders in kilts, seamen from the Liverpool tramps, French sailors with their silly-looking tams, Savoia Grenadiers, and the half casts of Shanghai's underworld. Customers were in every stage of drunkenness, from "feeling good" to staggering blindness. Monk's Brass Rail was like a time bomb, ready to explode at a slight side glance—"what the frig are you looking at"— or a slight misunderstanding— "hey, swabbie, I seen her first." You could rest assured, any minute a drunken sailor would ask a Seaforth Highlander what he had under his kilt, and it would begin.

We finished our drinks and went next door to George's Bar. Two Marines from Monk's Brass Rail teamed up and went with us. A wise Marine always knew that safety lay in numbers. Marines with Marines; sailors with sailors;

Grenadiers with Grenadiers. The two Marines who joined forces with us had been stationed in Peking, and like lost brothers we became instant buddies, ready to defend one another against all odds, if need be.

Customers in George's Bar were more subdued. Here they had ears only for the girls clinging to them in the half-light of dance-floor alcoves. The freewheeling painted beauties in ankle-length dresses slit up the sides, sitting on stools at the bar, called out to us when we entered: "Dar-ling, buy me one drink, pleeease." We bought them drinks, but not one of them had any information about Tsingtao, except to say girls from Tsingtao hung out mostly at the Palais Cabaret.

We ventured from bar to bar, having a drink in each place, and finding each dive wilder, more noisy and better than the last one. We lost count—the Crystal, the New Ritz and Mums, plus a few more. By now we had forgotten what we came for, and it was then that we stumbled into the Palais Cabaret. They could hear us coming, walking down Blood Alley four abreast, singing to the tops of our voices, frightened of no one— Highlanders or Grenadier, Seventh Fleet swabbie or British Marine. The manager met us at the door. He was White Russian, wearing a frayed white-linen suit. He abruptly, without asking, moved three bargirls from their seats and gave us their stools near the door. We ordered Hubba Hubba vodka and before we had the first sip, bar hostesses were upon us like flies. The Palais, Gilbert insisted, was noted for the best looking women in Blood Alley. It appeared that way, with something else—variety. We had our pick—Chinese, Korean, Japanese, Anamneses, Russian Eurasian, Filipino, Formosan.

Gilbert was right; the cabaret was popular. It was jam-packed, with some customers standing three-deep at the bar. The booze poured like water from an open tap: rotgut whiskey, vodka, and local Chinese beer. The heavy smoke-laden air was so dense it was impossible to discern the faces of those sitting at the other end of the bar. Still, through the haze, I thought I saw a face I recognized. But I had to be mistaken.

I tapped Gilbert on the arm. "Who does that remind you of?" I asked, pointing to a girl sitting with a Marine officer at the other end of the bar. Gilbert looked hard, squinted and looked again.

"No," he said and got up from his seat. Without explaining or commenting, he elbowed his way though the crowd, nearly causing a brawl with each step, and headed directly toward the girl and her Marine officer friend. I followed him, trying to keep up. I became momentarily separated from him, and when I moved in closer I could hear him screaming, "You son of a bitch! You bloody whore." I closed the distance, and the girl whom I thought looked like Monique was Monique, Melanowski's wife!

"You had better watch it, Marine," the officer said to Gilbert, getting to his feet. He didn't shout or threaten. He remained composed.

But not Gilbert. He was in an uncontrollable rage. I had never seen him like this before. He was always quiet and mild-mannered. Now he was like a demon released from a cage. Those standing around began to move back. I took my eyes from Monique and looked at the officer. My heart missed a beat. That son of a bitch! The officer was Lt. McCaffery, the Jap lover, the hometown boy who introduced me to Sofuku Geisha House in Tsingtao. He was with Melanowski's wife. My thoughts flared up. Had he started fooling around with her while Melanowski was out in the field with UNRA? That creepy son of a bitch, an ill excuse for an officer. I never did like him. He recognized me. "You had better call your friend off," he said to me.

"You giving me an order?" I fired back.

Monique hastily took a position and stood between him and Gilbert, for it was obvious Gilbert was going for his throat.

"You bitch," Gilbert continued shouting at Monique. "Where's Ski? Home waiting for you?"

"Hey, take it easy," Lt. McCaffery repeated, pushing Monique to one side. He was getting angry now.

Our Marines buddies had sensed that something was wrong and came running to our aid. "You are a son of a bitch," Gilbert shouted at Lt. McCaffery and made a lunge to grab him by his jacket, but hands from every direction reached out and held him back. "Let go of me," he shouted. "Let go! I'll kill the bastard."

This was serious. Gilbert was about to strike a Marine officer. Monique moved in and attempted to grab hold of my arm. "Let me talk to you," she pleaded.

"You go to hell," I shouted and pushed her hand away.

"Listen!" she cried. "Listen, damn you!"

"Listen, listen to what?" I repeated.

"Let me tell you," she said, looking directly at me and then at Gilbert. Her eyes filled with tears, and she reached out for my arm again, to steady herself. She looked solely at me now, attempting to dry her eyes with the back of her hand. Her voice choked up with emotion. She finally blurted it out: "Melanowski's dead." She hesitated, letting her words sink in. "You hear, Melanowski is dead." Our Marine buddies let Gilbert go and his arms dropped to his side.

The White Russian manager pushed through the crowd that had gathered, and seeing that things had settled down, suggested that Monique, Gilbert and me follow him. He told Lt. McCaffery to wait where he was. He led us to a back door that opened into a small courtyard.

Monique told us the story. Her husband, Melansowski, was killed when a convoy of half a dozen UNRA vehicles bringing in refugees to Tsingtao from the south was ambushed. All the drivers were killed, including Melanowski. The refugees were unharmed. A patrol of Marines was dispatched to retrieve the bodies but the gunfire became so intense, and they were so outnumbered, they had to turn back.

She talked about the evacuation from Tsingtao. Only military personnel and their dependents could travel on US ships. She told how White Russians with suitcases jammed with money pleaded for passage to Shanghai but the Americans had to turn them away and leave them to the mercy of unscrupulous ship captains for passage. Those without money attempted to flee aboard open sampans and bumboats.

I asked her about Ming-Lee but she had never met her and didn't know her. She suggested I contact Roy Lund. Roy had owned the Hansen Photo Studio on Chung Shan Road in downtown Tsingtao. He was a friend of all Marines and sailors. I knew him. He came to the aid of any Marine in distress. He loaned us money when we were broke, as we usually were between paydays, and he guided us in the right direction when we got into trouble. He was our Chaplin, without preaching religion. Melanowski had befriended him, and he was the one who was able to secure Monique's safe passage to Shanghai.

"But you were married to an American citizen," I said to her. "Didn't that cut the mustard?"

"No one would listen to me in Tsingtao. It was terrible. I had to get here on my own. Once I got here I went to the US Embassy. With thousands of dependents wanting to leave, they have lines of people waiting. But the consul was helpful. They put me in touch with Lt. McCaffery. He's working with the American dependents and refugees."

To Gilbert and me that still didn't matter, not at all. The way Lt. McCaffery was pawing her at the bar, he had to have more in mind than a passport.

"What about the other civilians?" I asked. "What about Little Lew? You remember him. You met him when you and Ski came to the PX one day."

Monique again welled up with tears. I braced myself for the worse, "Yes, I know," she said. "The Marines told me what happened to him. I can't bear the thought."

"Where is he?" I asked. "Tell me, what happened."

"They killed him," she sobbed.

Nothing she could have said could have come as a worse blow. Was I hearing right? "I am talking about Little Lew," I said, thinking she must have the wrong kid in mind, hoping she was wrong.

"Yes, it was him, Little Lew," she replied.

"Killed him! Who killed him? What are you talking about?" I demanded.

"The other kids," she said. "When the Marines left the university he stayed back, as long as he could, but he eventually had to come out. He put on his old clothes, but the kids recognized him when he stepped out the gate. They picked up stones. They stoned him to death. There was nothing the Chinese guards at the gate could do. There were too many."

What had we done? My teacher Mrs. Murray was right. She said our making Little Lew the company mascot would lead to no good. "What about when you Marines leave?" she had asked. Who thought we would ever leave China? Why didn't we listen to her? I left Monique standing there with Gilbert at her side, and they made no attempt to come after me. I found a back gate to the courtyard and walked through the streets of Shanghai back to the barracks.

The next morning I conned the company clerk in to giving me an early liberty pass and went to find Roy Lund. It wasn't difficult to do. He had opened a new camera shop right off the Bund. "Maybe Chairman Mao will let me keep it," he said after greeting me. "After all, the communists will want to take pictures, too."

Roy was in a very happy mood, but that soon changed when he confirmed Little Lew's death. "The street kids didn't envy him," he explained; "they hated him. Poverty does strange things to the hungry." Roy was deeply saddened too about Melanowski. "I liked that guy," he said. "He always talked about wanting to go home, and all that changed when he met that girl in Peking. The last time I saw him, he was proud that he was getting a fat belly. It was his measure of success. He'll never be going home now." Roy was also upset about Ming-Lee. "You shouldn't feel bad. It wasn't your fault." I explained what had happened to me, that I couldn't get back to her. "And if you could have, what could you have done anyway?" He agreed he would try to find out what he could about her. He suggested that I might try Katarina. "She had been in contact with Ming-Lee until the very end," he said. He didn't know her address, except that she was staying with her family in French Concession were the White Russians mostly lived. "There's a Russian bakery on the corner of Jeffrey. They might know her." I thanked him and was about to leave. He put a hand on my shoulder. "You better hurry. Many White Russians are returning to Russia. She might be one of them."

I found the bakery, by following the wonderful aroma of baked bread up the street. The proprietor asked that I be seated and sent his young son to find Katarina. He brought me a steaming cup of coffee and told me to wait. The bakery was like the one in Peking where Katarina and I went the first time we had coffee together. His customers were all European, mostly Russian. They all left the shop with bundles under their arms and pleased looks on their faces. The poor Chinese, they didn't know what they were missing.

I must have waited half an hour, and still no Katarina. I was getting ready to leave when the tinkling of the bell above the door made me turn in that direction. Katarina stood there. I had forgotten how lovely she was. Her skin seemed even whiter than before, and her hair darker. She greeted me by throwing her arms around me. Before we could exchange greetings, she announced, "I'm going home."

"Going home, you just got here," I said somewhat bewildered.

"No, silly, home to Russia," she replied.

Roy was right. She sat down, and while we held hands across the table, she explained her intentions. In excited words she said the US State Department announced that the descendants of all White Russians who were bilingual could return to Russia. The State Department had a registration office and they told Russian refugees they could come and register. American ships as well as Russian ships would transport them back home. They could take all their possessions.

"Russia is still our homeland," she insisted. "Most White Russians feel this way. They are tired of living as second-rate citizen in foreign lands. Many of us have decided to go back."

"But you once told me in Peking that you would never go back to Russia," I said.

"That was before," she said. "Conditions have changed."

"How do you know you will be welcomed back?" I asked.

"Your State Department guarantees our safety," she replied.

"That's a guarantee to get there. They can't guarantee anything after you arrived," I answered. She didn't respond, only winced her nose, and I continued: "And if some Russians decide not to go, what then will happen to them?"

"Come, you must meet my aunts," she said. "They will explain better than I can."

I actually wanted to meet Katarina's two aunts. I had not forgotten the stories she had told in Peking about her family. I especially wished I could have met her mother, remembering that her second husband, Katarina's stepfather, was a China Marine. They had married in 1931, but both she and her husband left Shanghai just before the Japanese arrived.

Katarina took me to meet her aunts Sunday afternoon. They lived in the same three-bedroom apartment in the French Concession that Katarina had told me about. The apartment was exactly as she had described it. It was more museum than a place to live. Every corner, every inch of wall, every space on top of tables and on top of the piano was used to exhibit some memento or other, many which dated back to imperial Russia. There were photos of Russian nobles in uniforms with sashes and sabers at their sides and chests full of campaign ribbons. There were regal looking Russian women dressed in ankle-length skirts with laces and frills, and wearing large hats rimmed with flowers. There were plaques and brass bowls with engraved names on the sides. Looking down from the walls were life-sized oil paintings of somber Russian nobles, both men and women. The rugs, one on top of another, were rich Persians and Afghans, and the drapes that shaded the light from the windows were right out of a Russian painting.

Her two aunts were a reflection of the apartment. It would be difficult to say if they molded the apartment, or that the apartment molded them. I couldn't imagine them any place but there, sitting as they were, surrounded by their faded past. They were pleasant enough. They asked me to be seated, and we began our conversation over tea. Katarina introduced me as Stephan—a fine upstanding Boyar name, she said when we were climbing the stairs to the apartment

"Stephan asked me what will happen to those of us who choose not to return home to Russia," Katarina said.

I studied the two women, aristocrats, turned milk cow farmers in Manchuria, and seamstresses, hairdressers and clothing-and-fur store owners in Shanghai, except they called them salons. I tried to picture them as young beautiful women, in their early 20s, when they arrived in Shanghai, as Katarina said they were. But I could only see two weathered old ladies with wrinkles and lines on their faces, and an over abundance of heavy make up, trying to be someone they were no longer. The older of the two women wore bright red lipstick, which she had applied beyond the contour lines of her lips. I wondered which one of them had turned down a film producer for an American sailor who sailed away and never returned. The other one, if I wasn't mistaken, fell in love with a Flying Tiger pilot, but he, it turned out, already had a wife in Oregon. I could see now why Katarina wanted to further her education. She didn't want to be like them. It was her means of escape, but the communists put an end to her studies and hopes.

"What will happen to those who don't want to go back?" the younger of the two repeated. "Why Father Wilcock will manage that, of course. He is making the arrangements this very minute."

I suspected she would say Father Wilcock. Katarina had taken me to meet him a few days before—Father Feodor Wilcock, an English-born Jesuit. He was a guy I had to admire:

barrel chested, pince-nez glasses, flamboyant with a black cape and a red lining that fluttered like a great winged sea hawk when he moved about. He certainly was colorful, and he didn't hesitate to tell me about himself. In 1929, he went to Rome to study at the newly formed Russian College established to train young men for work in Stalinist Russia. He was ordained in 1934, and his first assignment was to the borderlands of Poland and Czechoslovakia where he ministered to large numbers of refugees from the Russian revolution who had settled there. He managed to cross over into the Soviet Union several times, but he was quickly expelled by the Soviet authorities. Some of his fellow Jesuits in the Russian mission were not so fortunate. They ended up serving long prison sentences, and in some cases losing their lives in the dreaded Soviet Gulag.

When World War II began to engulf Eastern Europe, he went off to Manchuria and China to assist the White Russians who had taken refuge there. In Shanghai, he set up a Russian Catholic chapel and eventually a boys' boarding school. But with the Chinese communist forces closing in on the city, he was assigned by UNRA to supervise the hasty evacuation of Russians to a detention camp in the Philippines. The makeshift Russian settlement was to be on uninhabited Tubabao Island off of Samar. There were 40,000 White Russians in Shanghai, but after seeing the ships that were to carry them there—three old condemned cargo vessels—only 6,500 agreed to go.

"At least we will have American ships to take us home," Katarina said when her aunts brought up the subject.

"Russia! Russia! Katarina, how can we talk sense into you?" the elder said. I was surprised for I thought they would be in favor of returning to Russia, at least the older generation. I could see a heated argument coming.

Before we had come to visit her aunts, Katarina told me that she had given up hopes of finding a husband. It wouldn't have done her much good even if she had found someone. A few months before, in December 1948, the War Bride Act ended and it didn't appear that they were going to extend it. It was now a dishonorable discharge for any GI to marry a foreign woman.

"Until we got this offer, it was the dream of every single White Russian woman in China to acquire a passport," Katarina announced to her aunts. "We are stateless, we have no country, and we have nowhere to go. We are not Soviet citizens but refugees from communist rule." She looked at me and laughed. "Before the War Bride Act, the best prospect, of course, was an American passport. You single American males became our chief prey."

"Katarina," her aunt said with astonishment, "how can you say that?"

"Auntie, you know that's true," she replied. "Any foreign man! They could be young, middle-aged, senile, handsome, ugly as sin, tall, short, fat, thin, it didn't matter. The goal was a passport. British, French, German, any male who breathed and had a legal travel document would do, but you Americans were the prize catch."

"Katarina, you demean Russian women," the older aunt snapped.

"Not only Russian women but all Russians," the younger aunt said.

"I agree," the older aunt said. "The Bolsheviks cast us out. And they also cast out ballerinas from Moscow and St. Petersburg, first-class opera singers, and painters, musicians, and poets. White Russian girls in the ballrooms of Shanghai were famous for their beauty. Russians have made Shanghai one of the best-known artistic centers in the Far East."

"You are right, auntie," Katarina said in agreement, but I could sense she had more on her mind. I was right. "Agreed, the Russians brought a new kind of style to Shanghai, but also through their poverty and desperation. They gave the Chinese a glimpse of the fact that white people are not necessarily the infallible master race."

"Katarina, watch your manners," the older aunt said.

"Auntie, we are talking about the women, always about

the women, but what about our Russian men? We should pity them, the great Cossacks and Boyars that they were. Look around. A single man in Shanghai today has little hope of marrying a girl of his own race, or any race for that matter. He has nothing to offer. He has no national stature, no prospect of a well-paying job. What prospect is there for even a former officer in the Czarist army, or high-ranking naval officer? At best he could find employment as a guard for one of the rich mansions in one of the concessions, or else work as a cemetery keeper. Walk through the French Concession, around the Orthodox Cathedral in Rue Dourner. You see young Russian men begging from Europeans, even from Chinese, Eurasians, anybody. You see Russian men lying on the pavement."

Katarina went on, and my thoughts faded back to the image I had of a tall good-looking Russian man I saw in the *hutongs* in Peking. He had leprosy eating away at one side of his face, and had to turn to begging to survive.

No, after all was said and done, Katarina had made up her mind. She was going home to Russia aboard the next available ship. Not even the prospect of a husband could stop her.

After I said good-bye to Katarina and her aunts I had an appointment at the Seaman's Club to meet Gilbert and his Marine buddy from the 3rd Marines. I stepped out into the chill evening air, glad to be away from all the talk about White Russians, took a pedicab to the Bund and walked from there. I followed the Waibaidu Bridge over the Suzhou River. During the day, the bridge was usually crowded with pedestrians, cyclists and laborers pushing bicycle carts heavily loaded with wares, but now it was still and peaceful. I stopped and looked out over the river, and I thought how Shanghai at this moment was all mine. I was alone, on the Waibaidu Bridge, all by myself. That was something! Alone in Shanghai. I thought about all the time I had spent in China. Years. I thought about my age. I was twenty now, and time was slipping by. Was my time in China up? Was the time up for all China Marines?

I was late by now and hurried to the Seaman's Club. The club may have been called a "seaman's" club but there were more than seamen who stepped though the front door. Many of the foreign correspondents used the club as a meeting place. They took advantage of the Teletype machine that continuously pounded out messages on the top floor, bringing the news of the world in a noisy display of difficult-to-read words. On their way back from the Teletype room the reporters always stopped at the bar, and there they talked about what they had just read. Some interesting bull sessions went on there at the bar. When I could manage to get away, I went with a few other Marines to catch up on the news. Some of the stuff they talked about was hardly interesting, like "Czechoslovakia announces a five-year plan to attain economic independence from the West" or "Secretary of State Marshall resigned for health reasons and was succeeded by Dean Acheson."

The news that was closer to Shanghai always got everyone to sit up at the bar: "Chinese communists occupied Tientsin after a 27-hour battle with Nationalist forces," followed by "The Chiang Government moved the capital of China to Canton." If it wasn't for the Teletype machine, we wouldn't have known about the British frigate *Amethyst* which had come under fire from communist Chinese artillery and was aground in the Yangtze River. The British were having a tense standoff with the communists, and many British sailors had been killed.

What was happening in America always got a lot of comments from the guys. Everyone had something to say when *Look* magazine proclaimed that radio was "doomed" and that within three years television would completely overshadow it. What a marvel television must be, we said, for none of us had seen it. But what were soap operas? We asked the question when we heard the report that "The first TV daytime soap opera, 'These Are My Children,' was broadcast from the NBC station in Chicago."

Times were changing back home without us. RCA Victor announced a "newfangled product" to replace the 33-1/3 'long play' phonograph disk with a smaller, seven-inch record, with a big hole in the center, called the 45-rpm disk. And at the Academy Awards, "Hamlet" won best picture of 1948 and its star, Laurence Olivier, best actor; The Rodgers and Hammerstein musical "South Pacific" opened on Broadway. We all thought it was funny that they would do a musical on the Marines in the South Pacific. Hell, before the war no one knew anything about the Pacific. Now they were writing musicals about us.

More exciting was the news that an American B-50 Superfortress, the Lucky Lady II, had landed at Fort Worth, Texas, after completing the first non-stop, round-the-world flight. We all commented that only a few years before our planes had a hard time flying from Guam and Saipan to bomb Japan and make it safely back to base. But the most distressing news was the report that the United States had charged the USSR with interning up to fourteen million in labor camps. Were they going to add the White Russians in China to that list? I wanted to tell Katarina but there was no need to frighten her more. She had already made up her mind.

When I met Gilbert and his friend Leroy Thompson that night after seeing Katarina and her aunts, the Seaman's Club was quiet, a thing that didn't often happen. They were sitting at a table in the corner with a couple of empty bottles of Tsingtao beer on the table.

Introductions were made and I shook hands with Leroy. He had hands the size of catchers' mitts, and his grip was like sticking your hand into a vice. He was a boxer, and after meeting him you knew he had to be a winner. He was as tough as they came, but at the same time he was as mild as a Sunday school teacher. He had an interesting story to tell. He was with Charley Company, 3rd Marines, in Tsingtao, and left with his outfit two weeks before, about the same time I was floating around the China Sea aboard the *Hai Lang* junk. His battalion had loaded men and supplies aboard the *USS Chilton* transport and sailed straight to Shanghai. The men were living aboard and had the task of guarding American personnel and property and supervising their evacuation from Shanghai. He had just returned from Nanking that day, after helping evacuate Americans there. "It won't be long, and we'll all be out of Shanghai," he said. The Cruiser *Springfield* was standing by down river and would be the last ship to leave China.

I made a few more visits to see Katarina and her aunts. I felt that I should give them all the support that I could. Katarina tried to find out from friends in Tsingtao about Ming-Lee but all her sources had dried up. In the mean time, the feuds among the Russians and their family members continued. Some wanted to return to Russia; others didn't. Katarina and her aunts were waiting for news from a doctor friend who decided to go back first, and he planned to send for his family when he saw what the conditions were like. He would cable or else write. That was a month ago, and they had heard nothing. There was an Englishman, head of the British School, divorced from his Russian wife. They had children, and the wife decided to return with their son to Russia. There was little the father could do. Katarina went to see them off aboard ship. They were waiting news from her too.

The Saturday morning after meeting Leroy at the Seaman's Club, I checked out early on liberty and went to pick up Katarina. I promised her that I'd take her to the Trillion for lunch. When I knocked on her door, her aunts were there to open it. Both were in tears. They said Katarina had gone. She received word the night before that she had to be at the docks at 0600 the next morning with all her belongings. A US transport was taking some 3,000 Russians to Vladivostok. Departure time was at 0900. It was 0900 when I knocked at the door. "Why didn't she tell me?" I shouted.

"She sent a message, and the boy left it at the front gate. She waited for you. She delayed until the last minute, hoping you'd come. We asked her to change her mind. She wouldn't."

She had to be leaving from the US Navy Fleet Landing on

Soucho Creek. I caught a pedicab and had him peddle as fast as he could, but I was too late. The ship had cast off its mooring lines by the time we arrived and had already pulled away from the dock. Every available inch of space along the railing was occupied by Russians returning home. I desperately searched the railings from one end to the other but could not see her. I was hopeful now that she had missed the ship. Maybe for some clerical reason they hadn't let her board—her papers were not in proper order, or a form had not been filled out properly. An important stamp or signature was missing. My hopes were dashed when I saw her. She was standing alone near the stern of the ship. I ran along the dock waving frantically but the figures along the railing grew fainter and fainter as the ship slipped further away. She didn't see me.

I was so utterly confused about this whole affair. Did the Soviets really welcome their expelled citizens back home? One man who might have the answers was Father Wilcock. I went to see him. He was terribly busy, getting ready for the first boatload of refugees to depart for the Philippines, but he took time to talk to me. He was brutal and frank, and spared no feelings.

"What the world is well aware of," he began, "is that on the 4th of February 1945, Stalin, Churchill, and Roosevelt met at Yalta to decide how to divide German territory. What they don't know is that there was also a secret agreement, and that was to exchange each other's liberated prisoners and to return each other's liberated civilians as they were rounded up in Germany and China. In accordance with this secret understanding, the United States has to return White Russian civilians in exchang for Allied prisoners."

It all suddenly came to light. Mrs. Murray and her family, and many hundreds of thousands of other prisoners, were given free passage from concentration camps. Now it was America's turn to repatriate the White Russians.

Father Wilcock continued: "Everyone forgets that the

Soviet decree in 1921 stripped all Russians outside the country of their citizenship. Unfortunately, most refugees remained hopeful, and expected that their exile would be only temporary. Stalin had other ideas. You have to remember, many White Russians fought alongside German forces against the Red Army; this included their Cossack regiments who had left their homeland after the revolution. Stalin won't forget. Several hundred thousand Russians took up arms against the Soviet Union in the years following the German invasion in June 1941." He then gave me the example of General Pyotr Krasnov, a Cossack who had fought against the Bolsheviks back in 1918 and hoped that the British would sympathize with his situation, for they had decorated him with the British Military Cross. It did no good. Under the Yalta agreement, he too was sent back to the Soviet Union to certain death. He was for Stalin a prize captive.

I was sick at heart when I left Father Wilcock at his parish. Life had been so simple when we first stepped ashore in China in October 1945. Our biggest concern then was, could we get to the Prime Club before some swabbies booked our girls and we had to wait around until their time was up. We never heard of Yalta and the only White Russians we were concerned about were those serving borscht in their restaurants. Mao Tse-tung was someone who Chiang K'ai-shek could whip with his hands behind his back, with a little of our help, of course, and the Eighth Route Army couldn't shoot straight if they had to.

At the Seaman's Club we learned from the foreign correspondents that life in China was much more complicated than that. Troubles began when General Douglas MacArthur designated Chiang K'ai-shek as the sole authority empowered to accept surrender from the Japanese in China. The Soviets were forced to sign a Sino-Soviet Treaty whereby Moscow was compelled to accept the Nationalist government as the legitimate government in China. Stalin was not pleased when Americans airlifted Nationalist troops to key points in Japanese-occupied territory in the East and North, and 50,000

American Marines soon occupied port areas and airfields on the Nationalists' behalf in Tsingtao, Peking, and Tientsin.

Stalin was finally having his revenge. Now with his ally Mao Tse-tung gaining complete control, Russia was forcing the United States to honor the Yalta accord, and that was to repatriate all Russians in China. Katarina was the victim. And the China Marines had to go

When the first US ships returned from Vladivostok, they had horror stories to tell. We received more reports from the Teletype machine at the Seaman's Club. Thousands of refugees who disembarked on Russian soil found instead of being welcomed, they were immediately stripped of the new winter clothing and personal equipment that had been generously issued to them by the Americans and British. The stories told were that they were then shipped off to prison camps for long sentences, to receive the same treatment as all the Gulag's inmates. Ship captains and their guards testified that some prisoners never made it that far. They were shot behind warehouses on the quayside with low flying Soviet planes circling overhead to help drown the noise of the rifle fire. Some Americans were appalled when they eyewitnessed many desperate acts of suicide by Russian men and women who preferred their own deaths and that of their children to falling into the hands of the Soviet secret police.

I had hardly enough time to pack my seabag when our orders came to muster at 0500 for transport to the airport in Shanghai. Mao Tse-tung's troops were at the outskirts of the city. There was no fighting, and the handover was expected to be peaceful. At the airport I found Gilbert waiting in line to board the same C-47. We had little we could say to one another. None of the Marines there had much to say. Our destination was Hawaii. Once in Honolulu, we transferred to navy ships for the last leg of our journey to San Diego—back where it all started.

Chapter 22

FAREWELL CHINA

During World War II, there was a saying among the fighting Marines in the South Pacific, and later with the Marines in China, that the only gate they ever wanted to see was the Golden Gate in San Francisco. The *USS Marsh*, DE 699, the destroyer escort that carried Gilbert and me homeward bound, and a half dozen other Marines, was heading to San Diego and not San Francisco, but that really didn't matter. The Golden Gate stood as the symbol of our "going home," and we were going home.

I was up early, just as dawn was breaking, and found an empty gun turret to the starboard of the bow. I squeezed underneath the barrels of a twin 40mm cannon, and leaned out facing forward. I pined to see America come into view. Many thoughts raced through my head as I stood there searching the horizon; so much had happened since that day in April 1945, when we sailed away from San Diego. What a moment that was for a bunch of young, excited Marines. How innocent we all were. I thought about that most often when we were on Okinawa, like the time I was with Terry, hugging the bottom of a foxhole in the rain, terrified that a shell from the battery of heavy bombardment whizzing overhead might fall short; or like the time when I was aboard that junk in the China Sea, with a chain around my feet, wondering when they might shove me overboard. It was times like this that I though how happy we had been. Every detail of that departure had been engraved in my mind. There was a band playing a John Philip Sousa's march, and hundreds of people were gathered on the docks, waving and shouting, some crying, all wishing us well. And I remembered so well that lovely young lady in black slacks, high heels, and a low cut black blouse. I remember her throwing kisses, and she called out that she would be there waiting for every single one of us to return.

Well, we were back. The *USS Marsh* slowly entered the harbor, but there was no woman in black, no waving crowds, and no band playing a John Philip Sousa's march. Instead there were two sad-looking longshoremen waiting to catch the lines our seamen threw to them. There was no one else, just the two of them.

The men picked up the lines, which were attached to larger mooring lines, and pulled them in. Once they had the mooring lines in tow, they threw the looped ends over two bollards. Without bothering to see if the ship was securely moored, the men turned their backs and strutted back to their tin-roof office shack at the end of the dock.

What a dismal sight, a miserable navy dockyard in San Diego! I watched the wind carry a newspaper across the yard. It swept past a pair of unused rail lines, and piled up against a chain link fence. Sea gulls came to rest on the bollards.

I threw my seabag over my shoulder, and along with the others, headed toward the gate. A Marine guard in a helmet liner and a .45 at his side said a bus would be along in half an hour to take us to the base. He said we could go inside the guard shack, out of the cold, and wait there. A half hour wait, I thought; he could have said a day, or a year. What did it matter? Where was the band?

Outside the gate, I could see a red blinking neon on a bar across the way. It was mid morning, but it was open. "Not a friendly dump," the Marine guard said when I asked about the place. "It's a longshoremen's hangout, and they don't like navy types there." I had no quarrel with longshoremen, and I felt like a beer. None of the others wanted to go, so I left my seabag in the guard shack and headed toward the bar.

It was a dark, dingy place, and it smelled of stale beer. Sitting at one end of the bar were several dockworkers in overalls. They wore heavy boots and metal safety hats. They weren't very friendly looking. Above the bar was a television. My first thought was to ask the bartender, after I got my beer, to turn it on. I'd tell him that I had never seen television before. That might amuse him. He was cleaning a glass, and when he saw me approach, he placed the glass on the bar. "Something you want?' he asked. There was no cheer in his tone of voice.

"Yeah, a beer," I said.

"Is that right. Well, then, you got identification?" he asked in a raised voice for the others to hear. All conversation stopped. The bartender picked up the glass, turned it upside down and placed it on the bar.

"Identification? Why do I need identification?" I asked.

"You gotta be 21 to drink in here," he said.

"What the hell you talking about!" I said. I was hot under the collar now. "I just got off that ship, and you mean to tell me I can't get a drink."

"What I'm telling you is," he said, "you had better turn your ass around, march right for that door, and get the hell out of here."

Ten thousand gobs laid down their swabs—where in the hell are you, Terry and Chandler and Stevenson? Where in the hell are all you guys? I know, scattered out across America, sitting in your new civvies, watching television, getting fat on your wives' and your mothers' cooking? Where in the hell are you when it's time to help a Marine buddy clean up a bar, as you all had done so often in China?

There were no Marines to help me here. I was home, after almost four years, and couldn't even get a beer. Nor could I even tell these early morning drunks that when I left a couple of years ago, there were people outside waving flags and cheering, and a band was playing a John Philip Sousa's march. There was a girl in black and she said she would be waiting until every single one of us got back. Well, there were a lot of us who were't comming back, ever, but there was no reason for that girl in black not to be here. Would these guys sitting there, sneering at me, would they understand about Okinawa and China, about napalm-filled caves and suicide bombers and tortured comfort women and the *balu* on the march? Would it do any good to tell them about Hecklinger and Melanowski, and Little Lew. They might laugh when I told them about Little Lew, and might say he was only a little gook kid anyway. Would it matter to them that Katarina might be dead, or if she wasn't, she'd probably be in a labor camp in Siberia somewhere, and Ming-Lee might well be in a Chinese reformation camp.

All it mattered to them was that I was under 21 and not old enough to have a beer with them.

My family, of course, was thrilled to have me back. My sister sent an application for me to fill out, to enter Michigan State University under the GI Bill. I could get by without a high school diploma, but I had to pass a GED test first. Not to worry; it was easy. Electrical engineering courses were some of the best in the country. For an elective, I could take drafting. My father said it would help when we opened a shop. But I said I wanted to take Chinese studies. The answer came back. There were no Chinese studies at Michigan State. There were no Chinese studies at any college or any university in America. China was dead, they all said. There was no China anymore.

I guess they were right. We had to forget China, put it away, get China out of our minds. That's what everyone told us. Farewell China!

But China Marines can't forget. We just keep silent.

WHO NEEDS A ROAD?
The Story of the Longest and the Last
Motor Journey Around the World
By Harold Stephens & Albert Podell
ISBN: 09642521-5-5
487 pages, with photographs, $14.95

**THE STRANGE DISAPPEARANCE
OF JIM THOMPSON**
And Stories of other Expatriates in Southeast Asia
by Harold Stephens.
ISBN: 0-9642521-7-1
260 pages, with photographs, $14.95